Bad Pe

How a Maverick Owner Helped Break Baseball's Color Barrier

A Historical Novel by Tom Gantert

Cover art by: Gary Gantert

Published by: Shadow Play Publishing, 2024

PREFACE

Let's begin with the ugly because often there is nothing uglier than an accurate depiction of history.

The word "nigger" appears in this book 15 times. The term "jigaboo" appears nine times. The slur "coon" appears twice. These terms are poisonous. But in the era covered by this story, they were commonplace slurs the book's characters dealt with daily. It would be an insult to the legacy of those Black players to dilute what they endured throughout their lives, including during the early years of the struggle to integrate Major League Baseball. The use of racial slurs has been limited but they are an unavoidable part of the story. Larry Doby, who broke the color barrier in the American League, said the slurs were an everyday part of life during that era.

The idea to write this book began in 2019 after I spent more than 100 hours researching Negro League baseball to create historically accurate rosters for a sports simulation game company.

In the midst of my research, I experienced an epiphany, inspired by Black comedian Chris Rock's opening monologue at the 2016 Academy Awards.

There had been no Black nominees that year and the popular comedian mocked Hollywood for its lack of diversity.

"You are damn right Hollywood is racist," Rock told a room of mostly white people, including the most powerful in his business.

Rock explained to that crowd the solution to the problem.

"We want opportunity. We want Black actors to get the same opportunities as white actors. That's it," Rock pleaded. "Not just once. All of you guys [white people] get great parts all the time. What about Black actors?"

That led me to dig more into the Black people of Negro League baseball and I discovered many crossed paths with a white team owner named Bill Veeck.

Effa Manley, a woman who owned a Negro League baseball team in the 1940s, was one of those fascinating people. She appears in seven chapters of this book. Effa Manley was one of my favorite characters in this book.

The research also touched upon Satchel Paige, whom I had heard about for decades, but not in depth. Ultimately, Paige became a significant character in Bad Penny and appears in 24 chapters.

In the end, Bad Penny is not about Bill Veeck. Even though his name is mentioned in all but five chapters, his career in Bad Penny is a window to some of the most interesting people involved in integrating baseball and race relations in America.

CHAPTER 1

Veeck As In Wreck

July 12, 1979

This was the end of Bill Veeck. This was the end of disco music.

This would go down as one of the most infamous nights in the history of Major League Baseball.

Veeck stood on his prosthetic right wooden leg in Chicago's Comiskey Park, shrouded in a cloud of smoke on a muggy July night.

The owner of the Chicago White Sox baseball team, Veeck surveyed the carnage left by his latest promotion - Disco Demolition Night.

Disco records were to be blown up during a break between the two games of a Major League Baseball doubleheader between the Chicago White Sox and Detroit Tigers.

But the antic let a genie out of the bottle. Now the outfield was on fire, as thousands of rebellious rock-and-rollers dressed in jeans and T-shirts had taken the field hostage. They had no intention of giving it up, and the second game was scheduled to start in 30 minutes.

Veeck had earned a reputation as the P.T. Barnum of baseball by devising thousands of entertaining promotions dating back more than 35 years. Many were whacky, such as hiring a 3-foot-7 player to appear in a game.

But a few became industry-wide innovations, such as names on the back of jerseys so fans could identify players, and gigantic electronic scoreboards now common in the 21st century.

Altogether, these ideas turned the game upside down, and were credited to this visionary known as "Sports Shirt" for his refusal to wear a tie.

But on this night, dread was settling in with this doomed promotion.

Veeck looked to the field for Steve Dahl, the shock-jock radio host he'd hired to emcee Disco Demolition Night. Veeck scanned the mob of revelers and found him. The disc jockey wasn't hard to spot, looking ridiculous wearing a blue leisure suit topped with a World War II Army helmet.

The disco-hating fans whom the embittered Dahl had whipped into a frenzy had turned on him.

Dahl found refuge in a Jeep he drove to the outfield to start the show, where the plan was to demolish hundreds of disco records. As the mob took over, Dahl pushed the gas pedal to the floor and wove through the outfield to his escape exit.

The cherry bomb firecrackers thrown by drunk fans exploded near him, causing him to flinch as he scrambled to escape. Dahl dodged firecrackers, cups of beer, and even an Earth, Wind & Fire vinyl record hurled at the open Jeep.

The Jeep made it to the open center field gate and slid to safety as crew members quickly closed the gate doors, shutting out the mob.

Veeck shook his head in disgust. He was abandoned.

Three hours earlier, the day started as a Major League Baseball doubleheader.

The "Disco Sucks" promotion was the brainchild of Dahl, who had been on a mission to demonize disco music since his previous radio station fired him when it transitioned from a rock format to disco. On this night, the top three songs on the Billboard Top 40 were disco songs by two Black women. Donna Summer's "Bad Girls" topped the charts and her song "Hot Stuff" was No. 3. Anita

Ward's "Ring My Bell" was No. 2 on the charts.

For this night's promotion, Dahl had convinced Veeck to let him blow up a crate of disco records between the two games of a baseball doubleheader.

Organizers expected 35,000 fans, which would have been a successful turnout considering the White Sox drew just 15,500 people the previous night.

Instead, 50,000 people filled the stadium, with thousands more turned away. The park's capacity was 44,492, and team security was utterly unprepared for the overflowing drunken mob.

For the promotion, fans had to bring a disco album and paid just 98 cents to enter. Dahl's radio station – WLUP 97.9 - sponsored the event.

From the start, there were omens the night might erupt into chaos.

Harry Caray, the wildly popular baseball announcer, sat in his booth calling the first game in the fourth inning.

"This is Disco Demolition Night - it's a full house, and what a promotion!" Caray said, his words slightly slurred due to the beer he had been drinking in the booth. "Boy, they've got banners all over the place!"

Then a vinyl record flew out of the bleachers and landed in the outfield.

"And another record is thrown onto the field," Caray said, now getting annoyed at the constant stoppages of play.

Detroit Tiger outfielder Ron LeFlore wore his batting helmet in center field because so many records were being thrown at him from the bleachers.

After the first game ended, Dahl was handed a microphone and wandered into the outfield. He encouraged the fans to join along with his anti-disco chants.

"Us rock 'n' rollers here in Chicago think disco sucks!" Dahl yelled into his microphone, waving his arm to incite the crowd.

Dahl soaked in the rousing cheers and was intoxicated by his power over a simmering crowd craving to attack disco.

"Disco sucks!" he continued. "Disco sucks!"

Soon, tens of thousands of fans were chanting along.

"And we are not going to let them forget it!" Dahl yelled as he wandered around the outfield while the crowd chanted. "We are not going to let them shove it down our throats!"

Minutes later, Dahl triggered the explosion of piles of records that had been stacked in the center of the outfield, jettisoning many into the air amidst a cloud of billowing smoke and pyrotechnics.

Dahl flinched and turned away from the explosion. He was shocked by the vast crater left in the grass.

"What the hell?" Dahl thought.

With the remains of records scattered across the outfield, Dahl turned around to head back to the visiting team's dugout, believing the promotion had ended.

But then a few frenzied fans stormed the field, overwhelming the scattered middle-aged men and young women dressed in bright yellow vests posing as extra security guards for the event.

Within a minute, hundreds of more rowdy fans spilled onto the field. They came for a riot and now created one.

Veeck's heart sank as the promotion spun wildly out of control.

He limped with his peg leg to the middle of the infield with his microphone. Bill Veeck didn't look like a typical baseball owner in baggy pants and an untucked sports shirt hanging off his thin 6-

foot-3 frame.

Veeck was 65 years old and had forged a reputation as an entertaining promoter. Among his countless gimmicks during the 1940s through the 1960s, he would grill his players about their musical talents and have them perform in post-game concerts for fans, who dressed in their finest Sunday clothes during that era.

In 1979, the fans attending Disco Demolition Night didn't come to be entertained. They were not dressed for a formal occasion, but more suitable for a rock concert in blue jeans and T-shirts. They were out to destroy disco, not enjoy baseball. And Veeck realized too late that he had handed them the keys.

Veeck gazed through the dissipating smoke and saw fans lighting another bonfire in the outfield. He looked to his right and was horrified to see a drunk fan had climbed the foul ball pole and was dangling from the top, 25 feet in the air.

"Hey, you in center field!" Veeck yelled into his microphone. "Back to your seats! This is Bill Veeck! The television cameras are not on you!"

Instead, more fans started yet another fire in the outfield. To the rioters on the field, Veeck had all the authority of a high school principal on the last day of school.

The longtime team owner held the microphone in his hand but said nothing. He was at a loss for words. The situation was hopeless.

The organist made an effort to calm the crowd and started the first few bars of "Take Me Out To The Ball Game". Popular announcer Harry Caray traditionally sang the tune during the seventh-inning stretch of games.

And like all great captains, Veeck was determined to go down with his ship. He began singing, microphone in hand.

"Take me out to the ball game, take me out to the crowd ...."

Veeck sang as if it were just another seventh-inning stretch.

Veeck went down singing the unofficial baseball anthem while Comiskey Park was in flames.

Some young fans held hands and danced to Veeck's tune as they formed a chain and pranced around the infield in a scene reminiscent of Woodstock. Other fans raced around the bases with the intoxication of pretending to be real-life Major League Baseball players. As they rounded third base, a fellow rioter pretended to be an umpire and called them all safe after they slid into home plate.

As Veeck finished singing, more rioters turned to the enormous metal cage that was brought on the field after the first game for batting practice. The mob swarmed the 30-foot-high batting cage. Finally, the metal contraption collapsed like a college football's goalpost swamped by victorious revelers.

The fans let out a collective roar, aroused even more by the mayhem their mob was orchestrating.

WGN sports announcer Jimmy Piersall sat in the press box disgusted at what he saw as Veeck stood helpless in the middle of the diamond.

Piersall got the nod from the director that he was back on air live.

"Jimmy Piersall back at the ball game. This is one of the saddest sights I've ever seen in my life," Piersall said as he stood up with his headset on to get a better view. "This garbage of demolishing records has turned into a fiasco. I certainly hope there is an example being made here that something like this will never happen again, not only for this ballpark but all parks around the country."

There were now 7,000 hysterical fans on the field.

Under the stadium, 40 Chicago police officers stood in silence.

They didn't have long hair like the people rioting in the field. It was cropped-close, military style, and hidden by riot gear including helmets, shields, and batons. The riot police lined up inside the visiting team's clubhouse, and then slowly walked through the dugout and pushed past the few brave Detroit Tigers who stuck around to watch the spectacle.

The riot police advanced shoulder-to-shoulder to the top of the steps leading to the field.

The police captain blew a whistle, and the police jumped onto the field and advanced in a slow trot, never breaking formation.

The wild-eyed fans knew the reputation for brutality of Chicago's police force. They saw the wall of approaching shields, helmets, and batons and scrambled back to their seats.

Within two minutes, the field was cleared but lay in smoldering ruins. Rome had been sacked.

At 9:15 p.m., the second game was officially announced as a forfeit in favor of Detroit because the field was in no condition for a game. For only the fourth time in the past 20 years, a game was forfeited in Major League Baseball.

After the police reclaimed the field and the forfeit was announced, the mood in the press box had changed. The game was meaningless. Several sportswriters had called in low-paid freelancers to report the final box score over the phone to the newspaper editors back in the office. That would get the writers who covered the teams out early.

The White Sox were 11 games out of first place, and the Tigers were 14 games out. Most of the chatter in the press box during the first game before the riot was about favorite bands, the colorful mannerisms of new Detroit Tiger manager Sparky Anderson and the observation there was an overwhelming odor of illegal marijuana wafting in from the stands.

But newspapers thrived on chaos. The dozen TV and newspaper reporters knew they had just watched one of the biggest fiascos in the history of baseball unfold before them.

The newspaper reporters moved silently from the press box to the teams' clubhouse. There was no chatter in the elevator, instead replaced by the tension that tags along with a major developing story.

After the two-minute trip from the press box to the players' clubhouse, the reporters fanned out to get the reaction to the debacle.

In the locker room, a TV reporter with a microphone walked up to Chicago White Sox pitcher Rich Wortham and asked him for his reaction.

Wortham looked into the camera.

"This wouldn't have happened if they had a country and western night," Wortham said in a thick Texan accent.

There were 39 people arrested that night. Just 18 months after Disco Demolition Night, Veeck would sell the White Sox and never get back into the business, which he entered as a popcorn vendor at games during The Great Depression.

CHAPTER 2

The All-Negro Team That Never Was

Aug. 9, 1942

Bill Veeck walked down an aisle in Yankee Stadium with a newspaper tucked under his arm.

Two big front-page headlines read:

"FBI Arrested 116 German, 15 Jap Enemy Aliens In New York City" and "Satchel Paige Suggests An All-Negro Team For Majors"

While the Major League Baseball team owners wouldn't allow Blacks on their rosters, they didn't mind occasionally cashing in on Negro League baseball by renting their large stadiums to Black teams for special attractions - like a chance to see Satchel Paige play.

Paige was one of the biggest draws in baseball, white or Black, right behind the legendary Babe Ruth. On this day, the Negro League was sponsoring a game in Yankee Stadium between two all-Black teams, the Kansas City Monarchs and the Cuban Giants. Paige was pitching for the Monarchs.

Veeck navigated his 6-foot-3 frame into the boxed seat, dwarfing his already-seated friend, the 5-foot-3 Abe Saperstein, who founded the Harlem Globetrotters basketball team in 1926.

Saperstein's original concept with the Globetrotters was to field a great all-Black basketball team and barnstorm around the country playing against white opponents. As the Globetrotters overpowered their all-white opponents, they began improvising during games. Leading by a large margin, a Globetrotter would throw a behind-the-back pass to a teammate waiting underneath the basket. Another Globetrotter would do a windmill motion before another dazzling pass to a teammate for an easy basket. The referees allowed it, having never seen such antics. The white fans loved it. Saperstein incorporated it into the team's play. The act became a sensation.

The Globetrotters won nearly all their games, but it was the entertaining antics that captured the hearts of millions. They were loved by white audiences across Jim Crow America with their comic routines laced with showmanship. "Jim Crow" was a derogatory 19th-century term for Blacks and referred to a system of laws in the South that legalized the separation of races.

At this game, Veeck and Saperstein were both white men who stood out among the 32,000 mostly Black fans who came out that day to Yankee Stadium. The all-white Yankees drew as little as 3,000 fans in some games.

Saperstein and Veeck shared a common bond. They were both circus ringmasters at heart, a shared trait that contributed to a lifelong friendship.

In 1941, at the age of 28, Veeck bought the minor league baseball Milwaukee Brewers franchise. The Brewers led the minor league's American Association in attendance every year.

Veeck was already earning a reputation as a showman. He once traded for a player and had him jump out of a giant cake at home plate and then take the mound to pitch. After each victory, Veeck stood at the gate, thanking fans for coming and shaking their hands. He often gave away live lobsters, pigeons, and chickens at his games.

But Veeck was not content with being a standout in the minor leagues. He believed he was born for a bigger spotlight – Major League Baseball. His father, Bill Veeck Sr., had been a top executive for Major League Baseball's Chicago Cubs.

Saperstein was at Yankee Stadium on this day in 1942 to scout

Black players. Not surprisingly, his interest in Black basketball naturally spilled over into baseball's Negro Leagues. He was looking for players, whether it be basketball or baseball, he'd figure out later.

Veeck had come to New York with an idea that would shock the nation. He wanted his friend Saperstein in on the deal, but was uncertain as to how to rope his friend in.

Veeck began with some small talk.

"They are saying they are going to draw 30,000 people here today," Veeck said.

Saperstein knew the mighty New York Yankees would usually draw half that many fans for a game. He also knew Veeck hadn't come all the way from Milwaukee just to watch a Negro League game.

"Satchel Paige," Saperstein responded, explaining what would draw such a crowd.

"So, why did you come all the way to New York? To watch Satchel pitch … again?" Saperstein asked.

"Business," Veeck said. "And really, it was more to talk with you."

Saperstein put down his pencil. Veeck had his attention.

Veeck opened his newspaper and held it in his lap.

"This was the lead editorial in today's newspaper about Satchel Paige. Let me read it to you," Veeck said.

Veeck composed himself and read the article: "We do implore the heavy-footed wizard of the raised pitching mound to arrive in New York minus a display of temperament usually associated with Stepin Fetchit. Baseball can well do without such hi-jinks. The thousands of dyed-in-the-wool fans who pay prices ranging from 55 cents to $1.62 are entitled to witness real baseball, not hippodroming."

Saperstein chuckled.

Stepin Fetchit was the stage name for Black actor Lincoln Theodore Monroe Andrew Perry, whose act was billed as "The Laziest Man In The World." Many Blacks found it a demeaning stereotype. Fetchit defended his act, saying it made him the first Black millionaire actor.

"They compared Satch to Stepin Fetchit?" Saperstein nodded knowingly. "Some whites aren't comfortable with a showboating Negro in sports."

Veeck glanced around Yankee Stadium, soaking in all the sounds and scenes of a warm Saturday afternoon in August.

"And look at the crowd already," Veeck said. "Satch has brought the coloreds out to the ballpark. That's a whole new market!"

Saperstein suspected this was leading to a pitch. And he wasn't wrong.

But Veeck's pitch would have to wait a moment. Paige had walked onto the field on his way to the pitching mound as Veeck finished his last sentence.

Paige didn't wear as baggy a jersey as the white major league players traditionally wore. His tighter jersey and pants outlined his trim, athletic 6-foot-3, 180-pound frame. His gait was akin to a model on a runway, fluid with rhythm to his steps. He started his windup by making two windmill motions, then kicked his leg straight up and held it still for three seconds before releasing a blazing fastball. That was Paige's famous "Hesitation Pitch." That pitching motion appeared at times as a dance routine.

Several women in the stands moved up to the dugout area to get a better look at Paige.

Veeck was as mesmerized.

Saperstein noticed he had momentarily lost Veeck's attention.

"Seems baseball could use more vaudeville," Veeck said.

"You two were made for each other," Saperstein laughed. "He's just toying with them today. And his Monarchs team could play with the Yankees. I'm here to see a player named Buck O'Neil."

Saperstein jotted down some more notes.

Veeck had a sparkle in his eyes. He turned his head to Saperstein.

It was time to make his pitch.

"Abe, I am moving up to the big league. I'm going to try to buy the Philadelphia Phillies," Veeck said, waiting for his friend's reaction. The Philadelphia Phillies were a Major League Baseball team in the National League.

Saperstein put down his notebook.

"What about the current owner, Gerald Nugent?" Saperstein asked.

"Bankrupt. He's trying to get a loan from baseball just to get his team to spring training," Veeck said, smiling.

"What's his price?" Saperstein asked.

"We talked about him selling me the team for $250,000," Veeck said.

Saperstein laughed and threw his head back. Now, he got it.

"So, you came down here to ask me for money?" Saperstein asked, shaking his head. "You think you can pull together that much for a team that has lost over 100 games five years in a row?"

Veeck smiled.

"I'm about $200,000 shy at the moment," he said.

"There's something I'm telling you that's off the record. You got to keep it here for now," Veeck said.

Saperstein nodded.

"The league is about to have its first all-Negro team. I am putting together a colored team after the sale," Veeck said.

Saperstein was stunned.

Veeck continued: "I was thinking since you have so much experience and credibility with the Negroes as the owner of Harlem Globetrotters, I could use your help signing them."

Saperstein immediately shook his head no.

"Are you out of your mind? You're going to bring an all-colored team into a league that doesn't allow Negroes to play? That's the most ludicrous thing I've ever heard," Saperstein said.

"More ludicrous than a 5-foot-3 white man making a living owning an all-colored basketball team?" Veeck retorted.

"And think of the promotional draw this would be for fans!" Veeck said, his voice rising.

"We'd pull in whites and coloreds," Veeck said.

Saperstein's face was flushed.

"The Globetrotters don't play in the National Basketball League. We barnstorm. America appreciates Negro athletes," Saperstein said. "But only as long as they don't mix with white society. Segregation. That's why they have the Negro Leagues."

Saperstein paused.

"I'm trying to pull together another Negro League right now. There's some market for that. You're great at promoting your teams and getting large fan turnouts. But this - you're going too far," Saperstein said.

Veeck smiled.

"Hell, The Harlem Globetrotters would outdraw any of the pro teams in the National Basketball League. You guys are aces!" Veeck said.

Saperstein was still annoyed. He believed the Globetrotters would outdraw any team in any sport.

"Do you know what would happen if you brought an all-Negro team to Philadelphia? You'd start a riot," Saperstein said.

"Great. We could have it in between the doubleheader with the Giants after you jump out of the cake," Veeck said, nudging Saperstein with his elbow. "Are you reading what the Negro newspapers are saying about some of the Negro ballplayers? They say this fellow Josh Gibson is better than Ruth. I could sign him."

Josh Gibson was a catcher in the Negro Leagues whose tremendous hitting earned him the nickname "The Black Babe Ruth."

Saperstein calmed himself and nodded.

"I've seen them both play. Gibson is better. He's Ruth without the hangovers," Saperstein said.

Veeck smiled.

"You were the booking agent for a Negro League team. You know the Negro players. I could put this team together and – "

Saperstein cut off Veeck.

"And what?" Saperstein snapped. "You don't know a thing about what it means to have a Negro sports team or what the Negro players will go through for your latest stunt. Most cities won't even allow my players to stay in the same hotel as me. Sometimes, they sneak up the fire escape into my room to have a place to sleep for the night."

Saperstein knew what he was talking about. He wasn't just the owner of the Harlem Globetrotters. He was also the team's coach, bus driver, booking agent, and public relations director. His experience was vital to what Veeck had in mind.

Saperstein turned to Veeck, a tinge of anger in his voice.

"I've had ten people in my room some nights," he said. "We have to play 150 games a year just to make ends meet, and we barely make $50 a game. In one game, one of my players got injured. I substituted myself for him."

Veeck interjected.

"You play basketball? Bet that's a sight to see," Veeck laughed.

Saperstein smirked, too, understanding how absurd it sounded.

"I played nine sports in school," Saperstein said. "But my point is after I played in that game with my colored players, I went out to my car, and all my tires were slashed."

Veeck was silent.

Saperstein looked at Veeck as if he finally got through to him about how outlandish his latest promotion was.

"None of that scares me. How about becoming a part owner with me?" Veeck asked.

"Own an all-Negro team - in Philadelphia? This is beyond one of your stunts, Bill. You know the manager, Hans Lobert?" Saperstein asked.

Veeck nodded.

"He would never coach a Negro. So, you lose him right away. I would love to know a manager willing to step in and coach an all-Negro team," Saperstein asked. "Probably someone who doesn't have a family to worry about keeping safe."

Saperstein paused. He knew he would regret asking his next question.

"Just out of curiosity, how would you pull this off?" he asked.

Veeck smiled.

"Two separate spring training camps. One white. One colored. The white team is the one that everyone thinks will play Opening Day. Then the real team of Negroes will replace them at the last minute," Veeck said.

Saperstein gave Veeck a stern look.

"You haven't told anyone about this yet, have you?" Saperstein asked.

Veeck wryly smiled. He held up the newspaper with the Paige headline about baseball's first all-Negro team.

"Well, are you with me?" Veeck asked.

Saperstein smiled.

"I get to select the colored roster, right?" Saperstein asked.

CHAPTER 3

A Gentlemen's Agreement

Feb. 26, 1943

Kenesaw Mountain Landis had a chiseled face with a perpetual scowl that could scare a crying baby quiet.

At 5-foot-6, 130 pounds, Landis' diminutive stature contradicted his intimidating, tyrannical management style as the first baseball commissioner. Landis was the supreme ruler of Major League Baseball.

Once described as looking like Whistler's mother in slacks, Landis was born a year after the Civil War ended and named after a battle in the War Between the States.

Landis was a federal judge in the Northern District of Illinois when he took over as commissioner in 1921.

In 1907, Judge Landis achieved fame by ordering Standard Oil of Indiana to pay $29 million for violating federal rules on freight charges. That ruling, which was later reversed on appeal, gave him the reputation of being anti-business. And with the power to stare down big oil came an ego.

In 1921, Landis was hired as baseball commissioner after the infamous 1919 "Black Sox" gambling scandal when several White Sox players conspired to throw the World Series against the Cincinnati Reds. His non-negotiable condition on taking the job as commissioner was to be given absolute power over baseball.

Babe Ruth challenged Landis' authority in 1922, the commissioner's second year on the job, and lost. Ruth had played in barnstorming games after the season to make more money. These games involved players independently assembling teams and playing in select cities. Landis forbid Ruth's traveling band of all-stars from playing against Black teams. Ruth ignored Landis' edict and played against many Negro League teams in 1921 and then a collection of Black players on a barnstorming team in the spring of 1922. Even though Ruth had just completed his best year with 59 home runs, Landis suspended the best player in the game for six weeks in 1922.

That confirmed Landis as the power that ran baseball.

Maybe Landis had smiled once or twice in the more than 20 years since he stared down Ruth, but there wasn't a photo around to verify it. The bags under his eyes completed a lean, angular face resembling a powdered-wig politician who could be memorialized on American currency someday.

As commissioner, Landis made $50,000 a year in 1921, the equivalent of $807,200 in 2023. Yet, he had a singular focus on his job. He was married but resided the past 27 years in Chicago's luxurious Ambassador East Hotel, not wanting to be sidetracked by the duties involved in owning a home.

The 76-year-old commissioner was not smiling when Boston Red Sox owner Tom Yawkey came to his Chicago office in February 1943 to discuss Bill Veeck's bid to buy the Philadelphia Phillies.

With his square jaw and short, slicked back black hair with a hint of silver, Yawkey resembled the image of a high-level labor union official. The Boston Red Sox baseball cap he liked to wear looked out of place with his entitled persona.

As is said about the privileged, Yawkey was born on third base. He was adopted by an uncle who left him a $20 million inheritance at age 16. That is the equivalent of $362 million in 2023.

In 1933, when Yawkey had full access to his fortune when he turned 30, he bought the Red Sox for $1.25 million. In that first year, eight players on the team were older than Yawkey. Yet, they all knew to call him "Mr. Yawkey."

Yawkey and Landis formed an intimidating yet unlikely alliance.

Yawkey was a Yale-educated, trust-fund baby who seldom lost his composure with an impeccable vocabulary polished with an Ivy League education.

He adored his life as the owner of the Boston Red Sox. During the baseball season, Yawkey spent most of his time at Boston's Fenway Park while living at a suite at Boston's Ritz-Carlton hotel. Yawkey never bothered to buy a home in Boston. During the off-season, he lived in an apartment in New York's Pierre hotel that he bought from hotel owner and oil man J. Paul Getty. Yawkey also visited his 40,000-acre estate in South Carolina, where he liked to hunt.

Kenesaw Mountain Landis came from a different background. He was a self-made high-school dropout, not a child of privilege. He was a theatrical judge whose court decisions were often overturned. Landis also peppered his sentences with profanities seldom heard in his affluent circles. When his wife almost slipped on a sidewalk, he warned her, "Be careful, dear, or you'll break your goddamn neck."

Yet, Landis and Yawkey bonded over the goal of preventing Blacks from playing in Major League Baseball. They kept a tight social circle. Landis sat with Yawkey's wife at high-profile events like the Major League Baseball all-star game.

On this February day in 1943 they met in Landis' office where they were joined by Ford Frick, a 48-year-old former teacher and sportswriter. Frick was a retired semi-pro ballplayer who had risen to president of the National League, a position he had held for nearly a decade.

Frick, Yawkey and Landis could hear Philadelphia Phillies' owner Gerald Nugent approaching down the hall.

Nugent was not part of any elevated social circle. A World War I hero with two citations for bravery, he didn't have the generational wealth to keep a Major League Baseball team out of red ink.

Nugent's Phillies were struggling financially, and he was losing money. He wanted to sell the Phillies, who played in the National League, and get out of the business. But any sale of his team would need to be approved by the other National League owners.

That's why Nugent came to see Landis. There was a knock at the door. Landis didn't look up. Frick quickly realized it was his job to answer it. He walked over and opened the door.

Frick started the introduction.

"Mr. Nugent. Thank you for coming on such short notice," Frick said with a nervous smile.

Nugent looked around and was confused about why Yawkey, an owner from the opposing American League, was present.

"Commissioner Landis, Mr. Yawkey, Mr. Frick, it's my pleasure. And I owe the league a lot of money, so this is the least I could do. But no worries, once I sell the Phillies, it'll all be taken care of," Nugent said.

There was a moment of uncomfortable silence as Landis had not even lifted his head to make eye contact with Nugent.

Finally, Landis spoke.

"Have a seat," Landis told Nugent in an admonishing tone.

Nugent sat down in a seat across from Landis and next to Yawkey. Frick continued to stand.

"Your deal with Veeck is dead. By the end of the week, we'll have another owner willing to buy the team," Landis said.

Nugent was shocked.

"For $250,000?" Nugent said, citing the price Veeck had told him he would pay for his franchise.

"It'll be $85,000," Landis said. "And we'll forgive the loans."

Nugent was appalled.

"The loans were only $75,000," Nugent shot back.

"The sale will be announced in a few weeks," Landis said, ignoring Nugent's objection.

Nugent persisted.

"Why would I agree to a sale at a fraction of what Veeck was offering?" Nugent asked.

Landis stopped what he was doing and finally made eye contact with Nugent.

"You think that carnival barker was going to come up with $250,000?" Landis snapped. "Did you verify the financing?"

Nugent shook his head.

"I took the man at his word," Nugent said.

Landis stood up, walked around his desk, and stood toe-to-toe with Nugent.

"The owners won't approve selling the team to that man," Landis said. "Negotiations with Veeck are through."

Landis stepped back and leaned on the edge of his large wooden desk.

"Mr. Nugent, it's my job to protect the integrity of the game. Bill Veeck wanted to bring in a team of all Negroes to play in Philadelphia," Landis said, pausing to allow the gravity of the accusation to sink in.

"All Negroes, Mr. Nugent," Landis repeated. "Were you aware of this? This deal didn't happen overnight."

Nugent shook his head.

"Our discussions were strictly financial and very preliminary," Nugent said. "Nothing was signed. He assured me he could get the funding."

Landis returned to his seat.

"I assure you the owners won't sign the deal - for a myriad of reasons," he said. "The National League is now assuming all operations of the Philadelphia Phillies due to the financial condition of the franchise."

Before Nugent could respond, Landis ended the conversation.

"Thank you, Mr. Nugent. You can see yourself out," he said.

His face red with anger, Nugent looked at Yawkey and Frick, then turned away and walked out the door.

Frick closed the door behind Nugent.

"Sir? Did he know?" Frick asked.

Landis sat back.

"It doesn't matter. Veeck called me and said he would have an all-white team play in the spring games. And then on opening day, swap his all-white team for an all-Negro team that was practicing in a secret location," Landis said.

The commissioner lit a cigar.

"At least, that was what he planned to do," the commissioner said.

Frick was confused.

"He was just going sign a team of Negroes? In Philadelphia? Without telling anyone?" Frick said.

Frick considered the possibility.

"Has he lost his mind?" Frick asked.

"That's just the tip of the iceberg with this Veeck character," Landis said.

He ruffled through some newspapers on his desk. He found the article from a Milwaukee newspaper dated from July.

It reported that Veeck invited American Association president George Trautman to one of his Milwaukee Brewers games this year.

Veeck had angered the president of the minor league association earlier in the season by calling the league's umps "Trautman's blind boys."

Landis read from the article. It reported that when the seventh-inning stretch was going on, Veeck got on the PA system and said he had a special gift for Trautman, who was guided to the center of the diamond to receive it.

Trautman was expecting a gift. Instead, one attendant came out of the stands with a seeing-eye dog, and another attendant came out with a striped cane and a cup containing pencils. And Veeck got on the PA and said, "These are for your boys!"

Landis finished reading and put down the article.

"The fans went nuts. Trautman ends up looking like a goddamn idiot," Landis said, his lip trembling with anger. "Veeck did that to the president of the league. He brought in 9,000 fans to a minor league game."

Landis shook his head.

"The man who just walked out of our office was lucky to get 3,000 fans to a game this year in Philadelphia," Landis said.

Landis turned to Yawkey.

"You know, I knew Veeck's father," Landis said.

Landis reflected on the memory.

"He was an executive for the Cubs," Landis said. "The son is nothing like him."

Yawkey had never met Bill Veeck. He bought the Red Sox in 1933, the same year Veeck's father died. All he had known about Veeck's background was that Veeck owned a minor-league baseball team and had dropped out of an obscure Ohio college when his father died.

None of that sounded appealing regarding joining the ranks of reputable owners in Major League Baseball.

"He may draw fans, but he does it by mocking a respectable establishment," Yawkey said. "This is what Bill Veeck will bring. He has no respect for this establishment."

Yawkey turned to Landis.

"I am almost certain I can get William Cox to buy the Phillies. He and my father were in the lumber industry. He's the perfect fit – he is a Yale man," joked Yawkey, who also attended Yale.

Landis nodded but was still concerned.

"We will need more than Ivy League smarts to get around this. Keeping the Negroes out of baseball is starting to feel like trying to hold back the ocean tide," Landis said.

"How's that?" Yawkey asked.

Landis took a puff from his cigar.

"Veeck isn't our only problem, Tom," Landis said, one of the few people bold enough to call Yawkey by his first name. "In December, I have a meeting in Los Angeles with Negro newspaper publishers about their campaign to integrate baseball."

Landis paused and then another issue involving integration came to mind.

"And this Paul Robeson character? He's a Negro musician?" Landis asked, giving a bewildered glance to Yawkey and Frick.

Both shrugged.

"Well, he's going to be at our winter meeting this year to talk about allowing Negroes to play," Landis said. "Whatever this Robeson says, I'll make goddamn sure the owners don't play along."

Robeson was a New Jersey actor who made it big performing in Shakespeare plays in New York City and London in the 1920s and 1930s. As one of the most famous Black actors, he had recently become involved in the civil rights movement and pressured Major League Baseball to sign Black players.

Landis reached for another piece of paper on his desk.

"Then there's this Citizens Committee to End Discrimination in Baseball that wants mixed-raced teams to be added this year. And FDR's Fair Employment Act," Landis said.

"Just tell them the truth: Baseball has no policy against Negroes playing," Yawkey said, repeating the standard cover story baseball had claimed while trying to convince the public there was no orchestrated conspiracy to keep Blacks out of baseball.

Landis reached for another piece of paper on his desk.

"We have a gentleman's agreement throughout the league about no Negroes being signed," Landis said.

"And Veeck is no gentleman," Yawkey interjected. "No doubt he will capitalize on this."

The commissioner nodded.

"But the fans seem to love him, so we must tread carefully.

Signing an all-Negro team is a thumb at the nose of this establishment. If he is willing to do this, no telling what he might do to embarrass us," Landis said.

"We can't have Negroes playing in the big leagues. It just won't work. It's not us. The fans won't have it. There'd be riots, and we must do our part to keep cities safe. Not to mention what they might try to do to the Negro players," Yawkey said.

Landis looked to Yawkey.

"That position will be more and more arduous to maintain. I've done what I can, but we are walking a thin line," Landis said.

Landis had done many things to discourage Blacks and whites from playing against each other. During his tenure, barnstorming had become popular. Realizing Landis would face a rebellion if he stripped the players' ability to work that lucrative side job, he allowed it with restrictions.

Landis didn't allow players to wear their Major League Baseball uniforms in mixed-race exhibitions, in part because Black teams too often were beating their white opponents. A key tenet of the rationalization to keep Blacks out of Major League Baseball was that they were not good enough to make a roster. Landis didn't want the public to realize the quality of the Black players.

When some of the Black barnstorming teams began outdrawing Major League Baseball teams, Landis told the owners of the Major League Baseball teams that they could no longer lease their stadiums to the Negro teams, except for certain special events. Landis sought to shut down the barnstorming games knowing no other facilities could host the large crowds they were drawing.

Landis picked up another newspaper article on his desk.

"That goddamn Satchel Paige, he was drawing 30,000 fans a game with his traveling band of Negro all-stars. He's outdrawing our teams by three times. And they were thrashing our white teams with former major leaguers," Landis said.

"You know you have my support and the other owners. So where do we go from here?" Yawkey said.

Landis took another puff from his cigar.

"If we keep saying that we have no policy and it's left up to the clubs, Veeck or eventually someone else will sign a Negro," Landis said. "And he's not going away. We stopped him this time, but I fear this man will be like a bad penny that keeps turning up."

Landis looked to Yawkey.

"You know, his wife was with the Ringling Brothers Circus. She rode horses," Landis said. He puffed from his cigar as that image played in his mind.

"That's what he will turn baseball into, a goddamn circus. Hell, he'd get married in between a doubleheader with the Bearded Lady as a bridesmaid if it drew 10,000 fans," Landis said.

Yawkey stood up and walked toward Landis' desk.

"How about promoting the quality of Negro League baseball and 'equal but separate?' That's been good enough for the Supreme Court for almost fifty years," Yawkey said. "Nobody is saying they can't play baseball. They have an equal league. I have even watched a few games."

Landis laughed.

"Our owners make money by renting our parks for them to play. Of course, you want to keep them 'separate but equal.' That's what the other side will say," Landis said.

"Touché," Yawkey said.

"And they will argue it isn't really equal, especially if you look at the financials. And I heard that colored team in Boston - what are they? The Royal Giants? Puts on a better show than your Red Sox," Landis said.

Yawkey was offended by the jab and didn't respond.

"With our country at war and Negroes serving in the military, it doesn't help us," Landis said. "And all these goddamn-colored sportswriters have been campaigning to integrate baseball. They all write, 'We can stop a bullet, but not a baseball.'"

"Well, Judge," Yawkey said. "We can at least solve one problem easily. Bill Veeck. Let's just be done with him once and for all."

CHAPTER 4

A Big Guy With A Big Mouth

Aug. 17, 1945

Tom Yawkey's secretary was in practice of clipping relevant daily newspaper articles and leaving them on the Boston Red Sox owner's desk.

On top of the pile was a Boston Globe item mentioning a committee Yawkey had served on to identify which Major League Baseball players returning from wartime service were eligible to play in the World Series.

It mentioned Red Sox star Ted Williams, but with the Boston Red Sox sporting a 51-58 record and currently in the midst of a late-season six-game losing streak, Yawkey didn't think it mattered much even if Williams could get back in time.

A clipping from the Boston Chronicle, the city's Black newspaper, caught his eye because he generally was not a reader of the Black press. The headline read, "Committee Named To Study 'Color Line' In Organized Baseball."

Yawkey began to read it and was alarmed: New York Yankees president Larry MacPhail had been named to the committee. Yawkey knew what a disaster that was likely to be.

The New York state legislature became the first state in the country to pass a law banning discrimination in employment earlier in the year. Then months later, New York City mayor Fiorello LaGuardia formed a committee whose goal was to study the segregation of baseball and pressure New York teams to sign Black players.

LaGuardia appointed a Black minister, several prestigious judges, Brooklyn Dodgers' general manager Branch Rickey and MacPhail to the 10-man committee in early August.

Yawkey saw MacPhail as a liability. The two men weren't strangers. During the off-season, Yawkey resided in a posh New York City hotel. He and MacPhail had become drinking buddies after getting acquainted during the 1941 World Series in New York between the Yankees and cross-town rival Brooklyn Dodgers. MacPhail was president of the Dodgers at that time.

In 1942, MacPhail left the Dodgers to enlist in the Army. Now, in 1945, he was back and president of the New York Yankees.

MacPhail was valuable because he was a wizard at making baseball teams profitable. It was his stroke of genius that saw night baseball introduced in the National League during the 1930s.

He also had a long history of binge drinking and boorish statements that got him in trouble.

Ten years earlier, when MacPhail was general manager of the Cincinnati Reds, an incident arising from lewd remarks made to an attractive young woman in a hotel hosting a convention led to a drunken MacPhail sucker-punching a police sergeant. The sergeant responded with a punch that knocked MacPhail unconscious. When the reporters asked about it the next day, MacPhail denied anything happened - despite a black eye.

In the dark days of 1942 that followed the United States entering World War II after the attack on Pearl Harbor, MacPhail spoke at a sportswriters' banquet in New York City. MacPhail blurted to the crowd that the U.S. Air Force should get the biggest bomber they can build and crew it with baseball players and name that plane the "Kenesaw Mountain Landis" after baseball's then commissioner. And that, he asserted, would be professional baseball's contribution to the war effort.

United Press International sportswriter Jack Guenther covered the event and wrote: "Larry MacPhail is a big guy with a big mouth. He has a dubious talent for speaking his mind on any subject at any time. Many people who know him don't like him."

As owner of the Boston Red Sox, the more sophisticated Yawkey was beginning to emerge as the American League's most influential power broker. This was due in part to his financial fortune. He was a man used to getting what he wanted, and in the summer of 1945, he wanted to keep Black players out of Major League Baseball.

Yawkey had gained experience in accomplishing this when he faced political pressure in Boston to sign a Black ballplayer.

In 1944, Boston City Council member Isadore Muchnick was on a crusade. He saw the absence of Black players on the Red Sox roster as an injustice and was determined to remedy it. The council member threatened to deny the Boston Red Sox authorization to play games on Sunday if the team refused to consider adding Black players.

The pressure induced the Red Sox to give three Black players a tryout in 1945 – Jackie Robinson, Marvin Williams, and Sam Jethroe. After putting the three players through their motions on the field for just 90 minutes, team officials claimed none were good enough to play on the Boston team.

City Council member Muchnick was present, and reported hearing someone yell, "Get those niggers off the field!" during the closed event. But it was never determined which if any Red Sox official said it.

Sam Jethroe said that after his Boston tryout, Red Sox manager Joe Cronin told him they were good enough to play in the all-white Major League Baseball but that Blacks "were simply not being allowed at that time."

Yawkey had maneuvered his way through a racial minefield

without having to sign a Black player.

After the news broke on MacPhail's appointment to the race committee, Yawkey wanted to give MacPhail some insights on how to deal with politicians.

He asked MacPhail out for drinks on the first day Yawkey's Red Sox were in New York.

Yawkey was clever enough to shield himself from being identified as the man who stood in the way of signing a Black player. He just hired executives and managers who would never endorse the idea. And Yawkey became drinking buddies with these men.

But Yawkey had no control over MacPhail, a man he had little faith could handle the race issue competently. He had no control of the Yankees' organization.

Ahead of the Red Sox visit to New York City in 1945, Yawkey arranged for a private meeting with MacPhail at the fashionable Toots Shor's restaurant in Manhattan.

MacPhail was seated in an exclusive area of a restaurant and already on his fourth cocktail when Yawkey sat down at Toots Shor's Restaurant. It was the place to be for celebrities.

There was a general bar area where the celebrities would drink if they were in the mood for some publicity. Regular customers could approach for a simple autograph, but anything more attracted the attention of a nearby bouncer.

Yawkey secured the more seclusive back room for the private meeting, available only to the most influential customers. Regular customers were denied access.

Toots Shor, the owner of the restaurant, met customers personally who were meeting in a back room and led them to a booth. Shor had turned his restaurant into a New York City hot spot by personally serving and sparring with the celebrities.

When Yawkey arrived, MacPhail had already been seated.

"How many have you had?" Yawkey asked, knowing that at some point, MacPhail would be past the point of no return.

"This is only my second," MacPhail said, downplaying his consumption.

MacPhail was anxious. He was a good baseball tactician, but realized he was no politician and knew he had a knack for putting his foot in his mouth.

Commissioner Kenesaw Mountain Landis had died a year earlier. Happy Chandler had been selected by the owners as the new commissioner but would not officially take office for three more months. Chandler wasn't the strident defender of segregation as his predecessor.

Shor approached the table.

Yawkey ordered a martini and smiled.

"And how about you break out the gin you give Joe DiMaggio instead of the swill I had last time," Yawkey said, who enjoyed the lively banter with Shor.

"The only reason you got Joe's table is that he's overseas, or else I'd have you upfront by the kitchen," Shor said. "I tell you what, you win a World Series, and I'll get you the top-shelf gin."

Shor looked at MacPhail.

"Larry, why don't you bring one of the Yankees' World Series trophies next time?" Shor said as he walked away. "Let Yawkey know what they look like."

Yawkey looked at MacPhail.

"So, tell me about this commission you just got appointed to," Yawkey said.

MacPhail shrugged.

"It's stacked against me," he said. "And the commissioner hasn't offered much guidance on how to handle this."

"Happy won't be any help," Yawkey said, shaking his head.

"And neither will that son-of-a-bitch Branch Rickey!" MacPhail shot back. Rickey and MacPhail had a decade-old feud that started over the management of a minor league team in Columbus, Ohio.

MacPhail couldn't hide a panicked look.

"What do I do?" MacPhail asked.

"You have got to stall," Yawkey answered. "Just say this is an issue that merits serious study. And then take 18 months to study the issue."

MacPhail blurted, "The commission is going to say that there are enough good Negro players to make the majors."

Yawkey nodded. Anybody who followed newspaper accounts of the success Black barnstorming teams had playing against white teams stocked with major league players in the off-season knew that. But Yawkey knew white baseball executives could dodge that point.

"Use their own colored press against them," Yawkey said. "There's a Negro sportswriter who just came out and said he didn't think there were any Negro players that could make a major league roster. I'll have my secretary get you the article."

Yawkey paused.

"We don't have to make the argument. Their own sportswriter did it for us," Yawkey said, nodding.

Sam Lacy was a Black sports editor of The Afro-American in Baltimore. He wrote a column in 1945 in which he stated, "There are few, if any, Negro players who could qualify for play in the major leagues at this time."

The white newspapers in 1945 jumped on Lacy's claim and republished them.

Yawkey took a sip of his drink.

"And stick to the economic issues we have spelled out in the past on this. Negro League baseball is growing, and taking the best Negro players would damage the league. Major League Baseball makes money off renting stadiums to Negro teams. And Negro players are already under contract, so we couldn't sign them if we wanted to."

Yawkey took another sip from his martini.

"You don't have to write all this down," Yawkey said. "I will have my secretary get you the highlights."

Yawkey looked at MacPhail.

"And whatever you do, don't tell them that there is an agreement not to sign Negro players," Yawkey said. "And send them your response in a letter and stick to what we discussed."

On Sept. 29, the Black newspaper New York Age reported that MacPhail had submitted a four-page letter to LaGuardia's commission.

The letter stated that Black players were already under contract, there weren't any Black players good enough to make major league rosters, and the Negro League was disorganized and had to get themselves in order before Major League Baseball would consider taking on some of the Black players. The letter contained all of Yawkey's suggestions.

But then MacPhail abandoned his script and got political.

"It's unfortunate the groups of political and social-minded drum beaters are conducting pressure campaigns in an attempt to force major league clubs to sign Negro players now employed by Negro League clubs," the letter read. "I do not believe anything can be accomplished by signing Negro players for small minor league clubs. To give tryouts to players whom you do not intend to employ is sheer hypocrisy."

CHAPTER 5

The Only Woman In The Room

Nov. 17, 1945

The Hotel Theresa in Manhattan didn't allowed Blacks until 1937 when a Black millionaire realtor bought the 13-story hotel and ended the ban.

Eight years later, Hotel Theresa was a beacon for the top Black personalities visiting New York who could stay at a rare, welcoming five-star hotel.

In the autumn of 1945, the biggest names in Negro League baseball were meeting at the Hotel Theresa to discuss the prospect of losing their best players to all-white Major League Baseball.

Branch Rickey, general manager of Major League Baseball's Brooklyn Dodgers, had just signed Negro League star Jackie Robinson to play in the all-white Dodgers' minor league system. Rickey had ignored that Robinson was believed to be under contract with the Negro League's Kansas City Monarchs. So he was likely stealing the star Black player without compensation to the Negro League team owner.

At the podium in a room filled with Negro League team owners and executives was 54-year-old Cumberland Posey. He was a big man with a large jaw and an athletic body from years as a star basketball and baseball player on Black teams. Posey was the owner of the Negro League team the Homestead Grays.

"We have a response from the baseball commissioner about our official complaint filed by the Kansas City Monarchs over the Jackie Robinson signing," Posey said, holding up the letter.

A hush fell over the room. Posey paused, his mouth so dry he could barely get the words out.

"Commissioner Chandler said our complaint did not constitute a bona fide dispute for consideration by his office," Posey said.

Posey put down the letter.

"Major League Baseball commissioner Happy Chandler just told Negro League baseball he doesn't care if we have legal contracts," Posey said. "They aren't going to do anything."

A collective groan escaped from the audience.

All eyes locked on the lone white man in the room, who was standing next to Posey at the podium – J.L. Wilkinson, owner of the Monarchs, the team that filed the protest.

The 67-year-old Wilkinson had silver-white hair and a profoundly receding hairline. He had lost much of his hair but not the respect of many in that room. Wilkinson invested in stadium lights in 1930 and introduced night baseball to the Negro Leagues. This triggered a surge in attendance at his games. He shared that extra gate revenue with other Negro League owners to keep them afloat during the dark days of The Great Depression.

To improve the image of his players around town, Wilkinson bought suits for his Black players and urged them to wear them. He paid the medical expenses of many of his players. The players took great pride in playing for the Kansas City Monarchs.

On this day, Wilkinson knew his reaction to the rebuff by Major League Baseball over Jackie Robinson would determine the Negro League's response.

"Although I feel the Brooklyn club owes us some kind of compensation for Robinson, we will not protest to commissioner Chandler," Wilkinson said, his tone hiding extreme disappointment. "I am very glad to see Jackie get this chance, and I'm sure he'll make good. He's a wonderful ballplayer. If and when he gets into the major leagues, he will have a wonderful career."

Wilkinson paused.

"I won't stand in the way of the Negro player making the major leagues," he said.

Dressed in a three-piece suit, Clarence Wilson nodded and stood up from one of the room's tables to speak. Wilson was a Black assistant district attorney for the borough of Brooklyn, and well-connected politically.

"This will be my official statement to the press: I am delighted that Branch Rickey has taken the first practical step in eliminating discrimination in baseball. Every Negro will be grateful to him," Wilson said.

Wilson scanned the room and held up a newspaper.

"The newspapers are going to portray us as hurting a movement that just about every Negro group in this country has been fighting for – getting Negroes into the majors," Wilson said.

"This is what Tommy Holmes wrote," Wilson said as he cleared his throat and read from the article. Holmes was the sportswriter who covered Major League Baseball for the daily newspaper Brooklyn Eagle.

"The thing about the Jackie Robinson story today that strikes right out and hits you between the eyes is that the first Negro ever to be signed to a contract in organized baseball may be blocked from a bona fide test by members of his own race."

Wilson had a somber look as he read the final sentence of the article.

"Holmes finishes with, 'It may be years before another opportunity opens up for a Negro in organized baseball again,'" Wilson said.

The room was silent.

And then a woman's voice cut through it.

Posey recognized who was now speaking out and grimaced.

"That white boy sportswriter has never written a thing that didn't carry the water of Branch Rickey since Rickey started poaching our players," said Effa Manley, the only woman in the room.

Manley was tall and slender. Her skin color was light enough to pass for a white woman. She had a history of claiming to be white to get into hotels that banned Blacks. She was co-owner of the Newark Eagles Negro League team with her Black husband, Abe Manley. While Abe provided the money, Effa ran the team, doing everything from booking hotel rooms to negotiating salaries and buying the uniforms.

She took great pride in her team and insisted that her team jerseys were purchased from the same company that made uniforms for Major League Baseball. That was one of many ways she declared her Newark Eagles were on par with any white Major League Baseball team.

J.B. Martin, who used the money he made as a dentist to become Black owner of the Chicago American Giants Negro League team, shook his head.

"Effa," is all Martin could say before he was cut off.

"That reporter Tommy Holmes should not tell us how to run our business!" Effa shot back. "Have the newspapers done us any favors? They don't report our game results. They don't print our box scores! I should go and knock some sense into Tommy Holmes!"

Martin recoiled and Joe Bostic, a Black sportswriter in attendance reporting for the Negro newspaper the People's Voice, was also taken aback by Effa's threat.

"Effa," Bostic said in a respectful tone. "Tommy Holmes only has one arm."

Effa turned and stared at Bostic.

"Good! I'll rip the other one off and ram it up Happy Chandler's behind! Maybe see if that is recognized as a bona fide dispute," Effa spewed.

From the podium, Posey raised his voice and pointed to Abe Manley.

"Abe!" Posey barked. "Keep your wife at home!"

Abe Manley shrugged as some in the room snickered.

An incensed Effa Manley retorted: "We'll all be at home if we don't act. Jackie Robinson is worth $50,000. The Monarchs didn't get a dime!"

She shook her head.

"I'm tired of the weak-willed handkerchief heads afraid to stand up for ourselves! This will end the Negro Leagues if the whites just come and take all our best players!" Effa yelled.

The room went silent after Effa's slur. The handkerchief heads insult was akin to calling Blacks subservient.

Posey threw his arms up in the air and stormed out of the room as the rest of the participants realized the meeting was over.

The reality was the Negro Leagues were not well run and Effa Manley knew it. Among other problems, player contracts were not respected by Black players and other Black teams.

Roy Campanella, who played for the Baltimore Elite Giants, estimated that half the Black players in the Negro League didn't have contracts at all. He said he never had a contract in his nine years in the Negro Leagues.

And many Black teams found it nearly impossible to get financing from banks that kept many white Major League Baseball teams afloat during tough times. Many Negro League teams had to live day-to-day and couldn't afford a streak of poor attendance or the possibility of losing a star player.

They sometimes squabbled over money. In 1942, after a first round of Negro League games in Detroit's Briggs Stadium drew huge crowds, Black promoters argued over who had the rights to promote future games at Briggs Stadium. In one of those games, 34,000 fans showed up to watch Satchel Paige pitch.

Detroit Tigers owner Walter Briggs, Sr., also owned the stadium named after his family. Briggs was against integration of Major League Baseball and eventually was fed up with the squabbling by Black promoters over their cut of gate receipts. Briggs banned Negro League games for the rest of that year.

While Satchel Paige's game generated $24,000 in gate receipts [$464,907 in 2023 dollars], Briggs realized he could do the game promotions with fewer headaches with his own Tigers staff. Although Briggs did not want Paige on his all-white Tigers team, he would take a cut of Paige's gate receipts when his Negro League team played at his stadium.

The infighting and lack of organization had plagued the Negro Leagues since the start.

And now, many of the Negro League leaders privately feared Effa was right. Integration of Major League Baseball was the beginning of the end of Negro League baseball. The flight of Black stars to Major League Baseball would be their doom.

CHAPTER 6

The Queen Of Newark

July 6, 1946

Newark Eagles co-owner Effa Manley was watching her team from the top row of the stands in New Jersey's Ruppert Stadium. She was a details person, and that location gave her the best vantage point of how opponents played their defense.

That top-down view also exposed her to the smells of the garbage dump next door, which could be so overpowering that games would sometimes be delayed.

"Lord almighty, I knew we were downwind," Effa said as the trash odor started to waft over the stadium.

Her husband, Abe Manley, sat alongside her. Effa smiled proudly as her first-place team was the best of the Negro Leagues.

On the field, she saw six of her players who a month later would be voted to the Negro League all-star team. The best was a 22-year-old named Larry Doby.

Dressed in a suit and hat, Abe was holding a newspaper.

Reading from it, he said scornfully, "You see what Rogers Hornsby said about Larry? 'If he were white, he wouldn't be good enough to play with a semi-pro club.' Hornsby said all Doby can do is run."

Rogers Hornsby, who was white, was one of Major League Baseball's greatest hitters. Hornsby retired nine years earlier after having hit over .400 in three full seasons, an amazing accomplishment by any standard.

Effa shook her head.

"Rogers Hornsby. The man could hit the ball. I've never seen better. And I can't think of another good thing to say about him," she said.

"Well," Abe said. "He doesn't live in Newark."

Effa laughed. She looked into the stands and saw a small crowd of about 600 fans, almost all Black. A group of six white men stood out, sitting by the first baseline.

"You see the scouts, Abe?" Effa said.

"Yes, Ma'am," Abe replied.

"We're getting to the point where we'll have more big-league scouts at our games than fans," Effa said. "We're going to be lucky to draw half the fans we did last year."

Abe nodded.

"That's a lot of scouts watching players who they say aren't good enough play for a semi-pro club," Effa said, starring at the scouts. "You know, they're going to pick us clean."

Abe nodded. "Yep."

Effa was getting worked up, and Abe touched her knee to calm her down.

Looking back at the scouts again, Effa froze and murmured, "Son-of-a-bitch."

Abe noted her tone: a bee was in Effa's bonnet.

Abe felt Effa's hand nudge him and asked in a voice trembling with rage, "Is that Branch Rickey?"

Abe looked and prayed it wasn't.

"The Dodgers are playing tonight," Abe said. "Branch would be at their game at Ebbets [Field]."

But Effa was already out of her seat and heading to the other side of the stadium.

Abe groaned. He knew it was Rickey, and obviously Effa saw through his attempt to sidetrack her.

Knowing what was coming next, Abe rose to flag down some ushers and a security guard.

Effa's heartbeat sped up with every step closer to Rickey.

Rickey was slumped in his seat, making him appear even smaller than his 5-foot-8 pudgy frame. He was wearing his traditional suit with a bow tie and wire-rim glasses.

Rickey was wearing a hat, trying to conceal himself. He was hoping to avoid running into Effa Manley. Clyde Sukeforth, a scout for the Brooklyn Dodgers, and Robert Finch, Rickey's trusted assistant, were seated next to their boss.

Rickey pretended not to see Effa approaching, but couldn't prevent from tensing up.

"Hey," Effa shouted while still 30 feet away. "I was wondering what that smell was. I thought it was the garbage dump across the street."

Tensions had escalated between white and Negro League baseball. Rickey had recently signed Newark Eagle rising star Don Newcombe even though he was under contract with Effa's Newark Eagles. Effa and Abe hadn't been paid a cent to allow Newcombe to leave for the Brooklyn Dodgers' organization.

"Mr. Rickey! I hope you're not going to grab any more of our players!" Effa yelled, placing the man in the center of a very uncomfortable spectacle. "You know, Mr. Rickey, the contracts we have with our players would stand up better in court than those you have with the majors. You know, Mr. Rickey, we could make trouble for you on the Newcombe transaction if we wanted to. ... I have five players on my ball club that could make the majors right now. But this time, I expect to get paid for their services despite the fact I'd like to see any of my Eagles in organized baseball!"

Finally, Rickey had reached his boiling point.

"Your leagues are not run on a sound basis," Rickey shouted. "It isn't legitimate. It's more of a racket."

"We have our faults, but we are distinctly not any fly-by-night business!" Effa retorted. "Our all-star game in Chicago had a crowd of 50,000. We'd get 100,000 if you'd stop stealing our players!"

The Black security guards Abe sent to fetch his wife had arrived, and Effa knew her time was up. She nodded to the two security guards and smiled.

"Gentlemen," she said with a wink. "I'd appreciate an escort back to my seat. And I'll tip you kindly."

Rickey turned around and noticed the small crowd giving him a death stare. Effa was the "Queen of Newark."

"Beautiful weather," Rickey said to his seatmates, tipping his hat.

Rickey was willing to risk being the target of Effa's rage because he believed the moment was ripe for outstanding Black players to enter the all-white Major League Baseball.

His plan was to groom Jackie Robinson as the first Black player to break the color barrier. That would open the door in the Dodgers' minor league system for more Black players such as Larry Doby and Don Newcombe.

In 1946, the Dodgers had an extensive minor league system with 21 teams representing multiple levels of skill.

Despite the numerous minor league teams, part of Rickey's challenge was finding a minor league town willing to accept Black players. The general manager of the team in Danville, Illinois had told him he'd shut down the squad down before taking a Black player.

Just one general manager among the Dodgers' network was willing to take on Black players. That was Buzzie Bavasi of the Nashua Dodgers in New Hampshire, whose team played in the New England League.

Nashua manager Walter Alston didn't have a problem with two new Black players – Don Newcombe and Roy Campanella.

Newcombe finished with a 14-4 record that year and led Nashua to a championship.

CHAPTER 7

Bill Veeck Gets His Big League Team

Aug 2, 1946

The phone rang in Bill Veeck's new office in Cleveland's Municipal Stadium. He tried reaching for it, but his right leg was propped up on the desk and had started to bleed again.

Veeck had served in the Pacific Theater after joining the Marine Corps in 1943. In 1945, a recoiling 90-millimeter artillery piece smashed into his leg and crushed it. Doctors had advised amputation, but Veeck wasn't willing to give up on the leg if he had a choice.

He returned to the U.S. in August 1945 and, ten months later, convinced many investors, including comedian Bob Hope, to join his syndicate and buy Major League Baseball's Cleveland Indians.

But right now, Veeck couldn't reach the phone. Harry Grabiner, Veeck's right hand man and the new vice president of the Indians, walked over and answered it. He listened briefly and said, "Bill, it's for you. It's Jackie Price's agent."

Veeck grabbed his crutches, stood and took the phone.

He listened and smiled.

"Absolutely," Veeck said. "See you tomorrow."

"We got him!" Veeck shouted as Grabiner nodded.

"Who?" asked Joseph Hostetler, one of Veeck's lawyers who was also in the office.

"Jackie Price!" Veeck beamed.

Hostetler shook his head. The name didn't register.

"Never heard of him," Hostetler said. "He better be half Babe Ruth and half Jesus Christ because we are 22 games out of first place."

Veeck shrugged it off.

"Oh, he can't hit a lick," Veeck said. "Unless he's hanging upside down by his heels."

Hostetler shook his head in disbelief. This was another stunt.

"Aw, Bill, not again," Hostetler said.

Veeck smiled.

On Aug. 13, the Detroit Tigers were in Cleveland for a Sunday night game. The sun was still shining when Jackie Price strolled onto the field at 5 p.m. to provide some pre-game entertainment.

Veeck, Grabiner and Hostetler watched from the dugout as Price strolled by holding a bat on his way to home plate. He was accompanied by three clubhouse attendants carrying large metal poles. The attendants assembled an eight-foot-tall "H" shaped structure like a football field goalpost and attached large leather straps to the top bar. Then the attendants picked up Price, turned him upside down, and secured each foot into the leather straps.

This left Price hanging eight feet above ground, upside down and positioned perfectly in the batter's box.

Cleveland bench coach Bill McKechnie walked out to the pitching mound with a bucket full of baseballs. He then threw the first pitch.

WHACK! While hanging upside down, Price swung and ripped a shot past McKechnie that rolled into the center-field grass. The crowd roared. There were more than 65,700 fans there to watch the last-place Indians.

McKechnie threw another pitch half-speed, and Price again ripped a shot past him into center field.

"Isn't that incredible!" Veeck howled from the dugout while nudging Grabiner.

Max Patkin emerged from the visitor's team dugout with another bucket of baseballs. Patkin was a 6-foot-2 string bean, another entertainer hired by Veeck.

Patkin had a severe receding chin and a humongous hook nose that swallowed his thin face. From some angles, Patkin looked like a giant nose on a broomstick.

For his act, Patkin wore oversized baggy pants and a jersey five sizes too big. His clothes were so baggy that fans couldn't see any sign of his 155-pound body underneath. Instead of a number, his jersey just had a big black question mark on the back.

Patkin ran to the mound, but before getting there tripped and spilled the balls. He tried to get up, stepped on a ball, and flopped onto his back. He managed to stand up, bent over to brush himself off, and then peered between his legs to gauge the amusement of the fans.

When Patkin got to the mound, he grabbed a baseball and began an exaggerated pitching motion that included windmilling his arm while kicking a leg up and down.

When he finally released the pitch, it was right down the middle, and Price hit it right back through the mound. Patkin flipped over backward and onto the ground as the fans howled.

Still smiling, Veeck turned to Grabiner and said, "Max looks like he was put together by somebody who forgot to read the instructions."

Curious about the cheering from the stands, Lou Boudreau entered the dugout from the clubhouse. Boudreau was 5-foot-11, with good looks that earned him the nickname "Handsome Lou." He'd been a star athlete in college and had been the franchise's sole attraction from 1940 to 1945 during World War II when the Cleveland Indians' star pitcher Bob Feller was in the military.

In 1941, the team's previous owner Alva Bradley made Boudreau the manager while allowing him to continue playing shortstop. But, year-after-year the Indians had finished near the bottom of the standings. None of the fans held Handsome Lou responsible for the losses. Veeck wasn't so forgiving.

Veeck noticed Boudreau and then turned back to Grabiner.

"Wait until you see what he does after this," Veeck told Grabiner. "He will stand on the pitcher's mound and throw three balls with one hand."

Veeck then paused for effect.

"And he'll throw it to three different people!" Veeck howled.

Boudreau stood in silence watching the performance without a smile.

Veeck looked over and tried to draw Boudreau in.

"Lou," Veeck said. "Later on, he'll chase down fly balls and catch them while driving a Jeep!"

Veeck nodded to a Jeep parked on the field.

"You bought a Jeep for this?" Boudreau asked with a scornful tone.

"Of course not," Veeck answered. "I offered a dealership free advertising. No reason to pay for it."

Boudreau was unimpressed as the upside-down Price hit another ball up the middle into the outfield, and the crowd roared.

"He can't come close to doing that against a real pitcher," Boudreau said.

"It's a full house," Veeck said. "And the fans are here to see a show."

"And a last-place team," Boudreau said coldly.

Jackie Price finished his show. The attendants lowered him down from the metal poles and set him upright. He stood for a second to get his bearings straight and then took a bow for the cheering crowd.

The 33-year-old Price spent his entire career in the minor leagues. Veeck traded for Price when he owned the minor league Milwaukee Brewers.

He had finally made the majors. Price's wife divorced him a year ago because he wouldn't give up his baseball act. This day, he was a hit with the fans.

Veeck joined the crowd and clapped for Price, he saw Boudreau walk back into the clubhouse.

Veeck lost his smile and turned to Grabiner.

"Lou has no sense of showmanship," Veeck said, irritated. "And his managing skills will keep us in last place. I don't like our star player also being the manager."

When Veeck took over as president of the Indians two months earlier in June, Jimmy Dykes showed up at the press conference in Cleveland. Dykes had just been fired as manager of the Chicago White Sox and was a close friend to Grabiner.

Veeck's plan was to have either Dykes or Cleveland Indian catcher Al Lopez take over as manager. Lopez was at the end of his playing career and Veeck thought once Lopez retired as a player he could make a good manager. But before revealing that to the public, he wanted to privately talk to Boudreau about giving up his duties as manager and focusing on playing shortstop. That would mean a cut in salary for Boudreau.

Dykes was in on the switch as a top candidate but was supposed to keep it quiet. Veeck was horrified when he saw the former White Sox manager surrounded by newspaper reporters at the new owner's June press conference.

"We're new here," Veeck told the sportswriters when they asked if he would fire Boudreau as manager. "Common courtesy, if nothing else, would indicate that we give Lou a fair trial as manager for us."

Veeck could tell no one was convinced. And he didn't have to guess how Boudreau would interpret seeing the man who just a month earlier was managing the White Sox at the press conference.

Veeck tried to entice the newspaper reporters to bite on another storyline.

"Hey," Veeck said. "Did you hear Bob Hope is one of the investors? He's in Hollywood making a promotional film with Bing Crosby for us. Bing is part owner of the Pirates."

Ed McAuley, a Cleveland sportswriter, raised his hand and asked a question.

"Bill," McAuley asked, "Dykes and Grabiner are close friends. Harry hired Jimmy while he was running the Sox. Is Dykes your next manager?"

Veeck shrugged.

"Isn't anyone interested in Bob Hope anymore?" he asked.

CHAPTER 8

I've Heard Charles Thomas Crying For 43 Years

Aug. 26, 1946

New York Yankees general manager Larry MacPhail was drunk. This was not unusual; years later his own grandson would describe his drinking behavior as that of a "raving lunatic."

He was sitting in Chicago's Green Mill restaurant, reputedly an Al Capone hangout two decades earlier. It was miles away from The Drake Hotel, where the next day Major League Baseball's power broker owners would gather for their annual meeting.

This night, just six of those top executives, plus a friendly and influential baseball writer, were at the Green Mill to discuss the owners' strategy to keep Blacks out of baseball, and how to frame the issue when speaking to the public or press. The small group had booked the entire establishment to ensure their discussion would remain private.

The meeting wouldn't begin until 6 p.m., but for two hours before then MacPhail had been getting a head start. A young waiter placed another gin and tonic on MacPhail's table and removed the glasses from the four he had already polished off.

MacPhail took a swig from the new drink and then slammed the glass down, startling the waiter.

"The drink is supposed to be two parts gin, one part tonic!" he yelled. "Goddamn it! If I wanted a fizzed Coca-Cola I would have ordered that!"

The startled waiter apologized, promised to return with a stronger drink, and scampered off.

Stress tended to aggravate MacPhail's drinking binges. As the general manager of the Brooklyn Dodgers several years earlier, he had allowed an open bar to be placed in the team's press box. In 1941, when the Dodgers lost the seventh and final game of the World Series to the New York Yankees, a drunken MacPhail told sportswriters there he would trade away all of his players.

Tired of being embarrassed by his drunken scenes, in 1942 the Dodgers' owners let him go. Three years later MacPhail, an attorney who made a fortune working with bankrupt companies during The Great Depression, assembled a three-person group to buy the Yankees.

Now in his second year as Yankees owner and general manager, he hadn't won a World Series. This was after the team had won six of the previous nine World Series before MacPhail took over.

Major League Baseball team owners had long shared a quiet consensus to oppose allowing Black players in their organizations. That "gentlemen's agreement" was now in jeopardy: Brooklyn Dodgers' co-owner and general manager Branch Rickey had over several months quietly signed five Black ballplayers to his team's minor league system.

MacPhail was a longtime adversary of Rickey and was infuriated Rickey had done this without notifying the other owners.

But there was no ducking it now: Major League Baseball could no longer turn a deaf ear to the growing chorus calling for integration in their sport.

It was now 6 p.m. at the Green Mill, and one by one the other meeting attendees arrived at the restaurant and took their place at a table.

Washington Senators 35-year-old white vice president Calvin Griffith was the first. In 1946, his uncle Clark Griffith owned the team, but Calvin would later take ownership. Calvin's racism was already no secret to his inner circle. But years later, after moving his Washington team to Minnesota and renaming them the Twins, it became notorious when he revealed the real motive for the move when speaking to a community organization.

"I'll tell you why we came to Minnesota. It was when I found out you only had 15,000 Blacks here… We came because you've got good, hardworking, white people here," Griffith said in 1978.

In 2020, the Twins cited those remarks when removing a statue of Calvin Griffith outside the ballpark.

He was followed by Sam Breadon, the less-strident 70-year-old white owner of the St. Louis Cardinals. Just two years earlier Breadon had ended segregated seating in his ballpark, with the sections for different races separated by chicken wire. Branch Rickey, then a Cardinals employee, had long pleaded with Breadon to end the practice, but Breadon hesitated, fearing it would hurt attendance.

The Green Mill door opened slowly for the next guest, as two men lifted Walter Briggs Sr.'s wheelchair over the steps and rolled him to the table. Owner of the Detroit Tigers, the 69-year-old Briggs had been restricted to the chair since contracting polio in 1940. He would die in 1952 having never had a Black player on his Tigers, which led sportswriters to coin the saying, "No Jigs For Briggs."

The man who entered after Briggs was not an owner. It was J.G. Taylor Spink, the 58-year old publisher of The Sporting News, the most influential voice in baseball. In 1942 he had written a column titled, "No Good From Raising Race Issue," claiming that Black players didn't want to play in the all-white major leagues. He later boasted this editorial ended early discussions about integration.

In February 2021, the Baseball Writers Association of America removed Spink's name from an annual baseball writers award, citing his troubled legacy of racism. The Sporting News agreed with the decision.

Walter O'Malley, a co-owner with Branch Rickey of the Brooklyn

Dodgers, walked in next and sat at the table looking very uncomfortable. This Chicago owners meeting would be the first since Rickey had signed the five Black players, and O'Malley knew he would have a lot of explaining to do.

Boston Red Sox owner Tom Yawkey, the last to arrive, entered and sat at the table.

MacPhail opened the discussions by congratulating Yawkey, whose Red Sox had just beaten new-owner Bill Veeck's Cleveland Indians three games in a row, and were all but guaranteed to make the World Series.

"So, what do you think of this Veeck fellow?" O'Malley asked Yawkey, hoping to steer conversations away from his Dodgers signing Black players.

Before the other owner could speak, the intoxicated MacPhail was pounding the table with his empty glass.

"I'll tell you!" MacPhail bellowed, suddenly up and out of his seat. "I'll tell you about that son-of-a-bitch Veeck!"

The others stared.

"This fellow has put up a goddamn tepee in the middle of center field!" MacPhail announced, followed by a stereotypical "woo woo woo" Indian chant.

"Larry, not in center field. You mean out in the bleachers," the Senator's Griffith said, meaning to correct MacPhail.

"No! I mean center field!" MacPhail countered. "I saw it. A big tepee in the middle of the field. With an awful 15-piece swing band dressed as Indians. They played during the game!"

The table was silent.

Spink, The Sporting News publisher, spoke up.

"It's true," he said. "We did a story. A big tepee with a band inside. If a ground ball hits the tepee it's ruled an automatic double. A fly ball hitting it is ruled a home run."

Detroit's Briggs, a longtime traditionalist, shook his head in disgust.

"It gets worse," Spink said. "After getting evicted from an apartment, a 56-year-old man named William Stengel asked Veeck if he could live in the tepee. Veeck allowed it."

"Oh, please!" Briggs said, shaking his head in disbelief.

Publisher Spink shook his head.

"Mr. Briggs, I verified the story myself. A penniless man lives in the tepee, even during games," Spink said.

The table went quiet. But they all howled when Yawkey snarked, "Brother, Can You Spare A Pennant?" referencing the 1932 Great Depression-era song, "Brother, Can You Spare A Dime?"

Walter O'Malley spoke up: "I read about it too. That game pulled in 74,500 fans, a club record. Before Veeck arrived, even a Yankees game in Cleveland only drew 4,500."

He turned to MacPhail.

"Larry, your cut of the Cleveland ticket sales was also a heck of a lot more than the last time you played there," O'Malley said.

O'Malley shrugged.

"Business is business," he said.

Getting back the business at hand, Yawkey looked to O'Malley. The two were longtime friends.

"Walter," Yawkey said. "What the heck is Branch Rickey doing? We thought Negroes would be a problem with Veeck, not your Dodgers."

In 1945, Major League Baseball had privately polled its 16 team owners asking if they supported integration. The response was 15-1 against. The only owner in support was Dodgers' co-owner Branch Rickey.

O'Malley shook his head.

"You think I want coloreds and Puerto Ricans at the ballpark?" O'Malley asked.

He shook his head and turned to the Yankees' MacPhail.

"Larry, when you look out your window what do you see? I'll tell you: About 600 or 700 people lined up at an unemployment benefits office across the street there," O'Malley said.

"If you look you can see they're almost all Blacks or Puerto Ricans. They're not paying their way, and don't pay to come to the ballpark either. So why are we catering to these people?" O'Malley said.

"Well," Yawkey asked. "Why are you?"

It was a reference to the Dodgers' co-owner Branch Rickey signing Black minor leaguers.

O'Malley sat up looking uncomfortable.

"Because Branch promised that the colored players would win us a World Series," O'Malley said. "You're not the only son-of-a-bitch at this table that would give his right arm to win a World Series. Brooklyn's been in this league since 1884, 73 years, and never won a championship."

He was silent for a moment before concluding, "I want a championship."

There was a pause, and then MacPhail handed out a report he had assembled articulating the team owners' point of view on Black players. At the moment, he was too intoxicated to coherently read it out loud.

The report reiterated what he had told the 1945 New York integration commission, and Yawkey had told the Boston City Council.

It was a virtual "cheat sheet" for owners, the unpublished party line on integration: Baseball was being pressured by publicity hounds, and signing a few Black players would be pointless. Black players weren't good enough to make a Major League Baseball roster, and wouldn't get there without more time in the minors. Plus, Black players were already subject to legal contracts with Negro League teams. The owners would subsequently go to great lengths to keep the MacPhail report secret. It wouldn't become public until discovered by a U.S. Congressional committee five years later.

The next day, after the official owners meeting had ended, Veeck and Rickey stood in front of The Drake Hotel elevator heading back to their rooms. Both had just left the conference room - but not before handing back their copies of MacPhail's non-integration document to a security guard at the door.

The two knew each other but seldom crossed paths. They first met at a 1942 awards banquet hosted by The Sporting News, often referred to as the Bible of baseball. It had named Rickey as the Major League Baseball executive of the year, and Veeck as the year's top minor league executive. At that time both men had expressed interest in purchasing the Philadelphia Phillies.

Rickey had worked as a manager in the St. Louis Cardinals organization from 1919 to 1942, first as a team manager and then as its general manager. Bill Veeck Sr., father of the current Cleveland Indians owner, had enjoyed a working relationship with Rickey for 14 years.

But Bill Veeck and Rickey had little else in common.

Rickey was a conservative evangelical Christian who regarded segregation an insult to his faith. He had played in the big leagues for four years, with just 343 total at bats. But what was most remembered about his short career was a refusal to play on Sundays. Rickey also opposed swearing and alcohol.

At the elevator, Veeck nodded and said with a chuckle, "It was nice to not be the most hated man in the room for once."

"Don't sell yourself short," Rickey responded. "You've only been an owner three months. I have more than 30 years in the majors. But you've made up a lot of ground in a short time."

Veeck smiled in response, but then became serious.

"You know, I'm impressed by your dedication to signing Negroes," he said. "The other owners are worried it will scare away the white fans. I don't think it will."

Rickey was quiet for a moment.

"It's not about attendance," he finally said. "This isn't like fireworks and handing out live lobsters to fans."

Veeck accepted the dig but looked confused.

Rickey continued: "The greatest untapped reservoir of raw material in the history of the game is the Black race. The Negroes will make us winners for years to come."

"But it's not just about winning," he said with a pained look.

"In 1903, I managed the Ohio Wesleyan University baseball team. I recruited a catcher, a Negro named Charles Thomas. We had a game against Notre Dame, and had to check-in at a South Bend hotel," Rickey told Veeck. "The clerk there wouldn't allow Charles to stay in my room. I convinced him to allow it if Charles slept on a cot."

He paused, and sighed.

"When I got back from dinner, I found Charles crying and rubbing his arms. He said, 'It's my skin. If only I could wipe off the color they could see I'm a man like everyone else!'" Rickey said.

Rickey was silent as the memory of the sobbing Black man hung in the air.

"I've heard Charles Thomas crying for 43 years," Rickey said, and looked hard at Veeck.

"Were you serious about bringing an all-Negro team to Philadelphia in 1942?" he asked.

Veeck nodded, also touched by the Charles Thomas story.

Rickey sized up Veeck as a potential ally.

"We've got no army. There's virtually nobody on our side. No owners. No umpires. Very few newspapermen. And I'm afraid many fans will be hostile. We'll be in a tough position," Rickey said.

Veeck smiled. "Well, when you put it like that, count me in!"

"This is God's work," Rickey said seriously.

Veeck nodded.

"I do believe in God, but I'm not too clear on the other details," Veeck said.

The elevator reached the upper-level floors where the owners had suites. Rickey exited and tipped his hat to Veeck.

When Veeck reached his room, Indians' vice president Harry Grabiner was packing his bags.

"Harry," Veeck said. "For next year I'm thinking about switching our spring training camp from Lakeland [Florida] to Tucson [Arizona]."

Grabiner stopped packing and looked up. "Arizona?" he asked.

"Yep," Veeck answered.

"Why?" Grabiner asked.

"The Jim Crow laws in Florida. It's going to be difficult for Negroes to play in a segregated facility," Veeck said.

"Bill, we don't have any Negroes on the team," Grabiner responded.

Veeck turned to Grabiner and smiled.

CHAPTER 9

Bill, We Need A Favor

May 1, 1947

Branch Rickey lifted the phone in his hotel room to make a call. Jackie Robinson was in the next room with two FBI agents stationed in the hallway to protect him. A month into his first season as the only Black man to play in the all-white major leagues, Robinson was getting death threats.

Bill Veeck answered Rickey's call.

"What can I do for you, Branch?" Veeck asked.

"Bill, we need a favor, but I'll be straight with you. I have never seen anything like this," Rickey said with his voice cracking.

"What exactly is it you need?" the Cleveland Indians team owner asked.

"I need to take some of the pressure off Jackie," Rickey said. "It's too much right now for him to carry the load of the only Negro in Major League Baseball. There's a Negro kid - named Larry Doby. He's a player. Run. Field. Hit. The real deal. He's yours if you want to sign him."

Veeck was silent. He knew of Doby from his own scouts but newspaper reports had said Doby signed with the Dodgers months ago.

Rickey continued, "But if I give him to you, you must play him. You can't put him in the minor leagues. That puts a lot of pressure on the kid. But he's that good. Just keep him on the field and in the dugout. That's all I ask."

Rickey had been scouting Doby for more than a year. His original plan was to have Doby replace Robinson in the minor leagues after

Robinson was promoted to the Brooklyn Dodgers. But at this critical moment, Rickey felt he had to sacrifice Doby for the greater good of protecting Robinson. But it hurt to give him up.

Veeck paused and then broke the silence.

"Walter O'Malley approved this?" Veeck said, referring to the Brooklyn Dodgers owner. "I didn't think he liked me."

Rickey answered: "None of the owners like you, Bill. Truth be told, you would be the last owner Walt would want me to hand a player as skilled as Doby to. But we don't know of any other owners who would take on a Negro right now."

Veeck was nodding.

"Yeah, Walt Briggs won't let Negroes sit in the box seats at his stadium in Detroit," Veeck said. "What's the saying in Detroit? No Jigs For Briggs? No way he'd let them play for him. And Tom Yawkey in Boston would – "

Rickey cut off Veeck.

"Bill. We've done our research. You're it," Rickey said.

Veeck was quiet.

"I'll do it. Our fans can handle it. I think they would love to see a great ballplayer, and nobody is handing them out for free. We'll take the kid. And we'll play him as much as we can - with no minor leagues," Veeck said.

"You won't regret signing Doby," Rickey said.

Veeck hung up the phone and then dialed the number for Harry Grabiner, the vice president of the Indians.

"Harry," Veeck said. "Remember why I told you we had to move out of Florida and go to Arizona for spring training games last year? With Florida's Jim Crow laws …."

Grabiner was confused, not uncommon when dealing with Veeck.

"Why would that impact us? We don't have any Negro players," Grabiner said.

"Well, here's the deal - you always ask me what I've got up my sleeve next?" Veeck asked.

Grabiner groaned, "Oh. No."

CHAPTER 10

All You Got Is A Minstrel Show

July 2, 1947

Bill Veeck was driving to Newark, New Jersey, singing along with the song on the radio, "Smoke, Smoke That Cigarette."

He pulled into a weed-choked baseball stadium parking lot and parked next to the stadium office. A sign read, "Ruppert Stadium."

Veeck limped into the office of Effa and Abe Manley.

"How are you doing, Abe," Veeck said as he shook Abe's hand.

Effa Manley sat at a table and stared down Veeck.

"How are you doing, Mr. Veeck?" Effa asked.

"Please, call me Bill," Veeck answered affably.

With a big smile, Veeck took out a $15,000 check from his pocket and set it on the table.

"You have the paperwork?" Veeck asked. "Our scouts love Larry. This is a good opportunity."

Effa retrieved a folder and set it on the table. It was an agreement to sign over the contractual rights of Larry Doby to the Cleveland Indians.

"A good opportunity for you. You're only a tad better than Branch Rickey, not interested in anything more than the click of the turnstile," Effa snarled.

Veeck was taken aback and felt insulted.

"I'm paying you $15,000!" Veeck said.

Now annoyed, Veeck continued: "I could have waited for Larry's contract to expire and signed him. Or just ignore his Negro League contract altogether. That's what the Dodgers did with Don Newcombe, isn't it? It wouldn't have cost me anything."

Abe Manley took a couple steps back with a look of trepidation.

Effa pounced on Veeck's words.

"Branch Rickey came into the Negro Leagues and plucked a star and walked away without as much as a dime to the Negro League owner who had Jackie Robinson under contract. He did the same damn thing to me with Newcombe," Effa said. "When I told him I would fight it, he said, 'Sue me.'"

Effa paused for impact.

Veeck was listening.

"How did you end up with Larry?" Effa asked. "The Dodgers were scouting him months before your guys showed up."

Veeck tried to suppress his ire but began to realize he had vastly underestimated Effa Manley.

Effa knew that Branch Rickey would want another Black player good enough to play in Major League Baseball right away to take the heat off Jackie Robinson. She also knew the Rickey's Dodgers and the New York Giants were the only teams from the National League that scouted Larry Doby. Rickey wouldn't want to hand over a rising star like Doby to the cross-town Giants who the Dodgers would have to play numerous times during the regular season. But by giving Doby to the Indians, Rickey wouldn't have to face him unless they played the American League's Indians in the World Series.

"There's no way Rickey is giving Doby over to the Giants and watch Doby kick his butt for the next 10 years in his own backyard," Effa said.

Veeck was stunned. That made perfect sense. He never considered that Rickey didn't want Doby playing in the same city as his Dodgers and having to face Doby 22 games a year if he landed on a National League team.

Veeck looked quizzically at Effa. He had met his match.

"That's where your dumb ass comes into the picture," Effa said, shaking her head as her words tore into Veeck. She was almost talking to herself at this point as she unraveled how Veeck landed his first Black player.

"The American League has the most racist owners," Effa continued, now looking back at Veeck. "So, you're their best shot. The Dodgers hand you Doby, but only if you play him right away. He'll be in an Indians' jersey and batting before the ink is dry on this contract. So don't say you are looking out for Larry, or else you'd let him get some time in the minor leagues like every other good prospect you have."

Veeck composed himself, still bothered Rickey played him.

"I believe someday, Cleveland will make a statue of Larry when he's done playing. He's that good," Veeck said.

Still indignant, he asked Effa, "Do you want Negroes to play in the big leagues or not?"

"Negroes? There are more than 100 Negro players in our leagues. Why are you signing just Doby?" Effa asked.

"Because I want to win, and Doby will help me win a pennant," Veeck said.

"Baloney!" Effa shot back. "You sign Monte Irvin, Leon Day, Max Manning, Rufus Lewis, and Doby today, and you'll win a pennant with those colored boys. And by a dozen games."

Effa paused and looked Veeck straight in the eyes: "You sign one Negro, all you got is a minstrel show."

Veeck was speechless. And his thoughts were frozen. He was blindsided a few times by Effa during this conversation. And she wasn't done chewing up Veeck.

"So, the white man has decided we can play baseball with him. But to do it, you will wipe out one hundred years of Negro League baseball because he found out the Negroes are the top players. But you will only take the best players. My Newark Eagles could beat half the teams in the majors," Effa said.

Effa got up from her seat.

"So you take Larry," Effa said. "And that's going to kill the Negro Leagues. You and Branch Rickey are just 20th-century carpet baggers. We probably will have to shut down the Eagles without Doby. Hell, it's a shame you don't take Satch, too, if he weren't so old."

Effa looked to Abe, who had been silent during Effa's tirade. He learned that lesson years ago.

"How old is Satchel?" Effa asked Abe. "We can only guess. Nobody knows that man's age."

Abe chuckled.

"Right, nobody knows that man's age," Abe said. "His arm is forever 21, I think."

"So is his plum tree shaker, if you listen to all his lady fans," Effa said with a deviant look.

Veeck was surprised to hear such coarse language from a woman.

"Let me ask you, Mr. Veeck. What are you going to pay Larry?" Effa asked, now standing next to her husband.

Veeck straightened up. He finally felt like he could take back control of the conversation.

"We are paying him $5,000. That's five times what he'll make here," Veeck said.

"If he were white, you'd be paying him ten times that," Effa said.

"What are you paying that backup first baseman, Hal Peck?" Effa asked.

Veeck realized he'd been checkmated again. Peck was a veteran now in the twilight of his career.

"$7,500," Veeck muttered.

"You know, Peck couldn't even make my team. Are they going to make any statues of him? What are you paying Bob Feller?" Effa asked.

"We are paying Bob $80,000, but he's a six-time all-star," Veeck said.

"What's Lou Boudreau making?" Effa asked.

"He's at $25,000," Veeck said. "But he's also the manager."

Veeck couldn't prevent himself from grimacing at that reminder.

"And I hear you are trying to trade Lou. Larry's better than Lou. You know that. Larry plays the same position as Lou. That's why you were trying to get rid of Lou. You don't need two shortstops, and you know which one is better," Effa said. "But you're going to stick Larry in the outfield to not upset your white has-been manager. And you mark my words, Larry will have more homers in a season than Peck will have in his career."

"Lou's not a has-been," Veeck said. "He just won't give up being a manager."

Veeck regretted he had shared that information.

Effa nodded.

"You can't pay a Negro more than a white man," she said.

Veeck didn't answer.

There was a long, uncomfortable silence. Finally, Effa pushed over the contract to be signed.

"You keep helping out the colored man, Mr. Veeck. Baseball will probably make a statue of you, too," Effa said, breaking out in a loud cackle.

Abe snickered, reminding Veeck that he was still in the room.

Veeck finished the paperwork without a word.

"Baseball is a rich, white man's hobby. And we aren't rich or white," Effa told Abe.

"Nope. We aren't," Abe said.

Bill Veeck picked up his copy of the contract and nodded. He sheepishly walked out like a dog with his tail between his legs.

Veeck sat in his car and stared at the stadium, reflecting on what was just said to him. He sighed. Veeck started the car, and the song "Too Fat Polka" played on the radio. He shut it off and drove away, no longer feeling like he was the patron saint of Black baseball players.

For the next 20 minutes, one thought raced through his mind. "How in the hell did she know I was thinking about trading Boudreau?"

CHAPTER 11

He's Your New Teammate

July 3, 1947

Lou Boudreau walked into Bill Veeck's office at 10 a.m. The night before their team had been beat by just one run. Boudreau was tense, anticipating Veeck would criticize his management of the game, which was becoming increasingly routine.

Veeck looked up from his desk when Boudreau entered and then leaned back in his chair.

"We signed a new player," Veeck said.

"Who?" Boudreau asked.

"Larry Doby. A Negro," Veeck said, waiting to see his manager's reaction. "It will be in today's newspapers."

Boudreau was silent. He was bothered Veeck didn't consult with him on such a big decision. But his managing instincts took over.

"Where does he play?" Boudreau asked.

"Second base," Veeck said.

The Indians had Joe Gordon at second base. Gordon was voted the league's Most Valuable Player five years earlier and was a regular all-star.

"Where else?" Boudreau asked.

"Shortstop," Veeck said.

Boudreau shot Veeck an icy stare. That was his position.

"He can play anywhere," Veeck said. "He's not your replacement."

Boudreau was skeptical. It was already clear that Veeck didn't want him as manager. Now, he had found a potential replacement at shortstop.

"This kid can play. This isn't a gimmick," Veeck said. "We need help in the outfield. I'm bringing in Tris Speaker to help Doby make that transition. But it will take time."

Boudreau knew about Speaker, a Cleveland legend and one of the best fielding outfielders in baseball's history. Speaker was a former MVP who spent his prime with the Indians 30 years earlier. Speaker, now 59, was also a purebred Southerner, born and raised in Texas. He had ties to the Ku Klux Klan, well known among the players.

"Tris is OK with that?" Boudreau asked.

Veeck nodded.

"Larry's not going to the minors. He will be on the roster all year," Veeck said. "So don't feel rushed to play him."

Boudreau nodded.

"You going to tell the players?" Boudreau asked.

"I'll address the team in Chicago in two days, when Doby arrives," Veeck said.

On July 5, Boudreau arrived at Chicago's Comiskey Park at 9 a.m., about an hour earlier than customary. Veeck had asked Boudreau to get to the park early, anticipating the barrage of newspaper requests.

After arriving, Boudreau was cornered in the clubhouse by about a dozen reporters.

Boudreau looked around and didn't recognize half the reporters, meaning they were from out of town and not the traditional beat writers he had seen from city to city. That signaled to him this was big news.

"The acquisition of Larry Doby is a routine baseball purchase, in my mind," Boudreau said, reciting the words he and his wife had rehearsed for three hours the previous night. "Creed, race, or color are not factors in baseball success. Ability and character are the only factors."

Boudreau nodded and smiled after delivering his scripted lines. Privately, he had no idea how good Doby was or how his new teammates would react.

When Jackie Robinson debuted with the Dodgers just 11 weeks earlier, many of that team's players threatened to boycott games rather than take the field with a Black player. One of Robinson's teammates, Dixie Walker from Georgia, had sent a letter to Branch Rickey asking to be traded rather than play with a Black player. Walker also had circulated a petition among his Dodger teammates looking to bar Robinson from playing.

Boudreau reviewed his roster a dozen times to determine who would have problems with the Doby signing. Two instantly came to mind – Les Fleming and Eddie Robinson. Both played first base, and both fit the Tris Speaker profile of being Southern boys born and raised in Texas. Boudreau loved being a manager and was dismayed it could all blow up because of this signing.

Boudreau didn't trust Veeck's motives.

The previous season, Boudreau eventually accepted the need for a last-place team to employ side-show antics like using Max Patkin as the first-base coach. Patkin made his living as "The Clown Prince of Baseball" and fans enjoyed his antics. Patkin would "accidentally" drop his pants while coaching first base and expose bright-colored boxers underneath. As part of his show, Patkin would run onto the field with a half dozen baseball bats pretending to take batting practice and stumble and fall.

But this was different. Boudreau knew little of the Negro Leagues.

Like everyone else, he had followed Jackie Robinson's performance in the newspapers. How could he not? The entire nation was following the first Black player. And Robinson played at an all-star level through the season's first four months. If Doby played anywhere near as well as Robinson, he would soon be taking the job of a white teammate.

But Robinson had played an entire season in the minor leagues. Veeck was not giving Doby that luxury. Boudreau realized this would be a day he would never forget.

At noon that day, Larry Doby got off the train at Chicago's Union Station. He was met by Louis Jones, a Black public relations employee with the Indians. Jones had scouted Doby for the Indians the past few weeks.

"How was the ride, Larry?" Jones asked.

"Nice, Mr. Jones," Doby said.

Doby was wearing a casual outfit. This was Major League Baseball. Jones needed to make sure Doby comprehended the moment.

"Our first stop is to a tailor we have waiting for you," Jones said with a smile and a pat on Doby's back.

The 6-foot-1, 185-pound Doby fit perfectly into his new sports jacket and button-down shirt. From there, Jones and Doby took a cab to The Congress Hotel where team owner Veeck was staying. Doby knew he wouldn't be allowed to remain at the segregated hotel. He would stay with Jones at the DuSable Hotel, which accepted Black patrons.

Veeck was waiting in a conference room just off the hotel lobby where about a dozen newspaper reporters were milling around. Veeck wore his traditional sports shirt with all three buttons unbuttoned and a sports jacket. Veeck was renowned for this look, which earned him the nickname "Sports Shirt" among friends and reporters.

Doby was anxious and had hardly slept the last four nights.

Once he signed his Major League Baseball contract, it became official: Doby was now the first Black player on an American League team. Six newspaper photographers took their shots, and the newspaper reporters headed to the ballpark.

Jones was impeccably dressed in a suit and hat. He smiled at Doby, who was not yet comfortable wearing high-end clothing.

"Let me say," Jones said with a wink. "It's nice to have another colored man around."

Doby tried but failed to relax.

"What's your role here? How does it relate to me, sir?" Doby asked.

"My job is to do what Bill Veeck tells me to do," Jones said with a wink. "But I'm just four months on the job, so I'm pretty sure my job is to make sure that the Negro players he is going to bring in don't think they are the only Negroes in the organization."

Doby was surprised.

"He's going to sign others?" Doby asked.

"Well, that, my man, depends on you," Jones said. "In a way, both our jobs are on the line. But no pressure. Right?"

Doby nodded.

"What's Cleveland like for a Negro?" Doby asked his mentor.

Jones paused to think how he wanted to answer that question.

"Well, here in Chicago, we stay at DuSable. The rest of your teammates will be at the Del Prado. That's Cleveland, too. It's like every other place, just people here aren't as open about their racism like they are down South."

Jones continued: "There's a lot more Negroes because they needed us to build their tanks for the war. We just had a Negro man elected to the state senate, Harry E. Davis. But it's damn near impossible for a colored family to find a decent neighborhood to live in."

Jones paused.

"And don't read the papers," Jones said.

Doby shot him a surprised look.

"I just talked to a reporter in the lobby. The Akron Beacon Journal today is blaming your signing as the reason Lou Boudreau has not gotten a hit the past two games," Jones said with a shrug.

He paused and remembered another tip for Doby.

"And don't take your family to Euclid Beach Park," Jones said. "It's for whites only. I know a Negro who went with a white couple, and the police kicked them all out and gave the Negro a beating."

Jones smiled.

"I only tell you this because Bill may ask you to go with his family," Jones said. "He's a little slow on picking up that most white society doesn't agree with his thoughts on segregation. Bill took me to a restaurant once, and we had a great time. Then he called me back the next day and told me it was the first time they'd ever had a Negro served. Luckily, they knew I was married to Lena Horne, so they kept their mouth shut."

Doby's eyes widened, and an excited smile appeared.

"You're married to Lena Horne? The Lena Horne?" Doby asked in awe. Horne was an iconic Black singer and dancer.

"Was married. We're divorced. But remember, if he asks you to a restaurant, you better have eyes in the back of your head. He doesn't know our world. Maybe check your food, too," Jones said with a nod.

Doby and Jones saw Veeck walking toward them.

"OK, time to catch a cab to the ballpark," Jones said. "We have to wait until all the white people leave. We can't compete with them for a cab."

"Will we see each other again?" Doby asked. It was clear that the rookie greatly appreciated the mentorship.

Jones smiled.

"I have a feeling I'll be around as long as you are," Jones said.

Veeck had limped over to the two Black men.

"How'd you like the hotel?" Veeck asked.

"Just fine, Mr. Veeck," Doby said.

"Please, call me Bill. I'm sorry you can't stay in the same hotels as the rest of your teammates. And you won't be able to eat in the same restaurants. But you're just as much a part of the team as any of them. I'm going to introduce you to the team," Veeck said.

Thirty minutes later, Veeck, Doby, and Jones walked into the visitor's clubhouse at Comiskey Park. Doby was stunned by how much better the accommodations were in the major leagues.

There was a murmur among the players still in street clothes before getting ready for that day's game. Everyone stopped at the sight of Doby. Veeck looked around the locker room, walked to the middle of the clubhouse, and brought Doby.

"Everyone, this is Larry Doby. He's your new teammate," Veeck said with authority. "Any questions?"

No one said anything.

Veeck continued: "I've heard that some of you said you'd quit before playing with a colored player. Well, I'm here to tell you, if you don't want to play with Larry, right there's the door. He's a better player than a lot of you."

Doby was stunned at Veeck's bluntness and fidgeted nervously at the statement. Veeck turned to his manager Lou Boudreau.

"Lou. I'll leave you to the introductions," Veeck said.

With that, Veeck left the clubhouse, and Boudreau walked over and motioned for Doby to follow him. Boudreau walked over to player Joe Gordon.

"Joe, this is Larry Doby. Larry, Joe Gordon," Boudreau said.

Gordon shook Larry's hand. Boudreau went to the three next players, who nodded and shook Larry's hand. Boudreau then went to Eddie Robinson.

"Eddie, say hello to Larry," Boudreau said.

Doby extended his hand, but Robinson stood with a glower and refused to accept it. Instead, Robinson stuck a wad of chewing tobacco in his mouth and turned his back on Doby. A look of shame spread over Doby. Boudreau moved on to the next teammate Les Fleming, who refused Doby's hand. The clubhouse went dead silent.

Boudreau stopped the introductions after three more teammates turned their back on Doby.

"You can get ready over there, Larry," Boudreau said as he pointed to a locker in the clubhouse. Doby walked over like the unpopular new kid in school.

Doby had been in many Negro League clubhouses where there was playful banter between teammates, laughing and joking.

As Doby changed into his newly pressed gray road uniform, the Major League Baseball locker room had become so quiet he could hear the water running through the old pipes above him. Most of his new teammates avoided making eye contact. The silence was broken only momentarily by a player clearing his throat.

The tension was so thick that Doby felt he could choke on it. Doby had never encountered such hostility.

In high school, he starred on the football team with white teammates who appreciated him. In 1942, Eastside High School in Paterson, New Jersey held a testimonial dinner for Doby. He was given a wrist watch.

High school coach Bob Dimond told the audience: "I said it before, and I repeat it here again, I think Larry Doby is the greatest athlete to ever represent Eastside High School, bar none."

Other classmates and faculty took to the microphone one by one to compliment Doby.

Doby swelled with pride that night watching his mother light up over the tributes to her son. Doby's mother was wearing the nicest floral print dress he'd ever seen. She bought it for the event.

The next day, the New Jersey hometown newspaper The Paterson News gushed: "One of the finest tributes ever tendered a Paterson high school athlete was given to Larry Doby, Eastside's great colored ace, by over 135 of his neighbors and well-wishers last night."

Now, five years later, Major League Baseball was suffocating him.

As Doby fastened the last button on a jersey he had never dreamed of wearing in high school, he felt rejected and ashamed.

CHAPTER 12

Can I Get An Amen?

July 5, 1947

An hour after Larry Doby's devastating introduction, the Cleveland Indians were all on the field playing catch before the game - except for Larry Doby. He was standing by himself - isolated and alone.

Cleveland Indians' second baseman Joe Gordon was doing a newspaper interview and noticed Doby alone. Gordon called over to teammate Les Fleming.

"Les," Gordon said. "Go play catch with Doby."

Fleming laughed and walked away shaking his head. Eddie Robinson gave Gordon a smirk. Doby saw it all and felt ashamed.

Five minutes later, Gordon felt he had to act.

"Look, Bob. I'm sorry. I've got to cut this short," Gordon told the sportswriter.

Grabbing his glove from the dugout, he trotted over to Doby.

"Hey, rookie," Gordon asked Doby. "Are you going to just stand there, or do you want to throw a little?"

Doby was overwhelmed by the simple act of kindness.

Bill Veeck watched from the seats behind the dugout. He promised himself to remember this moment.

In the game's seventh inning, Doby was sitting on the bench with the rest of his teammates. Boudreau looked over to him.

"Larry, grab a bat. You are hitting for Stephens," Boudreau said.

Doby froze, his heart was in his throat. The Indians trailed 5-1, with one out and two runners on base. The game was on the line and Doby had been on the team for less than four hours.

On the second pitch, Doby swung and connected. It was a shot down the left field line and landed foul by a mere three inches. The stadium went silent briefly when the play was in doubt.

Doby swung and missed on the next pitch. He struck out.

"This isn't your nigger league, boy!" a white fan shouted from the stands as Doby returned to the dugout. "Go shine some shoes, boy!"

Doby ignored him and slumped on the end of the bench alone and put his head in his hands. The Indians lost 6-5.

The next day was a Sunday. About two miles from Comiskey Park, the pews in the Ebenezer Missionary Baptist Church were full. On a hot Sunday morning, the women in the all-Black congregation fanned themselves while men in suits loosened their collars.

A Black pastor stood at a podium. He looked over his congregation.

" ... There will be people who have been broken by their sinfulness, ashamed of things in their lives, who will wonder if there's even a ghost of a chance that they'll get into that kingdom," the pastor's voice boomed.

The Black pastor paused and wiped his forehead with a cloth.

"They'll conclude that the only possibility is for them to rely on God's grace, favor, and kindness in providing some way for them to come. They'll look at themselves and wonder if they will make it in. And, by the grace of the Lord, they will make it!" the pastor shouted.

Congregants nodded and shouted praise in agreement.

The pastor momentarily looked at his watch.

"But we won't make it …" the pastor shouted.

Everyone looked stunned by the admission.

"… to Comiskey Park on time to see Larry Doby play if we don't wrap this sermon up now. God loves you! God loves Larry Doby! Can I get an Amen?" the pastor pleaded.

The entire congregation roared with a hearty, "Amen!"

And with that, the pastor concluded his service and the congregation poured out of the church, revved up and excited. Many walked in the direction of the stadium, seen on the horizon, hollering and singing in excitement.

Four hours later, Lou Boudreau was in an office in the visitor's clubhouse after the White Sox had beat the Indians 3-2 in the first game of a double-header. He had pulled Eddie Robinson aside into his office to tell him that Doby would be playing first base the second game.

"Eddie," Boudreau said. "You are hitting .226. I'm giving Doby a shot. We haven't won in three games."

Robinson's face turned beet red.

"Is that what this is?" Robinson said. "A nigger taking my job?"

Boudreau took a step toward Robinson.

"Nobody is taking your job," Boudreau said curtly.

Robinson paused.

"Doby doesn't even have a first baseman's glove," Robinson said. "And no, I won't lend my glove to a nigger."

"Then he can wear his fielder's glove," Boudreau snapped back.

Doby sat at his locker, trying to avoid eye contact with his new teammates. He was about to make the first start of his major league career. He felt sick to his stomach.

Spud Goldstein, the Cleveland Indians traveling secretary, overheard Boudreau's conversation with Robinson. He walked to the team bus and returned lugging a huge wooden footlocker with his name on it.

Goldstein went into the clubhouse and dropped the footlocker in the middle of the floor.

"OK, guys, you know the drill. This is the getaway day, and we are back in Cleveland tomorrow for the all-star break," Goldstein said. "I need to collect all the equipment not being used so we can get out of here and all get home."

The players started throwing extra gloves and catcher mitts into the footlocker.

Goldstein looked at Robinson.

"Eddie," Goldstein said. "You aren't playing. That's the only first baseman's glove we have."

Robinson got up and tossed the glove in the footlocker.

Goldstein shut the footlocker and brought it back to the bus. Now, out of sight, he retrieved the first baseman's glove. He walked over to Doby, who was at his locker.

"Larry," Goldstein said. "Here's a first baseman's glove."

Doby was unaware of Robinson's refusal to share his glove.

"Oh, thanks, Mr. Goldstein," Doby said.

Goldstein smiled.

Robinson was standing next to Les Fleming in the dugout when Goldstein approached.

"Doby is wearing your glove today," Goldstein told Robinson. "If you have a problem with that, I'll bring it up to Mr. Veeck. Tomorrow, I'm buying the Cleveland Indians a second first baseman's glove. This will be for one day. If you like, you can have the new glove."

Goldstein nodded at Fleming and Robinson and walked away.

An hour later, the second game began. This time, Doby had a base hit in his first at-bat in the third inning and drove in a run. It was the first hit of his major league career. Many of the fans cheered. As Doby walked back to the dugout, he passed a white fan who had yelled a slur at him earlier in the game. Doby pointed to the back of his hand, pointing out brown skin.

Chicago White Sox owner Grace Comiskey stood next to Bill Veeck in her owner's luxury box, watching the play unfold.

"I've never seen so many colored folks in my stadium," Comiskey said to Veeck. "We are four games under .500, but we doubled our attendance from yesterday."

The White Sox owner scanned the crowd of 31,566. Just five days before on July 1, the White Sox drew a crowd of 13,988.

"I know," Veeck said with a smile. "Just wait until the Negroes in Cleveland see him."

"Well, you're paying a high enough price," Comiskey said. "You're on the bad side of almost every other owner in the American League."

"I was already on their bad side. Nothing new for me," Veeck said.

Veeck looked at Comiskey.

"What about you, Grace?" Veeck asked.

She smiled.

"We're not much different. As a woman, you think I can give up one inch?" Comiskey asked. "Hell, when my husband died and left me the team, I had to go to federal court to stay as the owner because the goddamn bank didn't think a woman could run a baseball team."

Comiskey paused.

"I won. When they suspended my manager four years ago for swearing at an umpire, I came out spitting fire. Good Lord, you think they would have tried that on any other owner in the league?" she said.

Veeck nodded.

"You've begun an experiment here that the whole world is watching. Doby doesn't just have to be good. He needs to be an all-star. Look at that Jackie Robinson. My Lord, that boy can play - and he still gets it for his color," Comiskey said.

"I'm not done," Veeck said. "I'm going to sign others. Maybe Satchel Paige next year. He may be too old."

Comiskey clasped her hands together. She smiled.

"Oh, he's a legend in this town. He came through barnstorming more than a few times," Comiskey said.

Comiskey turned to Veeck.

"You and Satchel Paige," she said with a laugh. "Now that is a match made in heaven. You won't need that man who hung upside down and took batting practice. Oh, my Lord, I saw the photo of that. It was hilarious."

Veeck missed not having Jackie Price around.

"I know you understand this, Grace - but most don't," Veeck said. "Baseball offers an escape from the problems of daily life. League management thinks this is just a business. But it's entertainment.

We don't always win - and some would even feel they wasted their money by watching their team lose. But if we can put a smile on their face and create a happy memory to take with them - then they are going to come back regardless if their team is winning or not. Good entertainment is good business."

Comiskey nodded.

"Now, if you ask the commissioner and other league owners, they're furious. Think you're disrespecting the game," she said.

"Well, unless they want to purchase thousands of tickets every game and fund my team - I don't care what they think," Veeck said.

CHAPTER 13

What You Did Opened A Door That Can't Be Shut

Sept. 9, 1947

On a sunny Tuesday in New Jersey, major leaguer Larry Doby was visiting his hometown of Paterson. He was at his old high school to watch the football team practice.

He parked his new 1946 Ford convertible in the school parking lot as 60 high-school teenagers ran around the field in helmets and pads.

During happier and less stressful times, Hinchliffe Stadium was Larry Doby's sanctuary. During the spring while in high school, Doby was also the star baseball player who played in the multi-purpose venue. The Negro League's New York Black Yankees played games at Hinchliffe Stadium during Doby's high school career.

He was the star and the only Black player on his 1941 Eastside High School football team. Doby scored three touchdowns in this stadium and kicked three extra points to help his team beat arch-rival Central 45-6 in a Thanksgiving Day game.

In his senior year, Doby led the football team to an undefeated season. The media declared the team state champions. The school district had been invited that year to bring their football team to Florida to play in a prominent national tournament. But with the state's Jim Crow laws, the promoters discovered Doby was on the team and demanded the district leave him behind. Instead, the school turned down the invitation refusing to play without Doby.

Now at the crossroads of his major league career, all that seemed a lifetime ago to Doby. He had just two hits in his last 20 at-bats spread over 19 games.

Henry Rumana, a 38-year-old white assistant football coach with a buzz cut of salt and pepper hair, was talking to local newspaper sportswriter Bob Whiting. Rumana looked up and broke out in a big smile when he spotted Doby approaching from the parking lot.

Rumana enthusiastically shook Doby's hand.

"You know, coach, sometimes I wish I were playing football again, right back here at Eastside," Doby said.

"Well!" Rumana shot back. "We'd love to have you back!"

The coach blew his whistle and called the players over.

"Gentlemen," Rumana said. "Let me introduce you to Larry Doby. He's the greatest athlete to ever set foot on this field."

Doby blushed at the praise. The team of all-white players looked at Doby with respect in their eyes.

Rumana blew the whistle, and the players took off to resume practice.

Whiting, a middle-aged white man, turned to Doby. Whiting had covered Doby for the Paterson newspaper during his high school stardom when Doby lettered in baseball, football, basketball and track.

"So, you made the big leagues!" Whiting said smiling. "Congratulations. Are you excited about next year?"

Doby flickered a nervous smile and hesitated.

"Mr. Whiting," Doby said. "Actually, I've been giving serious thought about going back to school. I have to think about my future. I'd like to take up physical education at Panzer [a state college in New Jersey]."

Doby paused.

"LIU [Long Island University] sent me a letter and said I could return there if I wanted to," Doby said.

Whiting was stunned.

"Uh, you know you can't play ball there," Whiting said.

Doby noted the sports writer's incredulous tone followed by an awkward silence.

"I'd still like to play ball with the Indians, but it gets pretty tiresome sitting around – if you know what I mean," Doby said. "The Indians have been trying me out in the outfield. And my hitting has improved – at least in batting practice."

When the football practice ended, Doby returned to the parking lot and took off for the 15-mile trip to Newark for a reunion with Abe and Effa Manley, whom he considered like parents.

He dreaded it, because there would be no hiding his failures. Abe and Effa Manley knew baseball. More than anyone, they knew what was at stake with Larry playing for Cleveland. And he couldn't stand the shame of letting them down.

A sick feeling set in his stomach as he drove into the driveway of the Manley's home.

Abe answered the knock on the door.

"Larry!" Abe said, giving him a bear hug. "Come on in."

Doby lit up.

Effa Manley emerged from the living room, also with a big smile.

"Larry Doby!" Effa said. "Where is that lovely wife of yours? I pray she didn't leave you after just a year because of how horrible you are playing?"

Doby laughed. The ice was broken.

"She's home," Doby said, feeling like a hundred pounds were lifted off him.

Doby and the Manleys went to the living room and sat down. The radio was playing a commercial.

"You just missed the Giants game," Effa said.

Effa could sense something was troubling Doby.

"So," she said. "What's on your mind?"

Doby exhaled.

"So, how bad would it be if I returned to college?" he asked.

Effa smiled.

"Why would becoming an educated man be such a bad thing?" Effa asked.

Doby was silent.

"Bob Feller wants me to play in Cuba for a month after the season," Doby said without an ounce of enthusiasm in his voice.

Effa nodded.

"What are you hitting?" she asked.

".138," Doby answered.

"Good Lord almighty, I weigh more than that!" Effa said with a cackle.

She walked over to her cabinet and pulled out her clipbook. In it, she read a newspaper article about Doby.

"I clipped this out and saved it. It's from the Detroit News, and some cracker named H.G. Salsinger wrote it," Effa said. "It's dated Aug. 12. OK. Here we go."

Effa paused and read: "Bill Veeck did the Negro race no favor when he signed Larry Doby to a Cleveland contract. If Veeck wanted to demonstrate that the Negro has no place in Major League Baseball, he could have used no subtler means to establish the point."

Effa halted and stared down Doby, who sat motionless, listening.

"Now, here's the best part. It's from Rogers Hornsby, the meanest bastard I've ever met," Effa said.

She continued reading.

"Rogers Hornsby, a distinguished judge of baseball talent, remarked after watching Doby in one game: 'If he were white, he wouldn't be considered good enough to play with a semi-pro club.'"

Effa put down the article.

"You feel bad because you are letting down the Negroes. You aren't a credit to your race anymore?" Effa asked.

Larry was quiet.

"I read in the newspaper that Mr. Veeck canceled a 'Larry Doby Day' the folks in Paterson wanted to have for you at Yankee Stadium," Effa said.

Doby looked up.

"He said it was too early. Maybe next year," Doby responded.

Effa snorted.

"Too early? He's just mad he didn't think of it first," Effa said. "That man never saw a promotion he wouldn't put on."

She smiled.

"You don't owe the Negroes anything, Larry," Effa said with a maternal tone. "You could never get another hit in your life, and you couldn't stop what's happening. We had five Negroes on Major

League Baseball teams this year. And we'll have more. I see the scouts. They know what they have in Jackie Robinson, and there's more coming."

"Yeah, but only Jackie is playing well," Doby said.

"Uh, yeah," Effa shot back. "That man is 28. And he played an entire year in the minor leagues to prepare for the National League, which isn't anything compared to the American League you are playing in."

"If Bill Veeck really was concerned about you playing well, he'd put you in the minor leagues for a year. Or two," Effa said. "Hell, your own manager, Lou Boudreau, spent two years in the minors. You can't go down because they need you to protect Jackie. That means something."

Effa paused.

"You want to go to college? You go to college," Effa said. "You paid your price, and you did your job. Baseball will never be all white again."

Larry nodded.

"Nobody knows baseball more than me," Effa said. "You know that. And I think you can be a star in the majors if you just quit trying to live five seasons in three months."

"Relax, you are 23," Effa said. "Jackie is five years older."

"What about coming back to the Eagles," Doby said, referring to the Manleys' Newark Negro team.

Abe and Effa glanced at each other.

"Honey, what you did opened a door that can't be shut," Effa said. "But when one door opens, the other is closing."

Effa looked to Abe.

"Unless there is a miracle, we are going to shut down the Eagles," Effa said.

"Shut down the Eagles?" Doby asked incredulously.

"The numbers don't work anymore," Effa said. "By next year, the best Negro players will be in the majors. That is where people will be going to watch Negroes play ball. Not our league anymore."

Doby was stunned.

Effa got up from her seat.

"Larry, come and eat with us," Effa said. "We are just getting ready to sit down."

Effa paused and turned around.

"Are the Indians paying your way to Cuba?" Effa asked.

Doby nodded.

"Well, then, don't you be quitting until after that trip," Effa said. "Cuba in December, oh, it's beautiful. It's 80 degrees and sunny every day."

Effa went to the kitchen, and Abe got up with a big smile to follow. But he stopped and looked at Doby.

"Young man, you really do have what it takes," Abe said. "Don't let anyone tell you otherwise."

Abe then swung his arms slowly, like he was hitting a home run.

"Pow!" Abe said. "I've never seen anyone hit a ball as far as you can."

Doby smiled.

CHAPTER 14

If I Were You, I'd Rent

Sept. 10, 1947

Bob Feller, star pitcher for the Cleveland Indians, had a bad outing as he gave up three runs in four innings. He was pulled from the game the Indians eventually lost 7-4 to the New York Yankees.

After the game, the Indians had to travel to Boston and boarded a train. Cleveland's Les Fleming had hit two homers and Feller's teammates had been ribbing the pitcher over a $30,000 bonus owner Bill Veeck had given him just a week earlier as an attendance bonus. The bonus was so large, it made national news. Feller's annual salary was $40,000.

Veeck was traveling with the team on this road trip.

"Hey, Bill!" Fleming shouted to Veeck as the Cleveland first baseman entered the train. "If Feller gets $30,000 for pitching like that, what do I get for two homers?"

Veeck ignored Fleming's question and headed to the back of the train where Larry Doby usually sat.

Doby didn't play in New York, missing his 11th straight game. Regular first baseman Eddie Robinson was out for the year with an injury but still traveled with the team. Fleming had taken over as the full-time first baseman.

Doby could sit wherever he chose on the train ride to Boston. That was not always the case. Two weeks later, the team would travel to St. Louis, Missouri to play the Browns. On that trip, Jim Crow laws would restrict Doby to the "colored section" of the train.

Despite Fleming's two homers, the loss had snapped a hot streak where the Indians had won 8 of 10 games.

Heading to Boston, most of the team filled the 18-seat section of a railroad coach car. Doby sat in an adjacent coach, which was fitting as he never felt more detached from a team.

Teammate Jim Hegan made a point to sit with Doby, making sure the Black player wasn't left sitting by himself. And Bill Veeck was right across the aisle.

Two hours into the six-hour trip, Fleming and Robinson were intoxicated after drinking several beers. Across the aisle from the two homebred Texans was manager/shortstop Lou Boudreau.

"Hey, Lou!" the drunk Fleming called out to the manager. "You know, Mr. Veeck paid a lot of money for that colored Doby, and he hasn't played this month!"

Boudreau tried to ignore Fleming's taunts, but inside, Boudreau was starting to resent Doby. Boudreau knew Veeck wanted him out as manager and believed Doby was part of a plan to sabotage his team. What better way to prove Boudreau couldn't coach than to plant a Black player on the roster?

"Mr. Veeck paid $15,000 for that nigger," Fleming said. "We could use another bat right now. Eddie's out the rest of the year."

Boudreau turned to Fleming.

"Les," Boudreau said. "Why don't you take it up with Mr. Veeck? He's in the next section."

Fleming took out a newspaper.

"Lou, here's what the papers are saying," Fleming said, his words carrying throughout the train.

He read from the newspaper article.

"Cleveland President Bill Veeck tried to unload Larry Doby, his Negro 'find' on several clubs in our league, but none of them would listen. Reason? They say, Doby, as well as the two Negro players signed by the Browns and since released, are nothing but sandlot performers," Fleming said.

Fleming paused.

"I don't blame them. Doby is nothing. But if Bill can't trade him, at least put that jigaboo in the minors!" Fleming said, his drunken rants now filling the train.

Boudreau didn't disagree and sensed that Fleming was only saying what was on everyone's mind. Doby had lost confidence at the plate. Sending Doby down to the minors was clearly the solution, but Veeck had forbidden it.

The Indians were 14.5 games behind the first-place Yankees, but a strong finish would make a good argument for Boudreau to remain manager.

The train coach went silent as Veeck walked through to get to the restroom at the front of the train.

"Mr. Veeck!" Fleming shouted.

Veeck stopped and turned to face Fleming.

"Bill, that's two homers I hit today. I've been working hard for you, and my wife wants a bigger house. I'd like a raise," Fleming said. "I am a steal considering what you paid for Doby!"

Doby's $5,000 salary had been printed in the newspapers.

Veeck paused. And nodded.

"Les," Veeck said. "If I were you, I'd rent."

And with that, Veeck turned around and walked away in silence.

Three months later, Fleming was traded to the Pittsburgh Pirates.

CHAPTER 15

Handsome Lou Is A Hero To The City

Oct. 3, 1947

Bill Veeck laid back after pulling his partially amputated leg onto the bed in a New York City hotel.

Harry Grabiner, a 56-year-old white man who had spent most of his baseball administrator career with the Chicago White Sox, was also in the room. He had 23 years on the 33-year-old Veeck.

Grabiner was now the Cleveland Indians' vice president and treasurer, and Veeck was the team's owner and general manager. They were in the big city to watch the first game of the World Series.

Grabiner was handsome with jet black hair slicked back and looked 15 years younger than his age. He was one of the few men to whom Veeck would listen.

They met to discuss Lou Boudreau and his hopeful imminent trade to the St. Louis Browns. Boudreau was the star shortstop and the manager when Veeck bought the team a year earlier. It was an unusual arrangement that Veeck didn't like.

Negotiations had failed to get Boudreau to give up his managing job and just play shortstop. If he was traded, the Indians would need a new shortstop and manager.

Grabiner had set up an interview with Jimmy Dykes, the current manager for the Chicago White Sox minor league team, as the top candidate to replace Boudreau as manager.

"What about Dykes and Doby? Will he be receptive of Negro players?" Veeck asked.

"Receptive?" Grabiner shot back. "Outside of you and Branch, I don't know many who are receptive. I don't think it will be a problem with just one Negro on the team."

Veeck gave Grabiner a look.

"Bill," Grabiner said.

"We may have more Negroes," Veeck said.

"Well, Doby has been a disaster," Grabiner said, shaking his head. "After Doby's second game, Lou just used him as a pinch hitter the rest of the year."

Veeck shook his head.

"That's what I'm talking about," Veeck said. "You mark my words. Doby will be every bit as good as Jackie Robinson."

Grabiner chuckled and shook his head.

"Jackie was rookie of the year," Grabiner said.

"They will build a statue of Larry after he retires," Veeck said.

Veeck paused.

"I tried talking to Lou again," Veeck said. "He won't budge. He likes the bigger salary of being a player and manager."

"Yeah, well, who wouldn't?" Grabiner said.

"He's a great shortstop, but not a good manager," Veeck said. "Anyway, so the deal to St. Louis is almost final."

The hotel room phone rang, and Veeck answered and listened for a minute. He then hung up.

"We better get a copy of today's newspaper," Veeck said nervously.

In the hotel lobby a few minutes later, Veeck and Grabiner bought a New York Times and opened the sports section.

The headline of a front-page story stated, "Lou Boudreau Through As Indians Pilot." Arch Ward, the sports editor of the Chicago Tribune, wrote the article. Dykes managed for the Chicago White Sox minor league system. Someone connected to the White Sox had leaked the story.

Veeck read the article and then handed the newspaper to Grabiner.

"I think I'd better get back to Cleveland," Veeck said.

Five days later on Oct. 8, during Cleveland's morning rush hour, there was a traffic jam four blocks long on Euclid Avenue.

Euclid Avenue was a primary thoroughfare in the heart of the city's business district, where 20-story office buildings blocked the midday sun. It was the route used by downtown Cleveland parades.

But at the moment, a line of 40 cars was crawling in the direction of the State Auto Sales dealership.

Max Friedman, a 29-year-old war veteran, had recently purchased the used car lot with his brothers after being discharged from the military.

From his corner office, Friedman could see cars waiting to get into his parking lot.

Friedman glanced at his advertising sign that was attracting the cars: "Sign The Petition To Keep Lou Boudreau Here, Pull In."

Several angry Indians fans had been driving in since the sign went up two hours earlier.

By noon, Friedman already had collected 1,000 signatures on his petitions kept in five notebooks. That's when he phoned Cleveland Municipal Stadium to ask if he could drop off his petitions.

He was expecting a secretary to take the call. Instead, just moments later, he was surprised to find himself on the phone with Cleveland Indians owner Bill Veeck, who asked him to come down to the team's office.

Friedman jumped into one of the dealership's loaner cars and 30 minutes later, he was ushered into Veeck's stadium office. Friedman wasn't sure what to expect.

Was Veeck angry?

Veeck was at his desk when Friedman walked in.

"I'd like to thank you for the flow of potential customers," Friedman said.

Veeck looked over the car salesman and then surprised him.

"I just read a book about the war," Veeck said. "There was a quote from Winston Churchill. 'Never let a crisis go to waste.'"

Friedman grinned and nodded.

Veeck liked Friedman's style – a salesman and promoter with conviction. Friedman was a believer, and right now, he believed in Boudreau.

"What do you know of Vern Stephens?" Veeck asked, bringing up one of the key players the Indians would receive if Boudreau had been traded. The question was a test. Veeck wanted to know if Friedman understood the trade's complexities in trying to win a championship.

"Good hitter," Friedman answered. "But his best years were the three years during the war when the best major leaguers were serving their country. Since the war ended, he hasn't done as well."

Veeck was impressed. Friedman knew baseball.

"But this isn't only about talent, Mr. Veeck," Friedman said. "Lou is a hero to the city of Cleveland. We understand he may not be the best manager."

Friedman paused.

"How many games do you think Boudreau costs you as a manager compared to how many you think he wins you as a player?" Friedman asked. "The difference is small enough that the Cleveland Indian fans will forgive. But, if you trade him, Bill Veeck will not be forgiven."

"We are in the same business, Mr. Veeck," Friedman said. "Pleasing customers. You trade Boudreau, and nobody will show up for your promotions."

Veeck opened the notebooks Friedman had delivered and reviewed the signatures. Each name came from a different person. This was legit.

"I've got more than 4,000 letters on this," Veeck said. "And they are running 4-to-1 against trading Lou. I haven't had this negative a response since I signed Larry Doby."

Friedman nodded.

"I'm totally in support of Doby," Friedman said.

Veeck was surprised by the admission.

"I'm a member of the National Association for the Advancement of Colored People," Friedman revealed.

"They accept white Jews?" a stunned Veeck asked.

"Jewish people played a pivotal role in starting the NAACP," Friedman said. "The Negro community and the Jewish community have a bond, Mr. Veeck. The Negro was a slave in this country as the Jews were slaves in Egypt."

"Please, call me Bill," Veeck said and continued listening.

"I was in the Army in Europe when we heard stories of the Chelmno concentration camp," Friedman said.

Underground newspapers in Poland reported that the Germans

murdered all the Jewish people in the camp once they realized the war was over. Estimates were that as many as 350,000 Jews were murdered in Chelmno.

Friedman was silent as the memory returned.

Veeck nodded respectfully to the suddenly serious fellow veteran.

"Thanks for dropping these off," Veeck said. "And let's keep in touch. I give away a lot of cars. There's nothing I'd enjoy more than giving away one of your cars in front of 70,000 fans. And it'd be a great way to promote your business, not at my expense."

Friedman smiled. He couldn't help but like Veeck, and Veeck's smile told him the feeling was mutual.

"You wouldn't consider trading Feller," Friedman joked.

Feller was the league's second-highest-paid player at $65,000 and had just won 20 games for the Indians the previous year. The fan outrage over dealing Feller to another team would inspire another petition drive.

"I just got a half dozen 1938 Buick Centuries I am trying to unload," Friedman said.

CHAPTER 16

The Apology Tour In Every Cleveland Bar

Nov. 29, 1947

Bill Veeck met with Lou Boudreau and signed the Cleveland Indian shortstop/manager to a new two-year deal in early November 1947. The team owner hoped this would heal their relationship. But too much damage had been done.

Boudreau felt humiliated. Veeck felt like he was held hostage with keeping Boudreau as a manager when he knew it was hurting his team's chance to win a championship.

But Veeck also realized how poorly he had handled the situation.

He misjudged how much of a pillar of the community Boudreau had become in his 10 seasons in Cleveland. Winning back those fans would now take a tremendous effort.

That effort started this day at The Harbor Inn, a tavern in the gritty section of downtown Cleveland known as The Flats.

Veeck told Cleveland sportswriter Ed McAuley he would go to every bar in the city to apologize for mishandling the Boudreau non-trade.

McAuley was waiting for the team owner at the tavern's front entrance. Hanging five feet above the door was a wooden image of Chief Wahoo, the Cleveland Indians' new mascot. Next to it hung a wooden sign that read: "Harbor Inn, Est. 1895."

The Harbor Inn occupied a two-story brick building with no windows on the ground floor. Inside, a bar stretched from the entrance to the back area where the restrooms were located. High-top tables extended from the wall opposite the bar. There was a four-foot-wide path where people could walk to the restroom or out the exit.

Veeck arrived and smiled as he saw McAuley.

"Mac, thanks for meeting me," Veeck said. "Don't make me look bad if you write a story."

McAuley smiled.

"Are you kidding? I wouldn't miss this for the world. I'd say it's brave of you, but honestly, I think it's a death wish. I mean, first you sign a Negro. That took nerve. But then trying to trade the most popular player in town?" McAuley said, shaking his head.

"You know," McAuley said, "The Cleveland sportswriters just named Lou the Baseball Man of the Year. I'm afraid this story could turn into a homicide investigation."

Veeck nervously laughed.

"Nobody would hold it against you if you didn't do this apology tour," McAuley said. "The newspapers have already said Lou got his two-year deal."

Veeck straightened up.

"Mr. McAuley, you don't set record attendance by being a poor businessman. And being a good businessman isn't just about managing money. It's understanding how to market and satisfy customers," Veeck said. "But Lou won't step down as manager. He costs us four games a year with his poor managing."

McAuley was curious.

"You wanted to bring in Jimmy Dykes to be manager," McAuley asked. "Dykes would never go for your parlor tricks. He's strictly by-the-book baseball. You understand marketing, but this time, you underestimated the fans' loyalty to a player. They'll forgive four losses from Handsome Lou - but they won't forgive trying to trade him."

Veeck nodded.

"Which is why I've got 90 bars to go to over the next two weeks. Make sure you print that. I'm going to every bar that will have me to apologize," Veeck said.

McAuley took out his notebook as he approached the door.

"I can't imagine how this will turn out. Either way, it'll make a good story," McAuley said.

Veeck pulled his pants leg up to reveal the wooden leg beyond his right knee.

"Maybe they won't beat a cripple," Veeck asked.

McAuley scoffed.

"In the Flats, they'll beat you with that wooden leg. And worse," McAuley said.

Veeck looked at McAuley with trepidation. He took a deep breath as he opened the door, and they entered.

Veeck was taken aback by the foul smell that greeted them. At 7 p.m., the bar was full of blue-collar workers fresh from the docks. The earlier business crowd had left, not interested in the spectacle.

It only took a few seconds for the bar to fall silent as both parties were trying to size up the other like an awkward blind date.

Finally, a middle-aged woman in the back yelled out.

"Hey, you stupid cunt, we are keeping Lou and sending you to St. Louis!" she yelled as the bar erupted in laughter.

Veeck relaxed a bit. He'd given thousands of speeches. He knew how to work a crowd and a profane, blue-collar group was right in his wheelhouse.

McAuley was nervous. He wanted to separate himself from Veeck.

"I'm a sportswriter with The Cleveland Press," McAuley yelled.

"We voted Lou Boudreau Man of the Year this year."

The crowd cheered.

Veeck shook his head.

"Thanks, Mac," Veeck said.

The middle-aged woman felt empowered by the crowd.

"Lou Boudreau is the best-looking man on your team. You don't have a decent-looking player besides him on the roster! And you won't find a better shortstop!" she yelled, drawing a cheer.

A drunk dock worker raised his beer and joined in.

"Fuck that! You wanted to trade Lou. And you signed the nigger Doby. If we wanted to see a nigger play, we'd go down to League Park and watch the Buckeyes play!" the dock worker said, referring to the city's Negro League team. "Boudreau is all this city had when Feller went to war!"

The bar roared its approval. The racial slur lit an internal fire in Veeck.

"I went to war, too. And I lost my leg," Veeck said in a calm, monotone. "But I didn't lose my desire to win. And I didn't forget how to do it."

Veeck looked around and assessed the crowd.

"You are going to knock the Cleveland Buckeyes, are you? They won the Negro World Series two years ago. Did any of you care?" Veeck asked.

The crowd yelled, 'Hell no!' and spewed more racial slurs.

Veeck nodded.

"Well, that's too bad. It's the closest you may get to any championship if you keep thinking the way you do," Veeck said, his voice raised a bit. "The Indians haven't won a championship since 1920."

"Lou is the only player worth seeing!" the middle-aged woman shouted.

"You know why?" Veeck asked.

The bar went silent.

"Because your dear previous owner Alva Bradley is no baseball man. He sells real estate and coal. He's a huge success at that. He's on the boards of several big companies. I see a lot of dock workers here. Alva sits on the board of the American Ship Building Company. It is one of the most successful businesses in America. But ship building isn't baseball," Veeck said.

"And you are going to do better?" the drunken dock worker yelled.

Veeck nodded.

"Alva ran his baseball team like one of his regular businesses. When we bought the Indians, Alva made a $200,000 profit on what he bought it for in 1927. He made a bundle. You got one damn second-place finish in 19 years!" Veeck said, now using a more animated voice.

The crowd grumbled in agreement.

"I'm going to change that!" Veeck said, earning some affirmative shouts in response.

"When a foul ball was hit in the stands, Alva made you give it back. Now, you will keep the baseballs that go into the stands as souvenirs. It's a small thing but a big gesture," Veeck said. "Here's what it says: Thanks for coming to the ballpark!"

The crowd shouted back encouragement. Veeck was winning them over.

"I know something most owners don't. This isn't just a game. It's entertainment," Veeck said. "And losing isn't entertainment. What's so memorable about coming to a game you lose?"

The crowd cheered.

"We want a winner!" a voice called out from the back.

"And ladies, we know baseball wouldn't be the same without you, so I added mirrors to the women's restrooms. The men know our Cleveland women are so damn pretty, and you deserve to see it for yourselves!" Veeck said, raising his voice so even those in the back of the bar could hear him.

The women in the crowd cheered.

"Did you like the beauty pageants we had? How many other teams celebrate their women's beauty?" Veeck said as the crowd cheered. "But let me tell you, all the promotions amount to nothing if I can't bring home a winner for you. Everything we do, we do for the fans. I want all of you to win a pennant. I want all of you to win a World Series!"

The room erupted in raucous cheers.

"Listen, I am the only owner you'll ever meet who was raised in a ballpark. My father was a sportswriter for a Chicago newspaper who wrote columns criticizing the Cubs. So, the Cubs owner Mr. Wrigley offered him a chance to run the team if he thought he knew better. My father won three pennants as general manager of the Cubs," Veeck said proudly.

The crowd respected the moment and was silent.

"Now, I know many of you don't like having a Negro on the team," Veeck said as he paused to look around the bar.

"But how much do you like the Yankees kicking our butts every year? We can't compete with them for money to pay the best players. They get more radio money in a week than we get in a month."

The bar patrons were now focused on Veeck, whose experience in public speaking had taken over.

"Right now, we have one edge over the damn Yankees. And that is the Negro player. The Yankees won't sign Negroes. We are. You don't like Larry Doby? Well, you will when he's the best goddamn player on the team. And he will be. Trust me on that. The Negroes will help us win a pennant," Veeck said.

Veeck stopped talking. No one was challenging him.

"I want you to know that I listen to the fans. And you told me loud and clear to keep Lou. And I'm going to every bar in Cleveland to make amends with all of you over Boudreau," Veeck said. "And I assure you Handsome Lou is staying in Cleveland. I'm signing him to a two-year contract."

The crowd cheered.

The middle-aged woman called out from the back.

"What if you don't deliver what you're promising?" she asked.

"Well, my phone number is in the book," Veeck said.

The bartender shook his head.

"Hold on!" the bartender protested in a skeptical tone.

He grabbed a phone book and thumbed through the white pages to the back, where Veeck's name would be listed.

The bartender chuckled.

"Well, I'll be damned. His number is listed in the phone book!" he said.

Veeck looked at the bartender.

"Everyone has a drink on the Cleveland Indians!" Veeck said. "Just send the bill to my office."

The crowd cheered as Veeck and McAuley left.

"That was pretty impressive," McAuley said.

"Mac," Veeck said. "I do believe this town has a drinking problem."

CHAPTER 17

Doby's Success Would Depend On A Confessed Klansman

Feb. 17, 1948

Larry Doby was prohibited from staying in the Arizona hotel with his teammates during spring training. Instead, the Black player stayed with a Black family.

This morning, he had to get to the ballpark to work on his hitting.

On his first pitch of spring training, Doby swung and whiffed.

Wearing their Cleveland Indians baseball uniforms, Tris Speaker and Rogers Hornsby watched from the dugout 30 feet away. Both were Hall of Fame players. Speaker was inducted in 1937, and Hornsby five years later. Both were born and raised in Texas.

They had one other thing in common: During their playing careers, both had befriended national sportswriter Fred Lieb and confided in him that they were members of the Ku Klux Klan.

Hornsby, 52, had been fired as the Chicago Cubs manager in 1932 by team president Bill Veeck Sr., the father of the current Cleveland Indians owner. The elderly Veeck fired Hornsby due to his combative demeanor.

Fifteen years later, Veeck Jr. had hired Hornsby now as a spring training hitting instructor, in part because he lived in Arizona.

Speaker, 59, was hand-picked by Veeck to help groom Doby for playing in the outfield, which is where the Indians decided to play the second-year player. Speaker had been a favorite of Indians fans during his 11 years playing for Cleveland and was considered the best defensive center fielder the game had ever produced.

Doby's success would depend on a confessed Klansman.

Speaker watched closely as Doby settled in for another pitch.

Doby swung again and connected, but still was flailing as the ball went foul down the right-field line.

"He has way too long a swing," Speaker said to Hornsby.

Hornsby was quiet.

Doby swung and missed the next pitch.

"He's got a hitch," Speaker said. "That may have worked in the Negro Leagues, but -"

"His swing looks fine to me," Hornsby said, cutting off Speaker. "I can't work with him. He isn't worth the time. Those jigaboos never listen anyway."

Speaker turned back to watch Doby.

Hornsby looked at Speaker.

"You're going to teach that boy how to hit? Shoot, you got a better chance teaching a sow how to square dance," Hornsby said with a laugh.

The next day, Speaker was waiting at the batting cage when Doby approached.

"Larry," Speaker said. "Where'd you learn that swing?"

"My high school coach, Mr. Speaker," Doby answered.

"Well, this isn't high school," Speaker said. "You won't hit your weight unless we shorten that swing."

Speaker took the bat from Doby and held it in a batting stance.

"Keep your arms in tighter," Speaker said, pulling his arms close to his chest. "You have them too far out. And your elbow is dropping."

Speaker lifted his elbow to illustrate.

"Just about every pitcher will throw you fastballs because it takes you too long to get the head of the bat around," Speaker said. "By the time you swing, the pitch is past you. In this league, there are enough guys that can throw a fastball right by you with that swing you have."

Doby listened intently.

Speaker handed him the bat back and looked over to a group of players on the field.

"Gromek!" Speaker yelled.

Steve Gromek, an eight-year veteran of the Indians, trotted over to the storied Speaker as if the command came from the burning bush.

"Take the mound and throw batting practice to Larry," Speaker said. "Nothing fast. Just fat cotton balls."

Gromek went over to the mound. He grabbed a baseball from the bucket and threw a pitch at about half speed.

Doby tried to swing but missed the pitch and almost tripped.

Speaker looked at Doby.

"Well, at least you kept your arms in tight," Speaker said, shaking his head with a grin. "Every day, 30 minutes a day, you are going to come here and do this until it comes naturally."

Speaker could tell Doby wasn't confident.

"Don't worry, it will come," Speaker said.

Doby arrived at the park at 8 a.m. the next day and saw Speaker in center field waiting for him. Speaker waved Doby over to meet him. Doby jogged over.

Speaker took his cap off and waved it toward the dugout. Hank Greenberg, a 37-year-old fading superstar trying to squeeze one more year from his aging body, walked up to the plate 300 feet away with a bat and a ball.

"OK, kid, Hank's going to hit a fly ball. Let's see you flag it down," Speaker said.

Greenberg tossed up a ball and released a mighty swing. The ball took off like a rocket.

Doby froze at first, then back-pedalled. Doby stumbled slightly and reached up as the ball bounced off his glove.

Speaker motioned Greenberg to hold off on taking another swing.

Speaker walked up to Doby.

"First thing, never backpedal," he told Doby.

He took Doby's glove. Doby noticed Speaker had no reservation taking a Black player's glove.

"Here, watch me," Speaker said.

Speaker waved his hat again, and Greenberg hit another rocket into center field.

Even at age 59, Speaker turned around, sprinted 25 feet and caught the ball.

He was a little winded when he jogged back to Doby and returned the glove.

"See the difference?" Speaker asked. "Don't backpedal. Turn and run to the spot."

Doby put his glove back on and chased down the next batted ball from Greenberg without a problem.

Speaker was impressed. Doby had instincts that couldn't be taught. He could judge a fly ball when it first came off the bat. And he had incredible speed.

"Every day, we work on your footing," Speaker told Doby.

Speaker started to believe Doby could be something special.

On March 4, the Cleveland Indians had their first scrimmage. The Cleveland veterans made up the A team, and the players likely to be sent down to the minor leagues were on the B team. Larry Doby was batting third for the B team.

Don Black, a 30-year-old veteran hoping to make the starting rotation, was on the mound. Black unleashed a fastball on his third pitch to Doby.

THWACK! Doby swung and crushed the ball.

The veterans on the field turned and watched the ball land 380 feet over the right-field fence. Doby had just hit the Indians' first home run of spring training.

Greenberg was sitting next to Speaker in the dugout.

"Where'd that come from?" Greenberg said.

Speaker let a smile escape briefly.

Over the next three weeks, Doby lit up the opposing pitchers in pre-season games against other teams. On March 12, Doby hit another home run that flew over the fences and landed in the parking lot.

Cleveland sportswriter Ed McAuley was sending stories back east for Indians' fans and was watching. He wrote in a March 25 article, "Doby is one of the most impressive athletes in camp."

Two days later, Doby had three hits, including two triples, as the Indians' B team beat the Chicago Cubs A team.

As the only Black player with any hope of making an American League team's roster out of spring training, Doby's hitting drew the media's attention.

Shirley Povich, a 42-year-old white reporter from the Washington Post, had made his name as a World War II correspondent. On March 27, he was down in Arizona to report on Doby.

Doby was in the batting cage getting instruction from Speaker when Povich walked over. Indians manager/shortstop Lou Boudreau was standing on deck waiting for his turn for batting practice.

"So, Tris," Povich began. "What's the story on Doby? He's hitting .333. Is he going to make the team?"

"That's not my call," Speaker said, turning to Doby. "But I've never seen a young ballplayer with such high potential."

Doby lit up. A compliment from Tris Speaker had weight.

Povich turned to Boudreau, who had wandered over to listen to what the newspaper reporter was doing.

"Lou?" Povich asked.

Boudreau patted Doby on the back.

"If Doby continues the way he has been going, I don't see how I can let him go," Boudreau said.

Still in the batting cage, Doby was trying to catch his breath. His heart was racing from the praise.

The Indians finished their final spring training game in Arizona on April 8. Over the next nine days, the Indians and New York Giants would play a series of exhibition games at local ballparks in cities in New Mexico, Texas, Oklahoma, Kansas, Indiana and Kentucky. It was a way to generate extra revenue in states that didn't have Major League Baseball teams. This was the only way for those fans to see professional ballplayers.

On April 8, the Indians left Albuquerque at 8 p.m. on the train to Texarkana, Texas. Doby had to ride in the "colored section" of the train, which had no luggage racks, smaller seats and the restrooms were smaller and often had no toilet paper. Teammates Jim Hegan and Joe Gordon were the only players that would visit with Doby on the train.

When the train arrived at 8 a.m., Doby was exhausted from the colored section's cramped quarters.

Just five years earlier, Texarkana made national news for a horrific lynching of a 25-year-old Black man. Willie Vinson had been accused of breaking into a trailer, grabbing a white woman, and putting his hand around her mouth before she got loose and screamed. Vinson ran, was chased and eventually shot in the stomach. While in the hospital, 12 white men dragged him out and pushed him into a car. Then they tied a rope around his legs, attached it to the car, and dragged him around the streets. The men ended the attack by hanging him 25 feet in the air on the winch of a cotton gin.

Sheriff Monroe Watts, a white man, told newspaper reporters the next day, "We've made no arrests and have no clues."

The only hotel that Doby was allowed to stay was two miles from where Vinson was lynched.

Larry Doby walked to his hotel as he couldn't get a cab in a town of 17,000 people, of whom 5,000 were Black. While walking, Doby saw "Buy White" and "Think White" billboards.

Two white people approached Doby as he was walking to the hotel.

"Wrong side of the street, boy," the man said, pointing to the other side. Doby skipped over and crossed the road.

It was 10 a.m. by the time Doby was in his room. That day's game started at 3 p.m. Doby figured it would take 30 minutes to walk to the park, so he left at 1 p.m.

Fencing around the Texarkana baseball stadium directed fans to an entrance about 20 yards behind home plate.

Knowing there would be no place at the stadium he could change, Doby was already dressed in his uniform when he arrived at 1:30 p.m. As he approached the entrance, he was stopped by two City of Texarkana police officers.

"Negroes don't come in the front," one officer said.

Teammate Joe Gordon appeared and walked Doby around to the outfield area where Doby had to enter.

As Doby took his position in center field, he could hear the racial taunts.

"Go home! Jigaboo!"

Doby turned and saw the white section of the bleachers where fans were yelling and taunting him. Black fans occupied a separate section separated by chicken wire.

Then he heard something whiz by his ear. It was an empty glass bottle that landed a few feet past him. Doby turned around and saw a rock flying at him, which landed 10 feet short.

Then another bottle landed near him. Soon, there were multiple projectiles headed at Doby, each getting closer.

Doby was stunned. He felt a tug on his jersey. Lou Boudreau had sprinted out to Doby in the outfield from his shortstop position.

"C'mon!" Boudreau said. "Let's get out of here!"

Boudreau escorted Doby back to the dugout. Doby's day was over.

In the safety of the dugout, Boudreau shared some important news with Doby. Boudreau told Doby he would be the team's starting right fielder when the regular season began.

CHAPTER 18

What's Wrong With Negro Baseball?

June 14, 1948

Eighty-one days. That was the time between Jackie Robinson's celebrated Major League Baseball debut with the Brooklyn Dodgers and Larry Doby's first game with the Cleveland Indians.

Unlike Doby's abrupt arrival and painful reception by the Indians, Robinson's ascent to the Dodgers had been as carefully orchestrated as a royal wedding. It was national news when Robinson was signed with the Brooklyn Dodgers on Oct. 23, 1945, the first evidence that integration of Major League Baseball was coming.

Then Robinson spent a year in the minor leagues with a Montreal team, a city far more amenable to a Black baseball player than any American city in the South.

In the fall of 1947, it was announced that Hollywood was making a movie about Robinson's life, with Jackie starring as himself. The next year, a biography on Robinson was published.

In contrast, Larry Doby was on the field with the Cleveland Indians just six hours after signing a contract in 1947. The public was far less aware of Doby's arrival.

Cleveland's top prospects played with the Oklahoma City minor league team which competed in the Texas League. That league included cities such as Houston, Fort Worth, Dallas, and San Antonio – all bastions of Jim Crow hostility to Blacks.

Larry Doby started the 1948 season with the Indians but had no book or movie deals. And Doby was fine with that.

On this spring day, the Indians were playing a charity exhibition game against the Brooklyn Dodgers in Brooklyn's Flatbush neighborhood.

For the first time Larry Doby and Jackie Robinson would be playing against each other in a Major League Baseball game.

But this milestone drew little publicity outside of the local newspaper, the Brooklyn Eagle. Doby's only media request that day was to pose with Robinson at home plate while shaking hands before the game. The Brooklyn Eagle photographer took the photo.

At this moment Robinson was being vilified in the Black community for an article he wrote that was a scorching criticism of the Negro Leagues in the June issue of Ebony. The article was published two weeks before the charity game. The cover of that issue featured a tightly cropped photo of Robinson's face with the headline: "What's Wrong With Negro Baseball?"

According to Robinson, the answer was "everything." His commentary in the article criticized the low salaries, trashy hotels with bed bugs, bad umpires and the shady owners. Gus Greenlee, the Black owner of the Negro League's Pittsburgh Crawfords, made his fortune illegally as a gambling racketeer.

"My five short months' experience in Negro baseball convinced me that the game needs a housecleaning from top to bottom," Robinson wrote.

Newark Eagles owner Effa Manley responded with a harsh criticism of Robinson's article.

"Frankly, no greater outrage could have been perpetrated. No greater invasion of the good sense of the American people could have been attempted," Manley told reporters. "No greater ingratitude was ever displayed. I charge Jackie Robinson with being ungrateful and more likely stupid."

Larry Doby was caught in the middle. He was very close to Abe and Effa Manley, and he was friendly with Robinson. Doby didn't want the media's attention.

Doby and Robinson occasionally spoke on the phone, but not about the horrific episodes of racism they had to endure.

Earlier in the year, Doby had to be restrained by Indians' coach Bill McKechnie from going into the stands in St. Louis with a bat to attack a fan who had been hurling racial slurs about Doby's wife, Helyn.

McKechnie tackled Doby to the ground and then told him, "Don't do it! This will be the end of you, not him!"

Both Doby and Robinson knew the score when it came to dark side of racism. They didn't need to share those memories.

Instead of their frustrations, they shared the precious moments of humanity in which they clung to get them through the loneliness of being a Black player in an almost entirely white league.

Sometimes it was the pockets of cheers they heard from the segregated Black crowds sitting in the Black-only section of the bleachers in St. Louis instead of the jeers and slurs from the white audience.

Other times, it was a generous "nice game" compliment from an opposing ballplayer or even a simple "See you tomorrow" comment from a teammate.

Doby had just experienced such a moment and wanted to share it with Robinson. The day before in the last game of a series in Yankee Stadium, Larry encountered a young New York catcher named Yogi Berra.

"Hey, Larry," Berra said to Doby as he approached the plate. "I'm sure glad they're only using you as a pinch hitter."

Doby was taken aback by the compliment.

The next day in the charity game, Doby singled in the seventh inning and scampered to first base, where Robinson was playing.

Doby got to first base and asked Robinson about Berra.

"Do you know the Yankees' catcher?" Doby asked.

Robinson shrugged.

"I saw him last year in the World Series," he said.

"Well, I was walking up to the plate - " Doby said.

Suddenly, Doby stopped talking and leaped back.

Brooklyn pitcher Rex Barney was trying to pick Doby off first base and threw over to Robinson. But Robinson was distracted listening to Doby. He didn't see the throw and it hit him in the chest, shocking both players.

The ball bounced off Robinson and landed 10 feet from him. Doby looked at the ball and decided it wasn't far enough for him to get to second base, so he took a few steps back to the bag.

Doby looked at Robinson with a big smile.

Robinson looked at Doby's mischievous grin and broke out in laughter.

Doby cherished moments like these. Once the game was over, he'd be back to being alone and isolated.

Robinson hit a homer in the game. Doby had two hits. The Dodgers won 6-2.

CHAPTER 19

Let Me Introduce You To Satchel Paige

June 28, 1948

Bill Veeck was desperate to find a good pitcher. It was late June 1948 and Veeck's Cleveland Indians were neck-and-neck with the New York Yankees in a battle for first place in the American League.

Veeck called his friend Abe Saperstein, who besides running the all-Black basketball Harlem Globetrotters, was also involved in Negro League baseball.

Veeck hoped that Saperstein could find him a good Black pitcher.

"I have just the pitcher you need," Saperstein told Veeck on the phone. "Leroy Paige. He can do the job for you."

Veeck sighed. Leroy Paige, better known as Satchel Paige, was believed to be 41 years old. His actual age was debatable.

"Oh, come on, Abe," Veeck said. "I'm serious. I need a pitcher who can get Joe DiMaggio and Yogi Berra out. Satchel Paige is as old as the hills."

Saperstein offered a deal. He would bring Paige down for a tryout and if Veeck didn't think Paige was good enough to play, Saperstein would cover all the expenses. It wouldn't cost Veeck a dime to give Paige a shot.

"OK," Veeck said. "Bring him down."

Saperstein first had to find Paige, who was in the middle of a nationwide barnstorming tour. Paige was nearly impossible to track down as he went from town to town, playing as many as three games a day.

Finally, after a few days of phone calls to hotels from Council

Bluffs, Iowa, to Wichita, Kansas, Saperstein tracked down Paige in San Antonio, Texas.

"Satchel," Saperstein said. "I got you a tryout with a Major League Baseball team!"

"Yeah, right," Paige said, and hung up.

Saperstein frantically dialed back and didn't give Paige a chance to talk.

"Don't hang up!" Saperstein pleaded. "No joke. You have a tryout with the Cleveland Indians and Bill Veeck."

"You got to be kidding," Paige said with disbelief. "I'll never get a chance to pitch in the majors. I gave up on the dream when they signed Jackie."

"Just pack your bags and meet me in Cleveland," Saperstein said.

It was 8 a.m. July 6, 1948, and Della Boudreau nudged her sleeping husband.

Lou Boudreau woke up.

"It's Veeck," Della said with a scornful tone. "He's on the phone downstairs."

"What does he want? We got a game today," Lou asked. "I'll be at the ballpark soon enough."

But he got out of bed, walked downstairs, and took the phone.

"Bill, this better not be one of your horseshit promotions," Lou said. "We're tied for first place with the Yankees and I need my sleep."

"Want to get in some batting practice?" Veeck asked.

"I'm hitting .358. Only Ted Williams is hitting better," Lou shot back.

"Just come down. I promise you. It's worth it," Veeck said.

The parking lot was empty when Boudreau arrived at Cleveland Stadium.

Inside the private clubhouse where players often changed into their uniforms, Boudreau spotted a naked Black man humming and playing a song on his guitar in the far corner. Boudreau didn't recognize the man or the song.

The school-aged boy serving as clubhouse attendant that day walked by Boudreau carrying clean towels. Boudreau stopped him.

"Who is that?" Boudreau asked.

"That's Satchel Paige!" the clubhouse boy answered with wide eyes.

Boudreau approached the naked man.

"Hi, Satchel. I'm Lou Boudreau, shortstop for the Indians. We've never met, but I sure have heard about you," Boudreau said.

Paige stopped playing the guitar and looked at Boudreau.

"I've heard of you, too," Paige said.

And then Paige resumed strumming his guitar.

Boudreau stepped out onto the field and saw Veeck standing at home plate. Boudreau still suspected this was some kind of weird promotion.

"I got a surprise for you. I want you to try out a young pitcher, and if you want to take a pass on him, that's your decision," Veeck told Boudreau.

Ten minutes later, Paige emerged from the dugout wearing a Cleveland Indians jersey.

"Let me introduce you to Satchel Paige," Veeck said.

"We just met," Boudreau said.

Veeck handed a catcher's mitt to Boudreau and motioned for Paige to go to the pitching mound.

Before taking the mound, Paige reached into his pocket and removed a napkin and placed it on one corner of home plate. Then he bounced back to the pitching mound.

Boudreau squatted behind home plate and waited for the pitch.

Woosh! A blistering fastball passed over the napkin and smacked into Boudreau's mitt. Then another. Then another.

After six bullseye pitches, Paige trotted in and moved the napkin to the other side of the plate.

Swoosh! Another stunning fastball hit Boudreau's glove, again passing right over the napkin.

Boudreau could guess how fast the pitches were coming in.

Boudreau was in his third year with the Indians when teammate Bob Feller's fastball ruled the major leagues. It was 1940, before there were radar guns available to measure the speed of pitches. But some baseball executives devised a publicity stunt to estimate the speed of Feller's pitch.

They would match a Bob Feller fastball against a police officer on a motorcycle and measure which traveled 90 feet the fastest. Boudreau was recruited to witness the stunt.

A suburban Chicago street was blocked off. The police officer on his motorcycle had a 10-foot head start and zoomed past Feller, who then let loose with a fastball. Feller beat the speeding officer by several feet.

Major League Baseball stated that the scientists present at the stunt calculated Feller's pitch was moving at 104 mph.

Behind the plate in an empty stadium eight years later, Boudreau could tell that Paige's fastball was comparable to Feller's.

After 12 pitches, Boudreau had seen enough and stood up.

He looked at Veeck and smiled.

"He will definitely help us," Boudreau said.

Veeck grinned and motioned for Boudreau to come to his office.

Veeck pulled out a contract from his desk.

"I'm sending this to the league office," Veeck said. "I know salaries are never kept secret. I'm paying him $40,000."

Boudreau was stunned by the salary. Boudreau was the star of the team and only made $35,000. Paige was going to make $40,000 and the season was already halfway over.

Feller, who had barnstormed with Paige in 1946, was still baseball's most recognized pitcher. Feller made $82,500 as one of the top-paid players in baseball.

"Lou," Veeck said. "Remember you questioned my dedication to winning?"

Boudreau nodded.

"Old Satch makes more than that barnstorming. The Monarchs bought him his own plane, he has so many engagements. Feller told me when he played with Satch two years ago, they made $100,000 barnstorming that year."

Veeck paused for that figure to sink in.

"They bought him his own plane and that son-of-a-bitch has his name painted on both sides of the fuselage," Veeck said.

"So, why did he give that up for $40,000?" Boudreau asked.

Veeck was a showman who knew that someone like Paige couldn't resist the stage and spotlight that only Major League Baseball could provide.

"More than anything, Satchel wants to be judged against the best and be recognized for it," Veeck said.

Boudreau smiled. He shook Veeck's hand. A feud was healing.

"That's it. No catch? Satchel doesn't have to jump out of a cake?" Boudreau asked.

Veeck shook his head, but with a gleam in his eye asked, "What do you think of a Kiss Handsome Lou Boudreau Night? First 10,000 women get in free."

"You can ask my wife, Bill," Boudreau said.

Six weeks later, on August 20, Satchel Paige became Veeck's best promotion.

Paige took the mound for a night game in Cleveland against the Chicago White Sox. The Indians were in first place by three games and were riding a seven-game winning streak.

Cleveland fans had finally cast away their doubts and become believers. The team's 28-year playoff drought was about to end. In early August, more than 70,000 fans came out four times to see the Indians.

On August 16, the celebrations took a back seat as the world learned Babe Ruth had died at age 53, 13 years after retiring from baseball. Ruth's doctors had not revealed even to Ruth that the home-run king had terminal cancer, fearing if word got out to the public it would cause a mass depression.

When newspaper reporters had asked Paige if he ever faced Ruth during his barnstorming travels, Paige said he did not. But former Black barnstorming teammate Buck O'Neil recalled a game in Chicago where Paige did pitch to Ruth. And Ruth hit the ball outside the park and over the trees. Paige was waiting for Ruth at home plate and congratulated Ruth. The game was held up for 15 minutes after Paige sent a ball boy to go recover the baseball. Paige had Ruth autograph the ball for him.

During a drizzling rain one day before Paige pitched, Babe Ruth was laid to rest. His funeral was on a Thursday and on the front page of virtually every newspaper in the country.

Ruth's death did not bring about the mass depression the doctors had feared. It had instead triggered a surge in passion for baseball.

The day after Ruth's funeral, 78,382 fans piled into Cleveland's Municipal Stadium on Aug. 20.

The people showed up for what felt like a revival and leading the congregation that evening was a legendary pitcher who, due to segregation, had played in his first Major League Baseball game just a few weeks earlier.

Despite his exclusion from all-white baseball, Paige was still recognized as possibly the only player whose talent could cast as big a shadow as Ruth. The Babe was dead, but the fans had come to see a living legend.

This was a baseball wake.

The opponent didn't matter. The White Sox were the worst team in the American League, with a 36-74 record and in the midst of a five-game losing streak.

When Paige took the mound in the first inning, he saw the people crammed into the park like it was the final lifeboat on the Titanic. It was standing room only, and fans found it difficult to lift their arms without hitting a person squeezed in alongside them.

In the fourth inning, Larry Doby singled in Lou Boudreau to give the Indians a 1-0 lead.

Paige strolled to the mound in the top of the ninth inning with the Indians still clinging to that 1-0 lead. Paige felt every eye in the stadium was focused on him. He had pitched magnificently in shutting down the White Sox for eight innings. And the hometown crowd was praying for Paige to win the game.

Paige could sense the fans were hanging on his every pitch.

He was no longer pitching just outside a cornfield in Iowa.

This was the moment Paige had waited for his entire life.

Paige did his trademark hesitation pitch with two outs in the ninth inning.

He lifted his leg, held it out perfectly still for two seconds, and then released the pitch. The White Sox's Luke Appling hit a weak grounder to second base. The game was over.

Paige had extended his scoreless inning streak to 22 innings.

The crowd roared its approval.

In the locker room, Paige was swarmed by reporters.

They said with a 5-1 record as a pitcher and a minuscule 1.31 ERA, he could be Rookie of the Year.

Paige smiled.

"But 22 years is a long time to be a rookie," he said.

A reporter asked Paige if the excitement of the game with a record-setting crowd was similar to when he pitched for the Negro League's Kansas City Monarchs.

Paige shook his head.

"It wasn't like this in Kansas City," he said.

Major League Baseball had at last given him a stage the Negro Leagues could never match.

Two days after that record-setting night, Veeck announced a press conference at Municipal Stadium. Veeck, Paige and Cleveland fan Carl Goerz showed up.

Three weeks earlier, Paige had tired of some claims that he was 60 years old. He said there was "no truth" to the rumor he was playing baseball before 1927. He had repeatedly told the media over the years that he would be 40 pretty soon.

Paige offered $500 [$6,400 in 2023 dollars] to anyone who could prove he played professional baseball before 1927.

Goerz was visiting his sister, Ellen, in Memphis when he mentioned Paige's offer. She went to the Memphis public library and combed through 1926 editions of the Memphis Commercial Appeal when she found it. There was a May 17, 1926 box score of a Negro League game between the Chattanooga Black Lookouts and the Memphis Red Sox. The box score listed a "Satchel" as pitching for Chattanooga. Alex Herman, who signed Paige to play for Chattanooga, confirmed it.

At the Cleveland press conference, Paige handed the $500 check to Goerz in front of about a dozen newspaper photographers and reporters.

"I must have slept a year somewhere," Paige told reporters.

CHAPTER 20

Good Ole Joe Earley Night

Sept. 28, 1948

Joe Earley had boyish good looks with a cleanly shaven face too young for a beard to grow. Just 24 years old, his smile betrayed a lifetime of horrors he witnessed on the front lines of World War II, where he had to decide who lived or died every day, serving three years with the Army Medical Corps in the European Theater.

Earley was dressed in a suit he had just bought for this occasion. His wife, June, wore a new dress, high heels, and a new hat. Earley thought this night would put them back financially and likely make them late paying their mortgage. He worked as a security guard at an auto plant.

But it was worth it. Cleveland Municipal Stadium was having "Joe Earley Night."

As they got to the stadium entrance, they were surrounded by a line of people to get in.

Joe walked near a meaty-faced man in a sweater and flat cap with a cigarette dangling in his mouth. Joe saw the man's puzzled look as he saw the giant "Joe Earley Night" banner hanging over the stadium entrance gate.

"Who in tarnation is Joe Earley?" the man bellowed to the crowd in a thick Irish accent.

"He's the trainer, I think," another voice behind Earley shot back.

June squeezed her husband's hand. They were both too intimidated by the growing crowd to speak up.

It all started four months earlier when Joe was reading a story in the Cleveland Plain Dealer announcing a Ken Keltner Day in recognition of the Cleveland Indians' third baseman.

"Why not have a Good Ole Joe Earley Night?" Joe asked Bill Veeck in a letter-to-the-editor that was published in a newspaper in May.

To Earley's astonishment, Veeck agreed.

Four months later, 60,000 fans were piling into the stadium and the wartime veteran was nervous.

As he and June neared the front gate, a man wearing a stadium uniform gave his wife and all the other women an orchid.

"It's an orchid that was flown in today from Hawaii," the man boasted as he attached it to June's suit jacket.

"It's beautiful," June whispered to herself.

At the gate, Joe saw Bill Veeck wearing his trademark sports shirt with the two top buttons undone.

Veeck spotted the Earleys and limped over, his long slacks hiding his artificial right leg.

"Joe! June!" Veeck beamed as he greeted the couple.

"Mr. Veeck!" Joe said as he looked around at the crowd. "I'm in awe."

Veeck looked at June and said with a wink, "Why, June, the beauty pageant is next week!"

June blushed.

Thirty minutes later, Veeck and the Earleys stood behind a microphone at home plate.

June looked around at the stands that were now filled with fans. She lit up. Joe was terrified, overwhelmed at being the center of attention.

"Mr. Veeck, we can't thank you enough for tonight. Joe was just being cute when he wrote that letter. We truly didn't expect this," June swooned.

Joe could hear his wife speak, but he was in a daze with 60,000 people all focused on him.

"June, we will make this a night you never forget. And call me Bill. Please," Veeck said.

With that, Veeck grabbed the microphone.

"Welcome, Cleveland Indians fans. What a great night to come to the park. And for all you beautiful ladies in attendance today, those orchids were flown in from Hawaii on an air-conditioned plane," Veeck said as a chorus of cheers drowned out the last words. "Because tonight we salute the fans!"

Veeck took a step back as applause filled the stadium.

"I have with me Joe Earley and his beautiful wife June," Veeck announced as his voice carried out into the stands.

Veeck was speaking, but Joe no longer heard him. He was frozen and for a moment feared he might faint.

"Joe wrote a letter to the editor after we had a fan appreciation night for third baseman Ken Keltner and asked, 'Why not have a fan appreciation night for me, Joe Earley?'" Veeck boomed.

The crowd roared. Joe was reeling, but June was smiling and soaked up the attention.

"I thought it was a grand idea!" Veeck said. "So, let's get it started."

The crowd roared again.

A fence near the bullpen opened, and a tractor towed a trailer carrying something onto the field. June and Joe turned to watch as the tractor got closer.

Veeck took over.

"Our first gift for the Earleys is a new home with designs from early American architecture!" Veeck said.

As the tractor advanced, everyone realized the tractor was carrying an old outhouse. The crowd erupted in laughter.

June was grinning and turned to her husband and nudged him and said, "Your mother can use that when she stays with us!"

The tractor stopped and Veeck continued.

"And next we have - a new car!" Veeck proclaimed.

A dilapidated Model-T car emerged from the bullpen fence area, backfiring and rocking on wheels that wobbled. The relic barely made it to the infield.

The crowd roared again with laughter.

Inside the press box of Cleveland Municipal Stadium, American League president Will Harridge was incredulous. The bespectacled Harridge was there to discuss ticket distribution for an increasingly likely World Series in Cleveland.

With just five games left in the season, Veeck's Indians were one win in front of the Boston Red Sox for first place.

"What is he doing?" a disgusted Harridge muttered to himself. "This is a war veteran, not a minor league commissioner you're humiliating, Veeck."

Back on the field, Veeck was fully engaged.

"The next gift is a box of nails and then a cow, horse, and nine piglets," Veeck said. As he spoke, a group of people approached, each bearing their gift.

June was laughing but Joe was embarrassed to be the butt of a joke in front of an entire stadium.

"Is everyone having fun?" Veeck yelled as the crowd roared.

Joe's throat was parched and he was dying for a glass of water. He feared Veeck was getting back at him for the ribbing delivered in his letter to the editor.

Veeck stood in front of the Earleys and nodded to the crowd.

"We will set an attendance record for Major League Baseball this year. And while I like to have fun, I can't tell you enough how much I appreciate the fans' support," Veeck bellowed.

Veeck walked over and put his arms around Joe and June.

"But I can show the Earleys! OK, guys, the joke's over," Veeck said as his tone changed. "You know we always like to have a little fun at the ballpark. But now, take a look over there."

A spotlight lit up and focused again on the bullpen fence area. This time, a sparkling new 1948 Ford Super Deluxe Convertible car was driven to the field.

"Mr. and Mrs. Joe Earley, here's your real car!" Veeck yelled.

Joe's face was a picture of disbelief. He and June both froze as the fans went wild.

The new car was just the beginning. It was followed by a series of expensive gifts, each delivered to home plate by owners of the businesses donating them. There was a refrigerator, TV set, and radio-phonograph console.

"How would you like a new refrigerator? And to settle down for a nice evening in front of your new television set or entertain with your radio-phonograph console?" Veeck said, now immersed in his role as emcee.

An overwhelmed Joe was trying to do the arithmetic inside his head, adding up how much these gifts could have cost.

Veeck the showman wasn't finished.

"Of course, you can't be comfortable without an easy chair. And just in case you need to visit family out of town, show up with your new luggage - and a complete wardrobe to fill it with," Veeck said.

New luggage, an easy chair, and a complete wardrobe for Joe and June rolled onto the field.

Veeck turned to June.

"I know Mrs. Earley is really going to love this one. Your life just got a lot easier with this – " Veeck said.

Then a new washing machine and dryer were rolled out. Now overwhelmed, June bolted from the home plate area to inspect the new appliances. June was in tears and nearly hysterical, nudging away the business owner who donated the machine. He stumbled backward before maintaining his balance.

Joe bent over in astonishment at the prizes, still trying to catch his breath. The pressure he had felt from the ocean of fans was at last overcome by the magnificent gifts.

Back at home plate, Veeck wasn't done.

"And I want Mr. and Mrs. Earley to know that I am also giving you both lifetime passes to any ballpark in the American League!" Veeck said.

The crowd roared.

In the press box, league president Harridge shook his head.

"He can't do that!" Harridge thought to himself. "He has no authority to give free passes to other ballparks."

Back on the field, the final trailer rolled onto the field. On it was a man who looked like a banker and a stack of small sticks arranged as if for a campfire.

With the microphone in hand, Veeck stood behind Joe and grabbed Joe's arm.

"Joe? You recognize that man?" Veeck asked.

Earley peered into the outfield. It took his eyes a moment to adjust to the stadium lights.

"That's Mr. Benton. He's the manager at the bank," Earley responded.

"Very good. Your eyesight is much better than mine," Veeck said. "I'll take your word for it. Now, can you see what's in his hand?"

Joe peered into the outfield again.

"Papers?" Joe said.

"Yes! Papers! Actually, your mortgage. But you won't have to worry about that anymore!" Veeck beamed.

Veeck nodded. The banker took out a lighter and lit the wood, and it instantly leapt into flames. Then the banker dropped the mortgage into the fire.

"It's all paid off!" Veeck yelled.

The man who had come to the ballpark worrying over a mortgage payment felt like he was in a dream. He looked at his wife sitting on the washer 30 yards away. He looked at the fans, cheering a man they had never met but knew was an Indians fan – one of their own. And on this night, that was all that mattered.

Veeck turned to Earley.

"Well," Veeck said. "You feel appreciated?"

Joe hugged Veeck and started to weep into his shoulder.

While Veeck held the sobbing Joe Earley, he looked around.

The farm animals had escaped the pen holding them.

Field attendants tried to corral the farm animals to be carted off the field, but the horse was now galloping to the outfield while the cow watched. Nine piglets were scurrying around the infield. The ballplayers and umpires joined in the chase to corral the livestock so the game could start.

The less-than-amused home plate umpire finally grabbed a chicken and took it off the field.

Harridge looked down upon the chaos and shook his head.

"Bill Veeck," Harridge muttered to himself, his voice dripping with scorn.

Joe Earley looked around at the field. He had no idea how to get the farm animals home once they were corralled. He saw his wife sitting on the dryer, her legs crossed and left leg wagging in excitement.

CHAPTER 21

Dreams Of A Beantown World Series

Oct. 3, 1948

When Tom Yawkey was orphaned as a child, he was adopted by his rich uncle Bill Yawkey.

Bill Yawkey died in 1919 and left his then 16-year-old adopted son a $20 million inheritance [$372 million in 2023 dollars].

Tom Yawkey did not shy away from using his fortune to get what he wanted in what would become a life-long obsession – to win a World Series.

In 1934, his first year as owner of the Boston Red Sox, he spent $250,000 [$5.8 million in 2023 dollars] to acquire the contract of star player Joe Cronin from the Washington Senators. He later kept the canceled $250,000 check on the wall of his Fenway Park office.

In 1938 Tom Yawkey bought a minor league baseball team for the sole purpose of signing a single player on that team - Pee Wee Reese.

Off the field, the team owner had contracted to have his Boston ballpark painted in a color called "Fenway Green." When the paint maker later announced it was discontinuing the color, Yawkey bought the company and continued the "Fenway Green" brand of paint.

The free-wheeling spending put off many of his fellow owners.

"He would rather win a pennant and drop $300,000 than lose a pennant and make $200,000," famed sportswriter Grantland Rice wrote about Yawkey in 1947. "This is an attitude that a good many club owners view with distaste."

But in 1948, Yawkey's spending appeared to have at long last paid off.

The last few days of the 1948 regular season were the most anticipated in the history of Boston Red Sox baseball. If things went well, it would also set the stage for a "subway series" between the Boston Braves versus the Boston Red Sox for Major League Baseball's World Series championship. The newspapers said such an event would make the city the capital of baseball.

The Braves had already won the National League pennant.

In the American League, the Red Sox trailed the Cleveland Indians by one game on the final day of the regular season. If the Red Sox won against the New York Yankees and the Indians lost their final game to the Detroit Tigers, it would produce an unprecedented tie for first place.

If that happened, the American League had already decided a one-game playoff would determine the champion.

For months, the prospect of a Boston vs. Boston World Series had kept the city abuzz.

Adeline Violas and her 11-year-old son Paul attended this final regular season game in Boston. In the 7th inning, comfortable with a 10-5 lead over the Yankees, a voice came over the stadium speakers announcing playoff tickets would be available as soon as the current game ended. Adeline immediately took her son's hand and ran to get in line ahead of the rush.

She wasn't the only one. When the last pitch finished off the Yankees, the park was already half empty.

A crowd estimated at 35,000 had squeezed into the two-lane Boston street pushing toward the ticket office. Some people were knocked down amid the scramble and 40 Boston police officers called in for crowd control were helpless.

Adeline and her son were part of the excited rush. She squeezed his hand to prevent the pair from being separated. A woman in front of her fainted. A young man ripped Adeline's dress as he tripped. A man in a fedora banged into Paul hard enough to send the 11-year-old boy to the ground.

Adeline elbowed people out of the way and yanked her stunned son up by the arm and then forged her way to an ad-hoc first-aid station. She plunked Paul in front of a nurse and then told her son, "Stay here! I'll be back!" Then the mother went back into the crowd.

The scene of people rushing to buy tickets outside Fenway Park after Boston won to force the playoff game was akin to a Times Square mob on New Year's Eve.

In the end, 40 people were treated for bruises and contusions. One person was sent to the hospital.

The 22,000 available playoff tickets were gone before Adeline reached the ticket office. But she did secure two tickets by sweet talking a United Press International sportswriter interviewing people at the medical tent.

Many of the stampeding fans who came away empty-handed chose to brave 40-degree temperatures and a 17-hour wait for another chance the next morning when 8,500 more tickets went on sale.

The Red Sox and Indians finished the American League's regular season in a tie with identical 96-58 records.

The league had decided that the tiebreaker would be a one-game playoff at Boston's Fenway Park. The winner goes to the World Series.

For the city of Boston residents, the chance of the Boston Braves and Boston Red Sox playing for the most coveted title in the country had been dancing around in their thoughts for months.

Boston Red Sox fans believed it was their form of Manifest Destiny that this would be the year they finally won a World Series.

Two years earlier in 1946, the Red Sox had won 104 games, the most in Major League Baseball that year.

But they lost a heartbreaking Game 7 in the World Series to the National League's St. Louis Cardinals.

In the eighth inning of that final 1946 World Series game, the Cardinals' Enos Slaughter broke a 3-3 tie when he scored all the way from first base on a base hit. Boston's beloved shortstop Johnny Pesky took the throw from the outfield just outside the infield, which should have caused Slaughter to stop at third base.

But Slaughter decided to go for broke instead of holding up and never hesitated while rounding third base and heading for home plate. For a moment, Pesky paused with indecision, shocked Slaughter would try scoring. Slaughter was able to beat Pesky's throw to the plate and scored what would be the game-winning run.

Tom Yawkey's dream of a World Series was crushed. No one in the Boston organization would ever forget it.

The phrases "Pesky held the ball" and "Slaughter's mad dash" would become common catchlines heard in Boston.

Now, the Red Sox seemed destined to make up for the past failure.

At noon on the day of the playoff game against the Indians, Boston City Council member Thomas McCormick arrived at city hall. It was about 90 minutes before the start of the game.

He was shocked to see the chamber all but empty, except for City Council president Thomas Hannon, the city clerk, the assistant city clerk, a single stenographer and only one spectator in the gallery. There were also two newspaper reporters and a photographer. But the other 20 council members were missing.

"Where is everyone?" McCormick asked.

"At the game," Hannon said.

"How'd they get tickets?" McCormick asked.

"City council members all get a ticket," Hannon said. "I'd be there, but I'm president of the city council. I figured I'd have to be here."

McCormick's face turned bright red.

"Goddamn it!" McCormick barked. "Why didn't anyone tell me I could have had a ticket?"

McCormick bolted out of the room.

For the first time in 10 years, the city council meeting had to be adjourned for lack of a quorum.

Hannon was left alone. He saw the photographer stand up and start to look around.

"No pictures!" Hannon demanded, worried how it would look that the entire city council was playing hooky.

CHAPTER 22

The Best Team Money Can Buy

Oct. 4, 1948

Boston Red Sox owner Tom Yawkey sat alone in his Fenway Park office 30 minutes before the start of the unprecedented American League playoff game between his Red Sox and the Cleveland Indians.

The Boston Braves had already won the National League pennant, setting the stage for a Boston versus Boston World Series if the Red Sox won.

On the wall behind Yawkey hung a framed 1941 article written by famed sports columnist Grantland Rice. It described Yawkey's drive to win a World Series.

"Winning an American League pennant is now an obsession, a matter of personal pride that goes beyond any concern with money," Rice wrote in 1941. "Tom Yawkey may not show it, but on the inside, he is a tough loser."

He could afford to be.

In 1933, during the depths of The Great Depression, Yawkey tried to buy two players' contracts from the St. Louis Browns for $75,000. When the Browns wanted an extra $25,000 [equal to $600,000 in 2023 dollars], Yawkey threw it in with little resistance.

"I can't spend two or three weeks fooling around arguing about $25,000," he told newspaper reporters in 1933. "I can make that much in the time I'd spend gabbing."

In 1935 he told another newspaper reporter, "My willingness to keep investing appreciable sums in talent is founded on a desire to bring the World Series to the best baseball city in the country."

"I'm buying ballplayers," Yawkey pronounced.

After just missing out on winning the World Series in 1946, Yawkey spent even more money on the 1948 team.

He pulled off what the newspapers called "The St. Louis Purchase."

After the 1947 season, with lenders threatening to foreclose on his stadium, St. Louis Browns owner Richard Muckerman sold his three best players to the Red Sox for $375,000 and a handful of fringe players in return. The $375,000 was more than triple the Browns entire team payroll.

Yawkey's latest spending splurge brought the Red Sox all-star players Jack Kramer, a pitcher, and Vern Stephens, a shortstop. Stephens had been the target of Cleveland owner Bill Veeck's 1947 bid to trade away Lou Boudreau.

New York Yankee owner Dan Topping complained to the Commissioner's Office that a rule was needed to stop owners from selling off their best players for money.

Yawkey also hired former New York Yankees manager Joe McCarthy, who won seven World Series with players such as Babe Ruth, Lou Gehrig and Joe DiMaggio. McCarthy also had a reputation as a heavy drinker.

The big spending had won over the Red Sox fans. And it also let Yawkey indulge a fantasy of himself as a professional baseball player. He often put on a Red Sox uniform and took batting practice before games while not allowing anyone to take photographs. It was one of the benefits of being the millionaire owner of the Red Sox.

But Yawkey's money was no guarantee of a championship on this day, the most important day of his life.

The only thing standing between him and making the World Series was Bill Veeck's Cleveland Indians.

Yawkey was at his desk when Boston mayor James Curley knocked on his door and entered.

Curley was a corrupt politician who had recently spent four months in prison for mail fraud. Before that, he was caught embezzling city money and was known for once punching a heckler.

Now 73, Curley understood a Boston vs. Boston World Series matchup would bring unprecedented attention to his city, and like any politician he wanted to cash in on it.

He sensed Yawkey's nervousness.

"It's all set, Mr. Yawkey," Curley said.

The mayor was 29 years older than Yawkey but, like everyone, referred to the Red Sox owner as "Mr. Yawkey" as a sign of respect.

"When the Red Sox clinch the pennant, I have approved for a series of fire alarms to go off around the city to alert the fans that we beat the Indians, and we are going to the World Series," the mayor said.

Yawkey nodded.

"Fire alarms throughout the city celebrating a Boston vs. Boston World Series," Yawkey said, relishing the thought of a five-alarm victory.

Yawkey got up from his chair to walk to the clubhouse and see if any players had arrived.

"Any idea who is going to pitch for us?" Curley asked.

"I am not sure," Yawkey said. "Let's go find out."

When Denny Galehouse arrived at the Boston Red Sox clubhouse, he was thrilled to find a baseball tucked inside his glove. That was Boston manager Joe McCarthy's way of letting pitchers know who would pitch that day.

Starting with Galehouse was a surprising move.

The newspaper reporters predicted McCarthy would choose Mel Parnell to pitch for Boston. Parnell had 15 wins and had the lowest earned run average of any of Boston's other starting pitchers. Parnell had last pitched on Sept. 30, meaning he had three days of rest, just one shy of the customary four days off between starts.

Galehouse had an 8-8 record, and more alarmingly, had given up six runs in six innings in his last two games.

But both teams had used up their top pitchers to get to the playoff game.

Galehouse felt good warming up in the bullpen moments before the game started.

He retired the game's first two batters when Lou Boudreau stepped to the plate.

On Galehouse's third pitch, Boudreau hit a long fly ball that appeared destined to be an out. As Boudreau ran toward first base, he watched Boston left fielder Ted Williams slowly walk back to catch it. Williams kept drifting back and back … until he ran out of room. Boudreau's wind-lifted ball was carried over the big Green Monster fence into the street for a home run. Cleveland led 1-0.

In the top of the fourth inning, Boudreau led off with a single into the outfield. Joe Gordon singled, and Ken Keltner followed with a three-run homer to give the Indians a 4-1 lead. And Galehouse was removed from the game.

Larry Doby stood in the on-deck circle, watching his teammates circle the bases.

A Red Sox fan wearing a Boston team cap sitting among about a dozen other young men began hollering racist smears to Doby.

"Hey, Doby, you stupid nigger. You should have stuck to shining shoes," the man wearing a Red Sox cap yelled.

An older Red Sox fan wearing a tweed newsboy cap joined in: "Doby! You think you're special, but you are just an uppity nigger - and Veeck is your master, boy."

Doby ignored the jeers and walked to the plate.

On the third pitch, Doby took a swing and lifted a long fly ball that caromed off the Green Monster in left field for a double. He scored on a ground out to give the Cleveland Indians a 5-1 lead. Doby refused to make eye contact with the fans as he ran into the dugout, chased by more racial slurs.

Doby sat next to Satchel Paige on the bench.

"Hey, Satch," Doby said. They smiled.

"You know what I love most about Boston's fans?" Paige asked.

Doby shrugged.

"So, you don't know, either, huh?" Paige said with a smile.

Doby laughed.

"You keep scoring runs, Larry - and I will keep pitching like I always have. Just not here in Boston! I'll wait until we are back home," said Paige, who was not in the lineup this game.

Boudreau came up again in the fifth inning, with the Indians leading 5-1. This time, Boudreau got hold of a pitch and smashed it over the Green Monster in left field for his second homer of the game.

The scoreboard showed it was the top of the eighth inning, and the Indians led 6-3.

Doby walked to the plate again.

The Red Sox fan wearing the team cap again started taunting Doby. This time, his voice sounded more desperate.

"It's the coon again! Coons dig through trash, and that's what you'll do when baseball is done with you. You aren't nothing but shit," the Red Sox fan yelled with a hint of panic in his voice.

Doby ignored the fans. On the second pitch, he ripped another double and made it to second base.

By the bottom of the ninth inning, the Indians led 8-3. A hush had fallen over Fenway Park. The largest home crowd of the year was dead silent. There were 34,000 fans stuffed into a stadium that held 30,000. Fans in the front row could hear players talking in the dugout.

With two outs in the ninth inning, Boston's Birdie Tebbetts hit a ground ball to third base and was thrown out.

The game was over.

Bill Veeck had been watching from the front row of the stands. He tried to jump onto the field with his players, but his newly fitted artificial right leg was making it difficult.

The Indians players had lifted winning pitcher Gene Bearden onto their shoulders. They were carrying him to the dugout when Veeck caught up.

As Veeck joined the growing crowd of hysterical Indians players, he met with Boudreau, who played the game of a lifetime with two homers and four hits.

"You still want to trade me?" Boudreau asked.

A speechless Veeck pulled Boudreau close and hugged him tightly. Boudreau squeezed back.

CHAPTER 23

There's A Fire In The Navy Yard

Oct. 4, 1948

A fire engine siren pierced the silence in the office of Tom Yawkey.

After the loss of a lifetime, the Boston Red Sox owner had retreated from the owner's box at Fenway Park to his office. He sat stone-faced. The season was over.

Until today, Bill Veeck was just a nuisance. Now, the circus showman had robbed the millionaire owner of his chance to win a World Series. Yawkey was starting to really despise Veeck.

Yawkey heard mayor James Curley hollering at someone in the hallway outside his office.

"Why are the sirens going off? Why are the goddamn sirens going off? We lost. Will someone tell them to turn off the god-forsaken sirens!" Curley yelled.

Curley slunk into Yawkey's office.

"The district chief says there's a fire at the Navy yard," Curley said.

Almost in a trance-like state, Yawkey responded, "Of course there is."

Ten minutes later, another man entered the owner's office.

"Hello, Mr. Yawkey. I'm John McDonough, chief of the fire department," McDonough said.

Yawkey didn't even bother to look up before speaking to McDonough.

"John, every citizen in Boston believes we have won the playoff game and are now going to the World Series," Yawkey said in a matter-of-fact tone.

"I'm sorry, sir. The first siren was legitimate – a fire at the Navy yard, but it set off a chain reaction and –"

With rage in his eyes, Yawkey cut off McDonough in mid-sentence.

"Chief McDonough, please make sure the other sirens are off," Yawkey said. "Immediately."

McDonough nodded and scurried off.

Boston General Manager Joe Cronin walked in. The rest of the Red Sox employees realized they should clear out.

"Joe, have a seat," Yawkey said.

Cronin sat down but was shaking.

Yawkey composed himself.

"Remind me what I pay Stan Spence," Yawkey asked, referring to the Red Sox starting right fielder.

"He makes $17,000," Cronin answered.

"That's more than three times what Veeck pays his Negro outfielder," Yawkey said.

Cronin looked puzzled.

"I'm not sure what Larry Doby is paid," Cronin said.

Yawkey smiled.

"Do you read the newspapers?" Yawkey asked in a condescending tone. "What do the sportswriters call us?"

"The Gold Sox," Cronin said.

Yawkey nodded.

"You are at least reading the sports section," Yawkey said. "Yes. The Gold Sox. You, of all people, should know that."

In 1934, in the heart of The Great Depression, Yawkey paid $250,000 to the Washington Senators to buy Cronin's contract as a ballplayer. That was the equivalent of $5.6 million in 2023 dollars, and covered the contractual rights to Cronin. Yawkey then paid Cronin $30,000 yearly to be a player/manager. It was a signal the then-new Boston Red Sox owner sent to tell everyone that money was no object in his single-minded quest to win a World Series. Cronin idolized Yawkey, even naming his son after him.

"Well, if you read the newspapers more often, you'd know, Joe. It's full of educational information. Doby was signed for $5,000," Yawkey said.

Cronin nodded.

"I'm not much of a reader, sir. But that's a steal," Cronin said.

Yawkey gave a dead smile.

"That's what we paid Neill Sheridan this year, and he batted one time all year. Yes, it is a grand bargain. And Spence hit .235, and he's 33. That's not such a great bargain. But we kept him in the lineup all year - why?" Yawkey asked.

Spence was an all-star for the Senators the year before but suffered through the worst year of his career in 1948.

Cronin attempted to answer, but froze when Yawkey held his hand up.

"We played Spence because we had no one in the minor leagues who was any better," Yawkey said.

Cronin was silent.

Just days before the regular season ended, Yawkey had ordered the firing of George "Specs" Toporcer and Phil Troy.

Toporcer had directed Boston's minor league system, which Yawkey blamed for not producing better younger players this season.

Phil Troy, the assistant general manager, was axed after 18 years with the team. It was rumored that Troy told Black sportswriter Mabray "Doc" Kountze that Yawkey was prohibiting the Red Sox from signing any Black players.

Kountze wrote for the Black newspaper the Boston Chronicle. He was the first Black reporter to be issued a press pass by the Red Sox. He had been a constant irritant to Yawkey about the lack of Black players on the Red Sox and played a role in setting up the Jackie Robinson tryout in Boston.

Troy's comments were an act of disloyalty Yawkey could not abide.

And now, the playoff loss triggered more firings.

"So tomorrow morning, you are to fire Nemo Leibold and Del Baker," Yawkey demanded.

Leibold was the manager of Boston's top minor league team in Louisville. Yawkey was clearly blaming the loss on the farm system.

But Del Baker? He was the team's third-base coach. His offense was having been a coach for Lou Boudreau and the Indians for two years before joining the Red Sox in 1945. The same Indians who had just crushed Yawkey's dream.

"Tell the media that Specs had to quit due to health concerns. The rest of them just resigned. I don't want anyone thinking we are overreacting to the most humiliating moment of my life," Yawkey said.

Cronin was confused.

"But Specs is completely healthy. He hasn't told me of anything wrong," Cronin said.

Yawkey nodded.

"Joe - I was referring to my health," Yawkey said.

"Specs has a young family," Cronin said.

"Well, let's hope that in their lifetime, we can deliver them a World Series. That's something that surely won't happen with their father running our minor league system," Yawkey sneered.

Cronin paused.

"Will the replacement be able to sign Negro players?" Cronin asked.

"Certainly, Joe. We will just hire the Harlem Globetrotters to play for us. They'd be far more entertaining than what I saw today," Yawkey said.

"Harlem is a long way away, Mr. Yawkey," Cronin said.

"They are further than you think, Joe. The Harlem Globetrotters are from Chicago, not Harlem," Yawkey said.

"Really?" Cronin said.

"Yes. The owner named them Harlem so people would associate the team as being all Negroes. It's brilliant marketing, actually. Their owner is Abe Saperstein, and he is a dear friend of Mr. Veeck's, whose team just beat us," Yawkey said coldly.

"Why is Veeck friends with the owner of a nigger basketball team?" Cronin asked.

"They're kindred spirits. They have turned what is a hallowed achievement - being able to perform at the highest level of a game - into a circus event. And today, we were beaten by a clown show," Yawkey said.

Yawkey's face was flushed.

"A goddamn clown show," Yawkey repeated.

Cronin recoiled. He rarely heard Yawkey spew profanities.

"I still don't understand why they call themselves the Harlem Globetrotters when they are from Chicago," Cronin asked, not having the common sense to move on from the Globetrotter conversation.

Yawkey didn't answer.

Yawkey feared that Cronin may not have realized he was being sarcastic about signing Black players.

"There are no Negro players capable of playing at the level we need to win a championship," Yawkey said.

Cronin nodded. He got up to leave to break the bad news to the men about to be fired.

"Joe," Yawkey said as if talking to a disobedient dog.

Cronin turned around.

"Did McCarthy say why he chose Galehouse to pitch?" Yawkey asked. The owner wanting an explanation why the Red Sox's manager Joe McCarthy chose the lesser-used 36-year-old veteran in the biggest game of the year.

Cronin swallowed hard.

"He locked himself in the bathroom last night with a bottle of Scotch, and when he came out, he said God told him to pitch Galehouse," Cronin said.

"God?" Yawkey said with a look of surprise.

"God," Cronin repeated.

Yawkey looked at Cronin.

"You can go now," he said. "And if a single reporter makes it up here ..."

Yawkey did not need to complete his sentence because Cronin understood the consequences.

Yawkey heard the sirens finally go off and sat back in his chair.

As Cronin left the office, he passed Helen Robinson in the hall. The 29-year-old Boston Red Sox switchboard operator had earned the respect of players and team officials by making the time to take messages instead of just transferring calls.

Robinson crept down the hall, knowing all too well the raw pain she was interrupting.

She was fearful of Yawkey, but peeked her head into his office.

"Mr. Yawkey. I'm terribly sorry to bother you. But the phones are ringing off the hook and callers are wondering how they can buy Red Sox World Series tickets. For some reason, they think we won tonight," Robinson said sheepishly.

"Talk with mayor Curley," Yawkey said without a flicker of emotion.

"Please shut the door, Helen," Yawkey said as he forced a smile that quickly evaporated.

The door was shut.

Yawkey sat at his desk. Alone.

Just one day earlier, the Red Sox had trailed the Indians by one game, entering the final day of the regular season. The Indians lost to the Tigers, and the Red Sox beat the Yankees to force the playoff game.

Yawkey watched the Red Sox beat the hated Yankees from his personal box seat near Boston's dugout that day. He had a radio with him and was listening to the other deciding game involving the Indians. He would run over to the Red Sox players in the dugout, yelling and gesturing with updates of the Indians' game.

When the Indians lost, Yawkey jumped on his chair and waved his arms frantically as if trying to flag down a cop to signal to the fans the Red Sox's hopes of forcing a playoff were still alive.

It was a moment of unbridled hysteria for a man known for his composure.

When the Red Sox beat the Yankees on the final day, Yawkey threw his brim hat into the crowd, and jumped up and down.

He never felt more alive.

Now, Yawkey was devastated with almost paralyzing grief. He'd never experienced such a flip in emotions in such a short time.

The integrated Cleveland Indians were going to the World Series after beating his all-white Red Sox.

Yawkey looked at his right hand trembling in rage. He could fire his entire coaching staff, but he could do nothing about Bill Veeck. At least, not yet.

CHAPTER 24

The Photo That Shocked The Nation

Oct. 9, 1948

When Larry Doby was drafted to serve in World War II, he tried to enlist in the U.S. Marines. The recruiter nodded, pointed to a door, and Doby found himself in the Navy. The Marines, much like Major League Baseball at that time, were not looking for a few good Negroes.

Doby was stationed in 1945 on Ulithi, a long string of islands between Guam and the Philippines. He and 9,000 other enlisted men were isolated on a sweltering half-square mile patch of coral that served as a supply depot to more than 600 ships.

There he met Mickey Vernon, a white Major League Baseball player five years older than Doby. Vernon and Doby played on the base's softball team, and a bond was cemented between them.

In 1946, the first year back from the war, Vernon won the American League batting title while playing for the Washington Senators, knocking off Boston's Ted Williams.

When Doby debuted in the major leagues the following year, he was floored to receive from Vernon a dozen of his personal Louisville Slugger bats as a token of their friendship. The treasured bats had Vernon's name and team engraved into the ash wood.

Louisville Slugger bats used by Major League Baseball players were handmade from trees in New York and Pennsylvania that were between 50 and 75 years old. Younger trees yielded a bat that was too heavy, and a bat made from an older tree was too brittle. Major league bats underwent a chemical treatment and sat for 18 months.

For Doby, the gift was more than just a souvenir from a batting champion. The Louisville Slugger bats were a symbol of acceptance he had craved but rarely received since breaking baseball's color barrier.

Now, he was playing in Game 4 of the 1948 World Series against the Boston Braves. He was standing at the plate in the third inning clutching his prized Louisville Slugger.

He swung hard and connected.

To Doby's sharply tuned eyes, the baseball looked as big as a cantaloupe. The sound when the bat struck the ball was a trademark "thud" produced by the barrel of a Louisville Slugger launching the perfect hit.

There was no vibration, and none of the stinging in his hand associated with hitting a foul ball. It was the purest of bat-meets-ball connections.

Doby's mind immediately raced back to the game against the Washington Senators in Washington D.C.'s Griffith Stadium five months earlier. He had ripped a shot that traveled more than 500 feet before caroming off a loudspeaker hanging 35 feet over the center field fence. The ball fell back onto the playing field. Under the rules, it was considered a live ball. Doby raced around the bases at full speed for an inside-the-park homer. It was an incredible display of his enormous power and speed. Only one man had hit a ball that far before – Babe Ruth. The Washington Daily Star's headline read: "Negro's Wallop Presses Ruth's Record Hit Here."

Now in his World Series' at-bat, in the most important game of his life, Doby felt that same stroke. He took off sprinting for first base and tore around second still at full speed, and 30 feet from third base, he saw coach Bill McKechnie furiously waving "slow down."

"Take it easy, son," McKechnie shouted to Doby. "That ball isn't coming back."

This time, there was no speaker in the way. The ball went clean over the fence. It was caught in the glove of 10-year-old John Lynch, a Cleveland boy squeezed in with the mob in a standing-room-only section 30 feet past the outfield fence.

Doby turned his head in time to see the ball lost on the other side of the fence, whereupon he reverted to a home-run trot the final 90 feet to home plate.

Lou Boudreau was standing there to shake his hand.

The Indians held on to win 2-1, giving them a commanding lead in the seven-game series. The Indians had now won three of the first four World Series games against the Boston Braves, putting them just one win away from the championship. The World Series was all but locked up.

Afterwards, a wild celebration was underway in the Indians' clubhouse. Winning pitcher Steve Gromek was in front of his locker being interviewed by sportswriter Ed McAuley.

"What was the difference today?" McAuley asked, his voice nearly drowned out by the surrounding celebration.

"What was the difference? He's standing right over there!" Gromek yelled, pointing to Doby. "That home run gave us the win. Larry! Larry Doby! Come on over here!"

A reticent Doby came over.

Gromek grabbed Doby and hugged him.

"We won!" Gromek yelled and then turned and kissed Doby on the cheek.

Doby hugged back. He was overcome by such an emotional public display of support from a teammate, a far cry from the 1947 introduction when so many refused to shake his hand.

Gromek looked at Doby, whose hug was a bit too enthusiastic.

"Larry! I can't breathe!" Gromek yelled as the pitcher and Doby broke out in laughter.

At that instant, a Cleveland Plain Dealer photographer took a photo.

Hours before Doby's winning homer, the Call & Post, a Black Cleveland newspaper, had stated, "They're Really Our Indians."

"Negro Cleveland is 100 percent behind this man Veeck and his Indians," read a front-page editorial dated the same day as Game 4 of the World Series. "These Indians of ours, behind the scenes, were winning over a powerful foe who for centuries has prevented our nation from reaching its fullest possibility. Those of us on this side of the railroad track where dark complexion and slum dwellings seem so readily to blend know this foe as Jim Crow."

Bill Veeck was sitting in his Municipal Stadium office the next day. Doby entered.

"You wanted to see me, Bill?" Doby asked.

Veeck nodded and smiled.

"We had 88,800 people last night. That's a record for the World Series," Veeck beamed. "Your home run is going down as one of the biggest hits in the franchise's history. We need one more victory, and we have Feller and Lemon pitching the next two games."

Veeck had that morning's Cleveland Plain Dealer newspaper on his desk. He held it up.

"And your homer made the front page," Veeck said.

Doby's beaming smile quickly faded. Next to the game story was a photo of Gromek and Doby hugging and smiling. The photo showed the faces of Doby and Gromek lit up in ecstasy, with

Gromek's left arm wrapped around his neck and his right hand clinging to Doby's shoulder. Doby looked closer at the picture and sat as he continued staring at it. Veeck was unsure what was happening. Something had stopped Doby in his tracks.

"Something wrong?" Veeck asked.

Doby tried to speak but couldn't get the words out. Tears welled up. Veeck looked down at the newspaper to see what had Doby so choked up. Suddenly, he understood it was the photo of Gromek and Doby embracing. The team owner smiled and put his hand on Doby's shoulder.

"I can't stay at the same hotels. I can't eat at the same restaurants. The players go out. I go back to the Negro-only hotel alone," Doby said so softly Veeck had to strain to hear it.

Veeck saw tears rolling down Doby's cheeks. Veeck stood quietly by his side and squeezed his shoulder for support. He patted him on the back and turned away so Doby didn't see the tears welling up in his own eyes.

Three days later, Veeck was in his office. The Cleveland newspaper read, "Tribe Wins World Series!"

Steve Gromek walked in.

"You wanted to see me, Mr. Veeck?" Gromek asked.

Veeck put down the newspaper and smiled. He handed Gromek an envelope. Gromek opened the envelope and was stunned.

"$5,000?" Gromek asked. "I heard we were getting bonuses for winning the World Series. Mr. Veeck, that's a full year's salary for some guys."

Veeck nodded.

"I wanted to recognize your contribution," Veeck said.

"I pitched in just one game," Gromek said. "That seems – so generous."

"Not all contributions are on the field," Veeck said.

Gromek was still stunned as he nodded and walked out in a daze. Gromek's first thought was to call his wife.

Veeck sat back in his chair with a warm feeling, opened the desk drawer, and looked again at the front-page photo he had saved: Gromek and Doby beaming.

A week later, Gromek entered Howard's Tavern in his hometown of Hamtramck, Michigan. Detroit Lions' pennants, Detroit Tigers' photos and other sports memorabilia decorated the walls. Some of the pictures showed the photos of the bar's semi-professional baseball team.

Gromek was wearing his 1948 World Series ring and smiled at the patron beside him. The man looked at Gromek and walked away.

Puzzled, Gromek asked the bartender, "What's up with Stan? It's like I owe him money."

"Oh, Christ, Steve. It's that photo," the bartender shot back.

"Photo?" Gromek asked.

"You and that jigaboo Doby. You couldn't have just shook his hand?" the bartender asked.

Gromek was stunned.

"It was just - what came natural at the moment," Gromek said. "I mean, that was the game we had to win, and Larry was a big part of it ..."

"Shit. If he had won me a World Series game, I would have kissed him," said a younger woman listening in.

The bartender glared at the woman and gave Gromek a cold look.

"You may want to have that to go," the bartender said.

Gromek nodded. He tipped his hat. He got up to leave and looked at the bartender and other patrons staring at him.

Gromek paused as he got to the door.

"I look around this place and see photos of cut-rate semi-pro baseball players. I am the winning pitcher of a World Series game with the largest attendance ever and was put on television. Everybody in this town saw me outpitch Johnny Sain," Gromek said.

"Johnny Sain," Gromek repeated for emphasis, referring to the three-time all-star pitcher.

Gromek surveyed the bar.

"This town has never seen anything like that. That photo was in damn near every newspaper in the country because it captured teammates enjoying one of the top moments of a lifetime. Nobody here would understand what accomplishing something like that would mean. This wasn't the Sunday afternoon beer league. And you should put that photo right at the entrance when people walk in. That picture would class up this dive," Gromek said.

With that, the World Series champion turned and left.

A week later, in Washington, D.C., a 36-year-old Black lawyer had two newspapers on her kitchen table. Once a week, Marjorie McKenzie wrote a sports column for the Black newspaper, the Pittsburgh Courier. Black U.S. Congressman Adam Powell Jr., who rented a room from McKenzie, sat at the table with her.

Pushing the two newspapers over to him, McKenzie asked, "Did you see this?"

The first newspaper displayed a photo of Doby and Gromek smiling after the World Series game. The other newspaper's photo was dated Oct. 7, 1948 – just two days before Doby's home run. It showed bespectacled 61-year-old Black professor George McLaurin sitting at a small wooden desk just outside a University of Oklahoma law classroom. McLaurin was looking through a doorway and into a room filled with all white college students listening to a lecture.

The retired professor, who had a master's degree from the University of Kansas, had gone all the way to the U.S. Supreme Court to gain admission to the university, but under state law the school was still required to keep its facilities segregated. The U.S. Supreme Court would end the "separate but equal" policy at the university in 1950.

Powell reviewed both photos. He looked up at McKenzie.

"Tells two different stories, doesn't it?" McKenzie said with a defeated tone.

McKenzie was silent.

On Oct. 23, 1948, the Pittsburgh Courier published McKenzie's column with the headline, "Doby-Gromek picture treated eyes to sight of equality in action."

She wrote: "That picture of Gromek and Doby has unmistakable flesh and blood cheeks pressed close together, brawny arms tightly clasped, equally wide grins. The chief message of the Doby-Gromek picture is acceptance. ... We can talk equality, we can legislate equality ... but we are most convincing when we can arrange for many people to see equality in action. That's why the Doby-Gromek picture is great."

CHAPTER 25

I Am Don Black. I Am An Alcoholic.

Don Black was dead.

That's what WHK, the radio station that carried the Cleveland Indians games, reported on Sept. 21, 1948.

Actually, Black was lapsing in and out of a coma in a bed at Cleveland's Charity Hospital.

Twenty days later, on Monday, Oct. 11, the Cleveland Indians won the World Series with a 4-3 victory in Game 6 over the Boston Braves in Boston.

Black was a pitcher on the Indians and forced to listen to the radio broadcast from his hospital bed.

After the final out, Black turned to nurse Maryan Coyne, feebly clapped his hands, and mustered a smile.

"I think they did OK," Black said.

Twenty minutes later he heard Cleveland Indians' star shortstop and manager Lou Boudreau give a post-game interview.

"Thirty men helped us win this championship ... you, Don Black, are one of the most helpful," Boudreau told the radio interviewer. "Every one of us who were able to carry on put out just a little more because you were unable to be with us. We won this for you, Don, and we want you to know how proud we are to call you our teammate."

Black bit his lip. He didn't want to cry in front of Coyne. The nurse recognized the moment and walked out of the room.

The Don Black saga that inspired the Cleveland Indians began three years earlier in 1945. Black was with Major League Baseball's Philadelphia Athletics at that time.

Black was so drunk at a team breakfast his head fell into the bowl of split-pea soup.

It occurred at Boston's Somerset Hotel on June 5, 1945. Black was in his third year of an up-and-down career that kept getting sidetracked by his excessive drinking.

Black's Philadelphia teammates tried to cover for him and get him conscious, but Philadelphia manager Connie Mack had seen enough.

"You don't have to do that," Mack told Black's teammates. "I've seen it."

Black was suspended for 30 days. He went back to his Virginia home to pump gas.

Convinced he couldn't stay sober, the Athletics sold his contract for $7,500 to the Cleveland Indians on Oct. 2, 1945.

"He has been a detriment to the team," Mack told newspaper reporters.

In March 1946, on the first day of spring training in Clearwater, Florida, Black made a promise to Indians' general manager Roger Peckinpaugh and manager/shortstop Lou Boudreau that he wouldn't drink alcohol.

On March 27, as spring training was winding down, Black was hit in the chin by a batted ball that required five stitches. After being treated at the local hospital, Black went to a Clearwater bar and got severely drunk.

Black stumbled back to the team hotel and went looking for Peckinpaugh to demand another advance on his $7,000 a-year salary. He had already been given a $1,500 advance earlier in March.

Cleveland sportswriter Ed McAuley found Black drunk in the hotel lobby and tried to convince him to go back to his hotel room. But Black kept on pushing McAuley away.

"Can't do that!" Black yelled, drawing the attention of people in the lobby. "I got to have some money. Right now. I don't care about myself. I'll quit the team and get a job somewhere! I'm not going to have my family worry about money!"

A few of Black's teammates tried to calm him down. Alerted by hotel employees about the disturbance, Boudreau and Peckinpaugh made their way to the lobby.

Black saw Peckinpaugh and shouted, "Hey! I need an advance! Or I'm going home!"

Peckinpaugh motioned to the players to get control of Black, which infuriated the intoxicated pitcher.

"Don't push me away! I need an advance!" Black yelled.

Eventually, hotel security calmed Black down and walked him to his room.

Boudreau and Peckinpaugh had now experienced what caused the Athletics to let Black go.

But the Indians weren't ready to give up on Black just yet.

During the regular season, Black had pitched in 18 games as a reliever but had problems staying sober.

Things came to a head on July 14, 1946. Boston Red Sox hitter Ted Williams hit a home run off Black in the fifth inning of a Sunday game. The Indians lost 11-10. Black started the game in the bullpen distancing himself from the manager, Lou Boudreau. Black avoided Boudreau in the dugout after he entered the game in the third inning.

Boudreau went to the mound to take Black out of the game in the seventh inning.

"You don't have it today," Boudreau told Black as he took the baseball from him and signaled for another pitcher to come from the bullpen.

As Black walked past Boudreau, the manager smelled alcohol.

The next day on July 16, Black was sent to the Milwaukee Brewers minor league team. The Indians had given up on him.

Bill Veeck had bought the Cleveland Indians that June. In July, comedian Bob Hope, one of Veeck's partners in the acquisition, told some newspaper reporters he heard some teams were offering the Indians $300,000 for star Cleveland pitcher Bob Feller.

A lack of pitching depth was the team's most glaring weakness, and Veeck knew the Indians couldn't afford to lose their best pitcher.

On Sept. 1, 1946 the Indians lost to the Chicago White Sox in Chicago and their record dropped 58-71. They were in fifth place, 32.5 games behind the first-place powerhouse Boston Red Sox.

Veeck had seen enough. After the day game, he took the train to Milwaukee and arranged a meeting with an old friend, Nick Cullop, manager of the Indians' minor league team, the Milwaukee Brewers. Veeck had hired Cullop as the manager back when he owned the Brewers in 1944. Cullop accepted the offer while Veeck was in a Naval hospital bed in California recuperating from his war injury.

On Sept. 1, Veeck met Cullop at the Landmark1850 Inn, a bar with German culture that fit Cullop's German ancestry.

"So, we need some help, Nick," Veeck told Cullop. "We need arms. Our pitching is bad. Do we have anything here we could maybe use next year?"

Cullop thought for a bit.

"There's Ewald Pyle. He's 34 and has 15 wins, by far the most," Cullop said. "I wish I could say that means anything. His fastball is average at best. He's been in the majors four times and washed out every time. Not a pony I'd bet on."

Veeck nodded. Pyle was not the answer.

"Anyone else?" Veeck asked.

"Don Black," Cullop said. "But you know his story. I mean, he has some great pitches. He has the best arm on the team. It's the bottle that is stopping him."

Cullop continued.

"I'll give you an example. He was pitching two weeks ago against the first-place Indianapolis team. He had them shut out after five innings. He looked like death warmed over. He's sweating through his shirt, and it's just 65 degrees. He goes out for the next two innings and gives up three runs. He's not in shape due to the drinking. He just ran out of gas," Cullop said.

Veeck nodded.

"When does he pitch next?" Veeck asked.

"The day after tomorrow," Cullop said.

"Tell him I'm in town to scout him and that he needs to straighten up and fly right, and this is his chance to get back in the major leagues," Veeck said. "I'm going to talk with him. Will he be square with me?"

Cullop shrugged.

"Sure," he said. "Children and drunks always tell the truth."

Black managed to stay sober the night before the Sept. 3 game. With Veeck in the stands, he pitched nine innings and only gave up three hits. He did his part, even though the Milwaukee Brewers still lost to Louisville 1-0.

But Veeck found a pitcher for his team.

After the game, Veeck approached Black.

"On your way back home to Virginia, stop in Cleveland. I want to talk to you," Veeck told him.

Veeck set a Sept. 10 meeting with Black in Veeck's office at Cleveland's Municipal Stadium. Veeck also asked Rudie Schaffer, the Indians' business manager, to attend.

Don Black walked into the meeting on time.

But Veeck noticed immediately Black's face was flushed and puffy. It was obvious the player had been drinking.

Veeck didn't mince words.

"I think you can have a spot on the Indians if you can handle your drinking," he told Black.

Black looked at Veeck. He shook his head.

"Alcohol has me licked," Black said as he slumped in his chair.

Veeck stood up and put his hand on Black's shoulder.

"Not if you can admit that," Veeck said.

Veeck had a plan.

Black's drinking had sent him into serious debt.

Veeck paid off $8,000 in debt that Black had racked up, the equivalent to $111,000 in 2023 dollars. To keep Black in Cleveland during the off season, Veeck got Black a job with one of the businesses involved in some of Veeck's promotions. And there was a reason for that.

The generosity came with a caveat: Black would have to join an organization started 15 years earlier called Alcoholics Anonymous. If Black accepted, local Cleveland Alcoholics Anonymous sponsors would keep an eye on him.

"Give this thing a try," Veeck told Black. "You won't have to worry about your debts. I'm paying them all off. The only man you're going to owe is me, and I'm not going to be tough on you. I know the A.A. people. I'm going to send them around to see you."

Black was silent. Finally, he looked at Veeck.

"What do I have to lose?" he asked.

The following spring training, Black told reporters he knew his career was on the line.

"I've made a lot of mistakes," Black said. "This is it. I know the score and intend to stay in condition and give it my best."

A sober Black began the 1947 season in grand form. He won his first two starts, including a four-hit complete game shutout in which the Indians beat the Chicago White Sox 1-0.

In his third game on April 29, Black was wild and gave up seven walks, including a free pass with the bases loaded to force in the winning run as his old team the Philadelphia Athletics beat the Indians 4-3.

After the game, Black found an Alcoholics Anonymous sponsor waiting for him. Veeck was worried the tough loss could trigger a relapse.

On July 10, Don Black again faced his old team, the Athletics. Just five days earlier, Black's teammate Larry Doby had become the American League's first Black player.

There were 47,871 fans in the stands, but not to watch Black. This was a twilight double-header, and Black was pitching the first of two games. The crowd arrived to see fan-favorite Bob Feller pitch the second game.

Cleveland fans had no idea they were about to witness baseball history.

Black started by walking the first two batters of the game.

But then, Black began to grind through the Athletics' lineup, getting one out after another.

When Don Black took the mound in the ninth inning, he hadn't allowed a hit.

He looked into the Athletics' dugout and saw former teammates Russ Christopher, Dick Fowler, Carl Scheib and Phil Marchildon, all pitchers standing on the dugout steps with their eyes riveted on Black. Two years earlier, they had tried to shield Black from Athletics' manager Connie Mack after he had passed out drunk, face down in his split-pea soup.

But now, Black was on the threshold of accomplishing one of baseball's most cherished achievements – a no-hitter.

Black noticed the crowd had grown silent. Even the beer and peanut vendors had stopped to watch this final inning.

Also standing at the steps of the Indians' dugout was Hal Peck, a former Athletics player who also witnessed Black's passing out that led to his 30-day suspension with the Athletics. Peck was now a teammate on the Indians. Black could see the anxiety in Peck's stare.

The players all knew Black was three outs away from baseball immortality.

Black looked for his wife Joyce in the seats near the dugout where the wives usually sat. He found her. She was crying and being comforted by the other Indians' spouses.

Black took a step off the mound and took a deep breath. Three outs to go.

Black retired the first two batters of the ninth inning. The only obstacle between him and baseball history was former teammate Sam Chapman, an all-star player the previous year.

Black unleashed a pitch, and Chapman swung and hit a slow grounder right back to Black. At that moment, the ball looked as big as a balloon to Black. He fielded it and threw it to first baseman Eddie Robinson, who caught it and tagged the base to end the game.

Robinson tossed the ball back to Black. The pitcher looked at the ball and hugged it, and then stuck it in his pants pocket.

At that moment, the Cleveland Press described the roar from the crowd as "yelling and screaming and whistling and the kind of applause that sticks to a man's ribs."

Owner Bill Veeck had planned a fireworks show for the crowd after the second game when the more popular Feller pitched.

"Forget that!" Veeck ordered the fireworks operator over the roar of the crowd. "Shoot off the fireworks now!"

The lights were turned off in the stadium and the fireworks went off.

Reporters mobbed Black after the game.

"You can chalk that victory up for Alcoholics Anonymous," Black told the pack of reporters.

Across the field, Athletics manager Connie Mack was happy for the man he had given up on.

"Whoever was responsible for Don joining the Alcoholics Anonymous - I say hats off to him," Mack told reporters.

A month later, Veeck put on a Don Black Night that highlighted the work Alcoholics Anonymous did. There were 4,000 Alcoholics Anonymous members who attended. However, the event was controversial because naming Black as a member stripped the anonymity regarded as essential to the program's success.

Black was just the second player in baseball's history to go public for being a member of Alcoholics Anonymous.

Rollie Hemsley was the first. He was playing with the Cleveland Indians when he called a press conference on April 16, 1940, on opening day.

Hemsley was an all-star catcher who wore out his welcome with four teams due to his heavy drinking before landing with the Indians in 1938.

Now, like Hemsley, Black had taken his struggles public.

A Sporting News editorial read: "Because Don so frankly admitted his debt to A.A., others who have been kept from achieving their true destinies in baseball, in industry, in professions, will take heart and seek aid which lifted the pitcher from the depths to the glorious peaks of no-hit, no-run achievement. Black now stands as a beacon of light for all those who have been handicapped by the demons that hide in the bottle."

Before the game, Black was honored by Alcoholics Anonymous. A Paramount Newsreel crew filmed the publicity event as Black received a check for $1,000, a gold watch and a gold chain.

Black managed to stay sober and started the 1948 season with the Indians.

Once a year, Veeck held a dance for his ball club. In 1948, it was held Sept. 10 at Hotel Cleveland's famous Bronze Room that had attracted celebrities like Eliot Ness, president Harry S. Truman, and first lady Eleanor Roosevelt.

Gordon Cobbledick, the sports editor of the Cleveland Plain

Dealer, was at the event. He saw Don Black sitting with his wife Joyce. Don was drinking a Coke.

Cobbledick had interviewed Black just a week earlier for a story about the pitcher's recovery.

Cobbledick approached and introduced himself to Black's wife.

Black asked Cobbledick when the story was going to run.

"In a couple of days," the sportswriter said.

Black nodded and looked at his wife.

"I'm living a new life," Black said. "I'm beginning to appreciate friendships I almost ruined."

Cobbledick turned to Joyce.

"Is he a new man?" Cobbledick asked.

Joyce started to tear up.

"It's hard to put into words," she replied.

She wiped the tears from her face and smiled.

"Just say we're happy now," she said.

Cobbledick's story for the Cleveland Plain Dealer ran on Sept. 12 with the headline: "Don Black's Greatest Victory." Newspapers across the country picked it up.

The next day, Black was pitching against the St. Louis Browns. He got through the first two innings without giving up a run.

He came to the plate to bat, swung, and fouled off a pitch.

Then, Black felt a twitch in his neck. He grabbed his head and collapsed at home plate.

Newspaper photos showed Black on his knees, clutching his head at home plate as nervous teammates tried to comfort him. An aneurysm near the back of his brain had burst.

Black was taken to the hospital. In the emergency room, he didn't recognize his wife.

"I got to win this game. We got to win the pennant," Black told doctors.

The Indians lost to the St. Louis Browns, 3-2, and fell three games behind the Boston Red Sox in the battle for first place.

Soon after talking to doctors, Black slipped into a coma. Dr. Spencer Braden of Charity Hospital had a grim prognosis for Black.

"He has a 50-50 chance to live," Braden told newspaper reporters.

On Sept. 22, Bill Veeck put on another Don Black Day. Instead, this time Veeck announced that some of the ticket sales proceeds would go to Black's family.

Veeck worked with the Boston Red Sox to change the day game to a night game so it could draw more fans.

The Cleveland Indians players, dressed in full uniform, walked up to the ticket gate and bought their own game tickets to boost the proceeds. Each teammate walked through Cleveland's Municipal Stadium turnstiles registering as a paid customer.

The attendance for the game was 75,382 fans. Black's family received $40,000, equivalent to $513,000 in 2023.

The Indians beat the Red Sox 5-2 to force a tie with Boston for first place with just eight games left in the regular season.

Dr. Braden operated on the aneurysm on Dec. 7 and Black was released from the hospital on Dec. 23. He spent Christmas with his wife and two young daughters. He was sober. But it was the end of his career in baseball.

CHAPTER 26

Report Says Doby Can't Buy Home

Oct. 20, 1948

Newspapers were piling up outside Helyn and Larry Doby's crowded one-bedroom apartment.

It had been a busy week for Larry Doby, World Series hero. Helyn picked up the latest newspaper and saw her husband on the front page once more. The story chronicled a Monday parade for Larry in his hometown of Paterson, New Jersey.

The parade route ended at the high school, where 3,000 residents gathered. The Dobys were given several gifts that included some jewelry. Helen was very appreciative but wasn't much for wearing jewels. She kept her gifts in a cardboard box. Their apartment was so small, it couldn't hold most of Helyn's items, so she kept them at her mother's home about a mile away.

The Paterson newspaper The Morning Call had dedicated an entire page to the Larry Doby celebration, with nine photos of that city's parade and Doby meeting local dignitaries.

Inside the apartment, Larry was sitting on the only piece of living room furniture, a four-seat couch. Helyn carried in the hometown newspaper and plopped down beside her husband.

Helyn had been a cheerleader at Eastside High School, where Larry starred in four sports. Larry asked her out on a date. Larry was an only child. Helyn had nine siblings. They clicked. They were now married for two years and four months.

Helyn began reading out loud the stories about her husband. She knew Larry took deep pride in the coverage.

"This article was written by Joe Gootter," Helyn said. "You recall Mr. Gootter? He covered you in high school."

Helyn then started to read an editorial out loud.

"Of all Paterson's champions in the world of sport, none has ever received a more spontaneous and wholehearted civic reception from his fellow townsmen than our national game hero of the World Series, Larry Doby," Helyn said.

She paused and looked at her husband, who tended to wear his feelings on his sleeve. That was one of Larry's most dominant personality traits, for better or worse.

"What did you find in Fairlawn?" Larry asked.

Helyn was quiet.

"I'm not sure we'd like it there. It's six miles away," Helyn said.

"What do you mean?" Larry asked. "I drove out there last week. I saw at least 20 homes with for sale signs."

"The asking prices are outrageous," Helyn said. "That's the way it is for colored folks out there."

Larry said nothing. Helyn knew the silence meant he was frustrated.

She tried to change the topic. A local boxing club was honoring Larry that evening. They were supposed to meet famous boxer Sugar Ray Robinson that night. Robinson was a welterweight division world champion.

"Is Ray going to be at tonight's Larry Doby Day?" Helyn asked.

Larry grimaced.

"You know he likes to drink and go out," Larry said. "You know me. Two beers, and I'm ready for bed."

Part of the reason Helyn loved her man was that he was content with their life. Neither of them liked to go out much unless it was an occasional movie.

Robinson was married to former Cotton Club dancer Edna Mae Holly, who was a celebrity in her own right. Robinson and Holly often fought like cats and dogs around the Dobys, which made them uncomfortable.

Sugar Ray and Edna were extravagant spenders. When they were all out together one night, Edna wore a $10,000 necklace her husband had bought for her.

This night, Robinson would be alone. This event was an evening of amateur boxing called the Diamond Gloves Show. It was sponsored by the Paterson Evening News and held at the Paterson Armory.

Larry had grown weary of all the public acclaim, but he knew he had to attend. Unlike Robinson, Larry didn't go to events without his wife unless Helyn opted out.

Helyn planned to spend the afternoon house hunting and then be home by 5 p.m. to get ready for the event.

When Larry and Helyn arrived at 5:30 p.m., they were met by state athletic commissioner Abe Greene. The evening's first bout was still three hours away. Greene laid out the program for the evening. Before the fights, Larry and his wife would be introduced. He would be presented with gifts and then give a short speech and pose for photographs.

Sugar Ray Robinson arrived 30 minutes later in his late-model Cadillac. Everything about the welterweight boxing champion oozed style.

Robinson had a reputation as a fierce fighter. In 1946, he won the welterweight world championship belt. In 1947, he unleashed a left hook that sent opponent Jimmy Doyle to the canvas. Doyle was counted out when he couldn't get back on his feet. He was sent to the hospital, where he died several hours later.

There was talk about charging Robinson with murder, but nothing came of it. Doyle had told his handlers he was fighting Robinson for money to buy his mother a house. When Robinson learned that, he gave Doyle's mother money to buy the house, taken from the proceeds of his next four fights.

Robinson had a record of 88-1-1 and on Sept. 23, 1948 at Yankee Stadium, he had beaten Kid Gavilan in front of his hometown Bronx fans. He got a massive $51,000 payday [$640,000 in 2023 dollars].

Robinson and Doby couldn't have been more opposite personalities. Robinson was a brash and flashy dresser. Doby was reticent and didn't like to draw attention to himself.

As an athletic race pioneer, Doby had a much more difficult path than Sugar Ray Robinson. That color barrier had fallen decades earlier in boxing, if not without conflict.

Jack Johnson became the first Black heavyweight boxing champion in 1908. When Johnson beat white boxer James Jeffries - dubbed "The Great White Hope" - race riots erupted across the country in 1910. A Black man named Charles Williams was discussing the victory on a streetcar in Reno and had his throat slashed by a white man who overheard him.

But breeching baseball's color barrier was a new thing. While the media had focused more on Jackie Robinson, Doby was the biggest name in his hometown of Paterson.

Sugar Ray Robinson was at ringside at 8:05 p.m. when Larry and Helyn were escorted into the ring to a standing ovation.

Larry was given a miniature diamond glove and a wristwatch with 17 jewels embedded in it. Helyn was given a bouquet of flowers.

Doby's speech to 2,800 fans was as dry as a bone.

"It's mighty nice to be home. I am very proud that I am a representative of Paterson," he said. "I'll try to keep Paterson on the map and be a gentleman at all times."

Doby paused.

"I am not very good at speeches, but I do know how to say, 'Thank you,'" Doby said.

He and Helyn exited the ring.

Many fans had bought drinks for Robinson, who by night's end was intoxicated.

"It looks like Ray will be staying with us," Helyn said.

Larry nodded.

As they walked out with Robinson, the boxer worried about who would drive his new Cadillac.

"Helyn will," Larry said.

"Wait!" Robinson objected. "That car is just a year old!"

"Ray," Doby said, now a bit annoyed. "Helyn's a better driver than me."

When the couple escorted Robinson into the apartment and turned on the light, he was stunned by the one-bedroom apartment.

"This is it?" Robinson said. "This is where the World Series hero lives?"

Larry was embarrassed. Helyn clasped his hand in support.

"We're having problems finding a house to buy," Larry said.

Sugar Ray Robinson passed out within five minutes after being put on the couch. Larry wondered if he'd remember much of the evening.

Two months later, the couple was still shoehorned into the cramped one-bedroom apartment. Helyn kept house hunting but her husband had given up hope.

At home on a Wednesday morning, Larry answered a knock on the door. He was wearing dungarees and not expecting company.

Standing before him was a 54-year-old Black man dressed in a suit. Larry's first guess was he was a banker. That didn't fit though. The man was Black and a wired notebook was stuffed into his jacket pocket.

"Can I help you, Mister?" Doby asked.

"I'm Harry Webber," the man said. "I'm a reporter with the New York Age."

"Come in, Mr. Webber," Doby said.

"Please, call me Harry," Webber said.

The New York Age was a long-time Black newspaper that in the coming years would become a strident voice for racial justice. But in 1948, Doby expected this would be another interview about his life as a World Series hero. He'd given so many interviews that the thrill of seeing his name in the newspaper had long been worn out.

Webber looked around the tiny apartment.

Doby was embarrassed.

"We usually don't have people over," Doby said sheepishly.

Webber nodded and saw a small table with two chairs. He looked over at Doby.

"May I?" Webber asked.

"Of course," Doby replied.

Webber sat down at the table.

"So, why is the New York Age interested in me?" Doby asked. "You don't look like most sportswriters I meet."

"I got a phone call from Sugar Ray," Webber said. "He told me about your situation. About how you can't find a home to buy in Paterson."

Doby was silent. He gave a skeptical look to Webber.

"You want to do a newspaper story on that?" Doby asked with trepidation in his voice.

"I do," Webber said.

Webber didn't say another word. Doby thought hard about the repercussions of such a story in his hometown.

Doby shook his head.

"What good would come from it?" Doby asked. "To call out my own city for racism?"

Webber nodded.

"I understand," Webber said.

Webber took his notebook from his jacket and put it on the table. He put his pencil down.

"So why are you doing this?" Webber asked.

Doby was a bit puzzled.

"Doing what?" he asked.

"Playing baseball with a bunch of white teammates who don't want you on their team. Playing baseball in front of fans in St. Louis who call you nigger and jigaboo, and the only Negroes allowed to watch are forced to sit behind chicken wire in the outfield bleachers," Webber said.

Webber paused, eyeing the reticent baseball player, and then answered his own question.

"You do it because you want to change it," Webber said. "You want to allow more Negroes to play in the majors."

Doby nodded.

"I want to show people we can live together and we can play together," Doby said.

Webber looked at Doby with admiration. Webber decided to tell his own story.

"I went to the University of Pittsburgh and got a master's degree in administration," Webber said. "Not many sportswriters have master's degrees. Surely not any Negro ones."

Doby laughed.

Webber smiled and continued.

"There was one other Negro on campus," he said.

Webber hesitated as the memory of the man flickered through his mind.

"His name was Scott McCoy, and he was from Pittsburgh. We would occasionally talk when we ran into each other. He was a year behind me in the school of economics. When we got the college yearbook, I remember they had little phrases for each student. Things like, 'Wonder why they all want to sit next to Winifred, especially during exams?' But for Scott, it was just his photo and hometown. No one bothered with any insights on him," Webber said.

Webber hesitated as the memories flickered past.

"When you graduated, the understanding was you would get a job at Mellon Bank," Webber said.

Webber paused. His smile evaporated.

"Well, about a dozen of us went to the bank, and I was the only Negro. The white graduates were taken to the top floor. I was taken to the basement and given the elevator operator's uniform," Webber said.

Webber paused. The pain of those long-past moments came alive in the older man's voice.

"After the meeting, we all met in the lobby," Webber said. "And I couldn't be the one to work the elevator while they followed my dream."

"So, I had a decision to make. I could work the elevator while the other white students took the banking job I wanted on the upper levels," Webber said. "I would be taking them in the elevator to the jobs I was told I wasn't qualified to have."

Webber shook his head.

"Who knows? Instead, I said no way. And I walked out," he said.

Webber's smile returned.

"And here I am sitting in front of you, the most highly educated newspaper reporter you'll ever meet," Webber said with a laugh. "But not a banker."

"You are on a path, young man, ... and it can be incredibly unpleasant, unbearable at times," Webber said. "Nobody knows that more than you. My dream was to be a banker. I lost that. Do I regret not fighting it?"

Webber didn't answer that question.

"But this fight is worth it," Webber said. "You know that more than anyone. Exposing the hypocrisy of racism. What's more important than that?"

"And you, Larry, are a magnificent voice for that cause," Webber said.

Doby lit up at that thought.

"Can I talk it over with Helyn?" Doby asked. "There's no way I do this without her approval."

Webber nodded. He opened his notebook and took his pencil in his hand.

Two days later, the New York Age broke the story that, due to racism, baseball hero Larry Doby could not purchase a house in his own hometown of Paterson, New Jersey.

The story contained this quote from Doby that Larry and his wife worked on for three hours the night before: "I honestly feel that I am more of a hero in Cleveland than here in my own hometown. In comparison, treatment in Cleveland has been wonderful. I am sure of a home there, and unless we are able to buy one in Paterson before spring training, we will move out to Cleveland to stay."

The story was picked up by newspapers across the country. The Des Moines Register ran it Christmas Day with the headline "Report Says Doby Can't Buy Home."

Three weeks after the story was published, Larry and Helyn Doby bought a home on East 27th Street in Paterson, less than two miles from his old high school and seven miles from the upscale white neighborhoods. Doby paid for the property with his $6,772 World Series bonus.

CHAPTER 27

The Fan Who Set The Record For Pole Sitting

May 31, 1949

Day One.

Charley Lupica climbed the ladder leaning against the four-feet by six-feet perch attached to a 20-foot utility pole that was planted on a roof 40 feet above the ground.

Lupica wore brown slacks, socks, loafers, and a white-collar shirt with "Cleveland Indians" imprinted all over it. On the platform was a canvas tent that left no room to stand, which would be the pole-sitter's only protection from the elements.

This was Lupica's new domicile. It was perched above the delicatessen owned by Lupica and his partner Ben DiMarco, located on Cleveland's 118th Street.

Nearby business owners had assisted in the platform's assembly. They were highly amused by a local business owner living atop a pole until the Cleveland Indians brought home an American League pennant.

Lupica was disappointed that no local newspapers had covered his stunt. They needed the publicity for the struggling delicatessen.

"Any luck with the reporters?" Lupica called down to DiMarco.

DiMarco just shook his head.

"They said they'd pass the tip onto their editors," DiMarco said.

DiMarco took the ladder down.

"I've got the store covered," DiMarco said. "I can't believe your wife went along with this. It was just a stupid bar bet. Nobody is going to hold you to this."

Earlier in the month, Lupica got into a heated argument with New York Yankees fans at a local Cleveland bar.

The opposing fans told Lupica, "If you like the Indians so much, why don't you sit on a flagpole until you die up there."

Lupica took the challenge to heart. He would stay up on that pole until the Indians won the pennant.

His perch on the pole was outfitted with an air mattress and a box of cigars. A large steel bucket served as the bathroom, with a rope to lower it to a large metal container DiMarco would empty as needed.

Charley Lupica added one final touch to the platform, a large beach umbrella to deflect the sun and rain.

At the moment it was 83 degrees, and Lupica was feeling the heat.

His wife, Gusty, who was six months pregnant, was taking care of the couple's three children at their home a few blocks away. She would miss being there for opening day of her husband's pole-sitting stunt.

Day Eight. June 7

Lupica had trouble sleeping due to the temperature swings. The thermometer fell to the low 50s at night before soaring back to the mid 80s during the day.

Lupica was not well prepared for the weather. The rain seeped through his canvas tent, soaking his air mattress.

At about 9 a.m. he heard a commotion down below. Looking down, he watched a Cleveland sanitation department security officer coming up through the delicatessen's roof entrance and approaching the pole.

Behind the Cleveland sanitation department security officer was a city of Cleveland police officer. Both security men stopped 10 feet short of the pole.

"Hey, buddy, time to come down," the sanitation officer demanded.

Lupica sat up. He was still drowsy. Lupica didn't know what time it was. And he had to go to the bathroom.

"Who are you?" Lupica asked.

"Captain Leo Schamadan of the city's sanitation department," Schamadan yelled. "I have officer Elwin Burmeister with me of the city's police department. Time to come down. Your little party is over. You need a camping license to be up there. And you are violating the city's sanitation codes with your bucket and rope. It's not the canal boat days anymore. Bucket and chuck it isn't allowed by city codes."

"The sanitation department has police?" Lupica asked. "What are you, the poop police?"

"You need a camping license," Schamadan repeated, ignoring the jab.

"Camping license?" Lupica said. "Does this look like Yellowstone to you, buddy?"

"Patrolman Burmeister is with the Cleveland Police Department, wise guy," Schamadan shot back. "You either come down, or we will take you down."

Schamadan took a deep breath. He was losing patience with Lupica.

"Look, if we allow you to stay up there, we'll have everyone in the city sleeping in the trees," Schamadan pleaded.

"I'm not coming down until the Indians win the pennant," Lupica said.

"What? Are you crazy? That won't be until October if they catch the Yankees," Schamadan said.

A crowd was starting to gather on the street below.

"Elwin, get him down," Schamadan told Elwin Burmeister, a Cleveland police officer.

Burmeister shook his head.

"I don't know how," Burmeister told Schamadan. "The ladder downstairs won't hold two people. We'll fall if he resists."

Schamadan paused. He looked up at Lupica.

"OK, pal. Here's what I'm going to do. I'm going to radio the station for a warrant for your arrest, and I'll have a crew come down and take down this pole if I have to," Schamadan said.

Schamadan headed down back to the police squad car that Burmeister arrived in.

Lupica's business partner Ben DiMarco came up to the roof to talk to Lupica. He saw officer Burmeister.

"Officer, the press is on the way," DiMarco said.

Burmeister cringed.

Ten minutes later, Cleveland Press reporter Jack Hume was on the rooftop.

Schamadan returned and walked up to the pole.

"The city attorney is drawing up the warrant right now," Schamadan said.

After ten minutes, officer Burmeister told Schamadan the city attorney was on his police radio. Schamadan smiled at Lupica and returned to the street as the newspaper reporter followed him.

Schamadan reached into the police squad car and grabbed the

radio. Another voice rang out.

"Captain Schamadan? This is Joseph Crowley, chief legal counsel. Is the man still on the pole?" the lawyer asked.

"Yes, sir," Schamadan responded.

"OK. Here's the deal. I had our legal team dig into the city codes. His perch isn't a hut, tent, or barracks. So, he isn't camping," Crowley said. "So just let him be. In a few days, the cold nights will send him home."

"What about the rope and bucket?" Schamadan asked. "Isn't that a violation?"

"We aren't pursuing it," Crowley said.

Schamadan put the radio back and looked to see Hume standing next to him.

"Well, you heard it," Schamadan said. "He can stay up there until the snow drifts bury him for all I care."

The Associated Press picked up Hume's Cleveland Press story. Within two days, Lupica's stunt was in hundreds of newspapers nationwide.

Charley Lupica, never known for much besides being the loudest man in the bar, was famous.

Day 49. July 19

It was 90 degrees. Lupica sat in his sweltering perch, stripped down to a sweat-soaked tank-top undershirt. The beach umbrella provided little relief. Posing for a newspaper photographer, Lupica held a clock-sized thermostat from inside the tent that read 117 degrees.

The national pole-sitting record was 72 days.

A red and yellow army-type Jeep pulled up in front of the

delicatessen. Jeeps for civilians were a rare sighting and still a novelty so this one drew people's attention.

Dressed to the nines, baseball legend Satchel Paige stepped out of the vehicle and headed for the rooftop.

When Paige got to the rooftop, Lupica was awestruck.

"Satch?" Lupica asked reverently. "Satchel Paige?"

Paige smiled.

"How are you doing, Mr. Lupica?" Paige asked.

"Please, call me Charley," Lupica responded.

Paige nodded.

"You want to come up and look around, Satch?" Lupica asked in a voice filled with anticipation.

Paige spotted the ladder. He picked it up and leaned it against the perch.

Paige took five steps on the ladder and stopped.

"This is as high as I go. I've got a thing about heights," Paige said.

Paige waved his hand before his nose and made a sour face.

"Charley. Almighty Lord Jesus, what is that smell?" Paige asked.

"To set the pole-sitting record, I can't go inside to use the bathroom. So, I got this," Lupica said, holding up a bucket and rope.

Paige cringed.

"That's disgusting, Charley - but I respect your commitment, sir! I just wanted to stop by and thank you for what you're doing. When you started, we were ten games back," Paige said.

As Charley knew well, with the Indians' victory the previous night, they were just 4 ½ games behind the first-place New York Yankees.

"It's my honor, Satch. You know, I saw you play years ago when you were pitching with the Negro team Cleveland Cubs. You threw a shutout. I was 14," Lupica said.

Paige barely recalled his stint in Cleveland in 1931. It was one of a half dozen teams he pitched for that year.

"Damn, Charley. That was a long time ago," Paige said, shaking his head.

"How are you holding up?" he asked.

"Good," Lupica said as he reflexively rubbed his jaw. "I have a bit of a toothache. But that's going to be fixed. My wife is eight months pregnant and due in a couple of weeks. Some neighbors are pressuring me to come down and be there when she gives birth. And the police gave me a hassle early on about sanitation violations."

Paige paused.

"They want you to come down for your child's birth?" Paige asked.

"Yeah," Lupica said.

The highly superstitious Paige dismissed the demand.

"How many kids do you have?" Paige asked.

"Three," Lupica said.

"Ah - you'll have another one," Paige said.

Paige nodded.

"You aren't missing out on anything you haven't done three times before. Besides, what a story your baby will have to tell someday," Paige said.

Day 59. July 29

Cleveland Indians owner Bill Veeck looked up from the street, trying to block the sun with his hand.

High on his perch, Charley Lupica was listening to the radio.

Veeck waved his hands to get Lupica's attention. Lupica turned down the volume on the radio.

"You must be Charley Lupica," Veeck yelled. "I'm Bill Veeck."

Lupica looked down and smiled.

"Thank you for not trading Boudreau," Lupica yelled back.

Veeck held his hand up.

"Hold on, I'm coming up. But give me some time. I've only got one good leg," Veeck said.

Once on the rooftop, Veeck thanked Lupica for his support.

"Charley, I'm humbled by your unwavering support," Veeck said. "We will try our damnedest to get you that pennant."

Veeck looked around and was taking in the spectacle of Lupica seated on his perch and asked himself, "How the hell did I not think of this?"

"I read in the newspapers your wife is expecting," Veeck said. "I want you to know my staff will care for her when the time comes. I gave her my assistant's phone number. When the time comes, we will get an ambulance to your house."

Lupica beamed and got a little choked up.

"Thanks, Mr. Veeck," Lupica said.

"Charley," Veeck said, "Call me Bill. If you have any second thoughts, we won't hold it against you."

"Not a chance I'm coming down," Lupica answered. "I guess I'm close to the world record. And we got Feller. And Doby is looking like an all-star. We are only 4 1/2 games back, and Ole Satch is pitching tomorrow. Besides, I told the newspaper people I was doing this. How would it look if I backed out?"

"Bill," Lupica said in an almost hushed tone. "Did I tell you Satchel came and visited me?"

Day 64. Aug. 3

Sportswriter Red Smith of the New York Herald Tribune came to interview Lupica.

Smith could see Lupica from the street, his feet dangling off the perch, playing catch with a young boy on the road as both threw a ball covered in black wire tape.

Smith arrived and signed the guest book to see Lupica. He was the 6,000th guest. Smith reviewed the registry and saw visitors from Belgium, South Africa, and Canada signed.

"This," Smith thought, "is bigger than I thought."

Lupica's business partner Ben DiMarco spotted Smith reviewing the registry.

"There are folks from 42 states so far," DiMarco told Smith. "There's one guy in the Cleveland newspaper who said today he's going to serve Charley a subpoena and make him come down to testify. He's just doing that to get Charley off his pole."

DiMarco was angry.

"Well, Charley doesn't know this guy or anything about this phony case. It's just a rat trying to make a name for himself," DiMarco said.

The 49-year-old Smith made his way to the roof, saw the wobbly ladder, and decided to conduct his interview on the roof.

"I have a syndicated column," Smith said.

"How many people will read it?" Lupica asked.

"It's picked up by more than 500 newspapers worldwide," Smith said.

Lupica nodded. Now he realized why so many salesmen had asked him to hold signs. He refused them all. This wasn't about money.

Every couple of minutes, a car would drive by on the street and honk in support or a passerby would yell encouragement to Lupica, and he would yell back.

Day 68. Aug. 7

At the top of the ladder, Ben DiMarco handed Lupica a sandwich.

"Charley, our business has been incredible since you came up here. The crowds have been huge. We can't keep stuff on the shelves," DiMarco said.

Lupica and DiMarco were drawn to approaching flashing lights.

An ambulance pulled up on the street below and a bulging Gusty Lupica gingerly levered herself from the passenger seat onto the sidewalk.

"It's time!" Charley's pregnant wife yelled. "It's coming!"

On the way to the hospital, Gusty had asked the ambulance driver if they could swing by to alert her husband.

"How'd you get the ambulance?" Charley asked.

"Mr. Veeck!" Gusty yelled back.

She paused.

"Charley, I decided we will name the baby after you if it's a boy. We can name the next one 'Boudreau,'" Gusty yelled.

Charley nodded with a look of acceptance.

Gusty maneuvered herself back in the passenger seat, and the ambulance drove off and went about 20 yards before stopping and going in reverse.

Charley wondered if he should be worried until Gusty stuck her head out the window and looked at Charley, and yelled, "Go Tribe!"

Charley's eyes welled up in tears as he watched the ambulance head off in the direction of the hospital.

The next day's birth notices in the newspaper told readers that Gusty Lupica gave birth to an eight-pound baby boy name Charley Lupica Jr.

Day 117. Sept. 25

When Charley Lupica climbed to the top of the pole on May 31, he figured he'd last no more than 30 days.

On the 72nd day, Lupica set the world record for pole sitting, which had become a fad during The Great Depression.

On the 80th day, a TIME magazine reporter and photographer visited, conducting an interview and taking photos for a spread in the nationwide weekly.

On the 106th day, a dentist had to climb up and temporarily fix an aching tooth.

Now, on day 117, the epic campaign ended in defeat. The Indians were mathematically eliminated from the pennant race.

Lupica was physically and emotionally washed out. The media pressure that elevated him to a folk hero had kept him up in his 60-foot perch far longer than he wanted or imagined.

The previous night, the temperature dropped to 41 degrees, and all

Lupica could think about was being back in a cozy, warm, dry bed.

Lupica had planned to crawl down the ladder once the season was over.

But Bill Veeck had other plans.

On that day at 9 a.m., a construction crew showed up with a crane and a giant hydraulic lift truck which looked like an oversized forklift.

Lupica remained on his platform while the crane gently lifted it and the pole onto the lift vehicle, still standing erect.

Accompanied by a police motorcycle escort, passing motorists honking their horns and well-wishers cheering from crowded sidewalks, the heavy equipment moved down the city street carrying Charley on his still erect perch. It was an eight-mile trip from 118th Street to Cleveland Municipal Stadium.

Despite the 117-day endurance test, Lupica stood from his perch and waved to the crowd of gawkers like a returning prince.

The hydraulic lift set Lupica's still-vertical conglomeration in a prepared spot in the left-field stands, where Charley had a perfect view of the field from 20 feet in the air. It was 11 a.m., the stands began to fill in time for the first pitch at 1 p.m.

An hour before the game started, 34,000 fans had filled the stadium, plus one more fan 20 feet above them.

The visiting Detroit Tigers finished batting practice and left the field. But the Cleveland Indians didn't take the field for their batting practice.

Instead, Veeck went to home plate, where a microphone awaited him.

"We were eliminated from the pennant race," Veeck announced, his voice carrying over the public address system.

There was a mixture of catcalls and boos from the disappointed crowd.

"We couldn't keep up with the Yankees. And I'm sorry. But I am grateful for the greatest fans in the league," Veeck said.

The crowd roared its approval.

"But for 117 days, one fan has shown his love for this ball club. And today, he's at the game," Veeck said as he pointed to Lupica in his flagpole, and the fans cheered wildly.

A stunned Lupica removed his cap and waved to the fans, turning left and right to address them all.

"Mr. Lupica. It's time to come down from your flagpole!" Veeck said as a standing ovation drowned out his voice.

The hydraulic lift picked up the pole, and as the outfield gates opened, it carried Lupica all the way to home plate. There Charley's wife and four children were waiting.

Veeck had arranged to have two nurses and a doctor on hand in case Lupica needed medical attention.

Lupica made it down the ladder without help. But as he took his first steps in nearly four months, he stumbled, and the nurses did their best to hold him up.

Lupica made it to home plate.

He hugged his wife, turned around, bent over, and kissed home plate.

The crowd rose again to give him another standing ovation.

Veeck had given the family gifts, including children's bikes and a new television and a better radio for Lupica to follow his favorite team.

Then Veeck took the microphone.

"Now, fans. We took Mr. Lupica and his flagpole with a crane and a truck. But he doesn't have a ride home. Any volunteers?" Veeck asked.

Laughs accompanied an abundant scattering of volunteers calling back from the stands.

"What? Nobody?" Veeck asked with a wink.

Then, on cue, a new 1949 Pontiac Chieftain sedan came onto the field.

"I'll tell you what, Charley. I'm so touched by your loyalty that we got you your ride back home," Veeck said. "Charley, enjoy your new car!"

The crowd gave out a roar. Lupica was stunned.

Lupica touched the car with a wondrous 'Is this really mine?' look. He smiled, looked up at the fans, and waved as they roared and clapped for him. He got inside the car and looked around. He grabbed the steering wheel and jumped up and down in his seat like an excited little boy.

CHAPTER 28

Stepin Fetchit Isn't His Real Name

Oct. 1, 1949

Just one more game remained in the 1949 season.

Cleveland Indian pitcher Mike Garcia led his team to victory against the Detroit Tigers with a 4-0 shutout performance. Now, he was being congratulated in the clubhouse.

The 1949 Indians' roster was constructed by owner Bill Veeck and was the most diverse in baseball. It included four Black players – Satchel Paige, Larry Doby, Luke Easter and Minnie Minoso. There were also two Mexican players – Mike Garcia, born in California, and Roberto Avila, born in Veracruz, Mexico.

Garcia served as the translator for Avila, who was just the fourth player born in Mexico to play in the major leagues. Avila couldn't speak a word of English.

As Satchel Paige congratulated Garcia, Avila said something in Spanish.

Paige looked questioningly at Garcia.

"What is Beto saying?" Paige asked, referring to Avila in the Spanish word for "Bobby."

Garcia smiled.

"Satch, the same thing he's been asking me all year: How old are you really?" Garcia said.

Teammate Bob Lemon jumped into the conversation.

"They mention Satch in the Old Testament!" Lemon said as the players laughed.

Paige looked at Lemon.

"You talk like you pitch! Loud but not smart!" Paige said. "What do you know about anybody's age?"

Lemon smiled.

"All I know is there was a colored man on that barnstorming team of yours out on the coast last winter. He told me he was 47 years old, and I heard you call him 'son.'"

"Shucks," Paige said in a defeated tone.

The end-of-the-season road trip in Detroit was a special occasion for the four Black players. Cleveland Indians owner Bill Veeck was putting them in a deluxe hotel that accepted Black players. The five-star Gotham Hotel was a reward for a good season.

It was 8 p.m. when Larry Doby entered his fancy hotel room in Detroit that he would share with Satchel Paige that night.

Doby sat on his bed savoring the luxury of the Gotham Hotel. This was the Taj Mahal compared to the flop houses where he and his Black teammates usually stayed. The beds here didn't smell of urine, and there was no sign of bed bugs that infested so many of the low-grade rooms where Blacks were allowed.

The Gotham Hotel was one of the half-dozen Detroit hotels that accepted Blacks. Just six years earlier, Black businessmen John White, Walter Norwood and Irving Roane had purchased the hotel and opened it up to Blacks.

Blacks were still barred from most hotels in the city. For years, Blacks were not allowed to sit in the premiere boxed seats at Briggs Stadium, home of the Detroit Tigers.

Doby looked around. The only sign Paige had been in the room was a revolver Paige always kept with him at night. The gun sat on the small nightstand between the two beds. Doby could see the bullets in its cylinder and it made him nervous.

Larry Doby was expecting a phone call from Jackie Robinson at 8:30 p.m. It would be the highlight of the evening for a young Black player isolated from his white teammates.

Robinson had played four sports when he attended college at UCLA before becoming the first Black player in Major League Baseball. One of those four sports was basketball.

Robinson and Doby's relationship preceded both of their entries into Major League Baseball. In 1946, Doby had played on Jackie Robinson's Black barnstorming baseball team that played against white players. Robinson and Doby were friendly, but not close friends.

In 1946, a year before he was rushed into the majors by Bill Veeck, Doby had sought a spot with his hometown Paterson Crescents basketball team, part of the professional American Basketball League. But Blacks were no more welcome in professional basketball at that time than they were in baseball.

In 1947, Doby connected with Robinson and played on the same semi-pro basketball team located in Canton, Ohio.

More recently, Robinson invited Doby to go barnstorming on a Negro League baseball team he had put together that would play in the fall of 1949. Doby agreed and would join Robinson's Black Brooklyn Dodgers' teammates Roy Campanella and Don Newcombe. But Paige hadn't been invited, which Doby found curious, considering the crowds he had been drawing for decades.

Embittered by years in the wilderness of Black baseball, Paige harbored a deep resentment of Robinson's selection as Major League Baseball's first Black player. Doby had no problem with Robinson getting the fame and attention being the first had brought him.

On this night's phone call, Robinson would go over the details of the upcoming barnstorming tour.

Doby was sitting on his bed when Paige walked in an hour later.

"Hey, Satch," Doby said. "You just missed Jackie. We had a long talk."

Paige nodded.

"What is going on with Jackie?" Paige asked.

"He's in Philadelphia," Doby replied. "He just heard Ben Chapman may be looking to get back into the majors."

Ben Chapman was the former manager of the Philadelphia Phillies who bombarded Robinson with racial insults in 1947, during the rookie's fifth game as a major leaguer. Chapman yelled racial slurs from the dugout all game at Robinson and accused him of sleeping with the white wives of his teammates. The newspaper reports of such horrid verbal attacks caught the attention of the baseball commissioner Happy Chandler.

The commissioner's response was to order Chapman and Robinson to pose together for a photo in May 1947 that would be distributed to the newspapers. Neither Chapman nor Robinson wanted to do it but went along to a point. They refused to shake hands but did agree to hold a bat together while posing for the photo.

Chapman was fired a year later in July 1948, and became the owner of a minor league team in Alabama. Robinson was naturally relieved he no longer had to deal with the man. But in August 1949, it was announced Chapman's team was being sold and that he wanted to return to managing in the major leagues.

"So, Jackie is worried Chapman might be back with another National League team," Doby told Paige.

Doby was interested in a feud between Robinson, Feller, and Paige. But he wasn't going to mention Paige's involvement.

"Hey, why do Mr. Feller and Jackie not get along?" Doby asked.

At that moment, Paige was rummaging through his suitcase looking for his stash of cash. He smiled and pulled out a wad of money.

"They have a poker game going on in the penthouse," Paige said without looking at Doby. "I'd ask you to go, but I know you don't gamble."

"Helyn would kill me!" Doby said with a laugh.

"I told Mr. Veeck I'd stay out of trouble," Doby said. "He said I couldn't fight back or associate with Caucasian women."

Paige froze.

"Can't associate with Caucasian women?" Paige said, shaking his head. "Those are my biggest fans."

No longer distracted, Paige waved the wad of money at Doby.

"Here's why Feller and Jackie don't get along," Paige said. "Money."

Doby sat up.

Paige continued: "In 1946, we were barnstorming in Los Angeles and drawing huge crowds. Jackie thought he deserved as much as a cut as me and Feller."

Doby nodded.

"Jackie is from Los Angeles," Doby said. "He went to UCLA. That makes sense."

Paige gave an exaggerated frown.

"Son, did you see how many fans came out when I pitched here earlier this season?" Paige asked. "It was standing room only. Feller and I were doing good business. Jackie wasn't even in the majors yet."

"Satch," Doby said. "Can you take the gun with you? I don't want it on the night desk."

"If anything moves at night, you'll be glad I have it," Paige said.

"What if I move at night?" Doby shot back.

Paige ignored Doby's request. He took a newspaper from his duffle bag and handed it to Doby.

"Here, you can read this," Paige said. "I got it because there's an article on me. Stepin Fetchit is trying to star as me in a movie about my life. Who knows? Maybe we could get a mannequin to play you."

Paige laughed. Doby took the newspaper.

"Stepin Fetchit would be perfect for you," Doby said with a hint of condescension.

Paige picked up on Doby's disrespectful tone, which wasn't Doby's style.

Paige sat on the edge of the bed.

"Larry Doby. What's eating you?" Paige asked.

Doby set down the newspaper.

"I heard your interview today with the sportswriters. The whole, 'They ain't gonna hit Ole Satch no how,' routine," Doby said.

He paused.

"You are adding to the racism by encouraging the Negro stereotypes," Doby said. "When you come in the dugout and do the Amos 'n' Andy routine … You and Stepin Fetchit and the 'world's laziest man' routine."

Amos 'n' Andy was a popular radio show throughout the 1930s and 1940s about two Black characters voiced by white actors.

Many Blacks found it to be racist and objected to its crude stereotyping.

Doby and Paige admired each other but weren't really friends. Doby had great respect for Paige's baseball accomplishments and summoning the courage to confront him had not been easy.

"You are one of the most successful Negro athletes ever," Doby said, his tone full of respect. "And you speak like you're a kindergarten dropout."

"You just tell people what they want to hear," Doby said.

Doby was repeating a sentiment that was growing in the Black community.

In October 1948, Black newspaper editor William Walker of Cleveland's Call & Post wrote a piece chastising Paige on this account: "There are many Negro fans who are hoping that the ageless pitcher will not again be a member of the Cleveland team. There is much resentment against Paige for his constant clowning and fitting perfectly into the Amos 'n' Andy type. There is no question, but Paige's continued presence on a major league team will do much to discredit Negro players."

Views like Walker's were becoming more prevalent.

The difference between Doby and Paige on how Blacks should present themselves in public was an indication of how World War II had marked a watershed in Black Americans' struggles for equality.

After the war's victorious conclusion, it became impossible for most white Americans to deny the significant contributions and sacrifices their Black countrymen had made. In 1948, three years after the Japanese surrendered in 1945, President Harry Truman signed an executive order to desegregate the military.

Satchel Paige and Larry Doby were on opposite sides of a

generation gap created by these world-shaking events. Before the war, Blacks had little cause for optimism regarding their chances of achieving equality and civil rights. Little had changed since the failed attempts of the post-Civil War "reconstruction" era to advance fairness for Black Americans.

Paige, born and raised in the South and 17 years older than Doby, had far less optimism about the plight of the Black man in America.

In 1942, Paige told a New York Daily News reporter that mixed-race baseball would not work, a viewpoint that outraged the Black civil rights movement.

"You might as well be honest about it," Paige was quoted as saying about integrating Major League Baseball in an article that was picked up by newspapers across the country. "There would be plenty of problems, not only in the South, where the colored boys wouldn't be able to stay and travel with the teams in spring training, but in the North, where they couldn't stay or eat with them in many places. All the nice statements in the world from both sides aren't going to knock out Jim Crow."

That was the world in which Satchel Paige grew up and came of age.

Members of Larry Doby's generation now had a different outlook. Like him, many had served in the war. They realized it had become much more difficult for the nation to continue to deny their civil rights.

Doby sat back in his bed. He felt relieved he finally said what weighed on his mind for months. He opened the newspaper to the article on Paige.

"I believe in carrying myself with pride to seek respect and speak with some of the intelligence I was born with," Doby said.

Paige was silent for a moment.

"Stepin Fetchit isn't his real name," Paige said. "It's Lincoln Theodore Monroe Andrew Perry."

Paige stopped to think about all the names.

"And he's got twice as many cars as names!" Paige said, laughing. "And he's the only Negro I know whose made more money than me."

Paige nodded in admiration of that accomplishment.

"Laziest man in the world? That man did nine movies in 1929. I know. I counted them once when we were out and about in LA," Paige said.

Paige stared down Doby.

"But Lincoln doesn't count his movies. He counts the money. He says he's made a million. He's the world's laziest man? He's the world's richest Negro. He owns 12 cars, including a Rolls Royce," Paige said.

Paige also had his own stable of luxury cars. It was a big reason he was always looking for the next high-stakes card game.

"The problem with Stepin Fetchit is he's broke. Women, cars and the horses - if one doesn't get you, the others will," Paige said with a laugh. "Don't I know it?"

As he was preparing to leave for a night of gambling, Paige took a stylish hat out and put it on.

"How do I look, young Mr. Doby?" Paige asked with a smile.

Doby nodded.

"Like a million dollars, Stepin," Doby said, breaking out in a smile.

As Paige turned and went to the door to leave for the night, he stopped.

"You know, young Larry, I pitched here in Detroit before," Paige said.

Doby was surprised.

"When?" he asked.

"It was back in 1941," Paige said. "I pitched against the Chicago American Giants. We had 34,000 people show up. It was the first time a Negro team had played in Briggs in more than 20 years."

Walter Briggs became the owner of the Tigers in 1919, and until 1941 had never allowed the Negro League teams to lease his stadium. No other Detroit area venue had near the capacity as Briggs Stadium. While the Detroit Tigers' games sometimes attracted as few as 2,800 fans, games between the Black teams consistently drew 30,000 fans, almost all Black people.

A week after Paige's 1941 victory in Briggs Stadium, the Detroit owner announced that no more games between Black teams would be allowed at his venue.

"The Tigers owner was shocked at how popular our teams were," Paige said. "And he wasn't going to be a part of that anymore."

Paige's smile disappeared.

"Go ahead and fight the system, Larry," Paige said. "I'm going to keep working it. My way will make you a whole lot more money."

CHAPTER 29

If Marriage Is Grand, A Divorce Is Ten Grand

Jan. 18, 1949

Bill Veeck peered out the cab window during the ride from the airport, excited by his first visit to Hollywood. He was absorbing a tourist's view of Tinseltown.

The taxi stopped in front of a small, one-level office building at the edge of a local business district. The building was wedged between a pharmacy and an empty diner.

Veeck entered the office of Herbert Kline, a moppy-haired, 40-year-old film director.

The baseball team owner was surprised a Hollywood director had such a small office.

"Hi, I'm Bill Veeck," he announced.

Kline was sitting at his desk reading a contract. He put it down and got up to meet Veeck.

"I was hoping I may get to meet George Brent," Veeck said. "I'm a big fan."

"I'm sorry, Mr. Veeck, but he won't be able to make it. He's got another film he's finishing up," Kline said.

"Please, call me Bill," Veeck said. "Not any chance of Bette Davis showing up, I suppose?"

Kline laughed.

"No. Brent hasn't worked with Miss Davis in several years," Kline said.

The film director realized Veeck wasn't aware that Brent's star had fallen since the war ended. The actor was now living off low-budget bombs. This next proposed movie with Veeck would likely be another one.

In his earlier days, Kline had far bigger ambitions. At age 29, Kline pretended to be a member of the American Nazi Party to film Adolf Hitler's invasion of Czechoslovakia. He released that documentary in 1939 under the title "Crisis."

This project that brought Veeck to Hollywood was to be called "The Kid From Cleveland" and was far less ambitious. It was a quick cash-in on the success of the 1948 World Champion Indians.

The gimmick was to feature some team players and even the owner in cameo roles.

"So, is this Hollywood?" Veeck asked.

Kline shook his head.

"It's officially unincorporated. More LA County. Not really the jurisdiction of the police," Kline said.

Veeck limped over to Kline's desk.

Kline pulled out a document.

"So, let's get down to business," Kline said. "You've seen the proposal?"

Veeck nodded.

"It looks great," Veeck said.

"Here's the idea," Kline said. "A kid sneaks into the baseball park and is playing hooky. He gets caught by stadium guards. The team takes him under their wing, and he flies straight."

"There'd be cameos from the players," Kline said. "And you."

"What about Satchel Paige and Larry Doby?" Veeck asked.

"We can include them, too," Kline said. "Negroes aren't a problem.

We can even have a scene where Satch shows the kid how to throw one of his trademark pitches. LA loves Satch."

Kline put the paper down.

"Mr. Veeck, the cameos are unpaid, but you get the standard guild rate as a percentage of the profits," Kline said.

Veeck and Kline finished the initial paperwork to start filming the movie. They shook hands and Veeck departed.

On the sidewalk, Veeck spotted a college-aged man heading his way. Veeck, at first, thought he may have been an actor hoping for a role in the movie.

"Mr. Veeck! Mr. Veeck!" the man shouted.

Veeck stopped, and the man reached out to shake Veeck's hand.

"You're Mr. Veeck? Right?" the man asked.

Veeck nodded.

"Yes, I am," Veeck said.

The man took out an envelope and placed it in Veeck's hand.

"You've been served," the man said as he turned and walked away briskly.

Veeck was stunned. He opened the envelope and froze.

Two weeks later in Cleveland, Bill Veeck was sitting in the office of his attorney, Ed Lurie.

Veeck sat in a chair as Lurie hung up the phone.

"That was Bob Hope," Lurie said. "He says, 'Hi.'"

"Did you tell him about the movie?" Veeck asked.

Lurie grinned.

"He's got three movies coming out this year," Lurie said.

The lawyer grew serious as he opened a folder with Veeck's legal paperwork.

"I looked over the divorce filing by Eleanor," Lurie said. "Three kids and 14 years of marriage. She's claiming abandonment."

"I'm going to fight it," Veeck snapped.

"You want my advice, Bill?" Lurie asked.

"The free kind?" Veeck retorted.

"There's no way out of this. She's got a good case," Lurie said.

"For what you charge, I was hoping for something more agreeable," Veeck said.

"You pay a general manager to be agreeable. You pay me for the best legal advice in the city. And here it is. You spend every waking moment at the ballpark, and on the slight chance you aren't there, you're giving a speech to the chamber, the Elks, Kiwanis, or whatever group will pay to hear you. I mean, Christ, Bill, how many people even knew you were married? Unless they noticed the ring on your finger - not many," Lurie said.

The attorney paused for a second.

"I read in the newspaper that you said you give 500 speeches a year," Lurie said.

Veeck nodded.

"Well, you can bet that will be presented in court in meticulous detail," Lurie said. "Not to mention, you've been spending time with that model from the Ice Capades."

Veeck got defensive.

"She's a publicity aide. Before that job she was an unemployed model," Veeck said.

Lurie chuckled.

"An unemployed model? Hey, aren't we all?" he asked.

Lurie paused.

"How serious is it with this publicity aide?" Lurie asked.

"Serious," Veeck said.

Lurie nodded.

"Well, you are a resident of Arizona now, Bill. And Arizona law requires you to wait a year after a divorce to get remarried," Lurie explained. "You contest this, and it drags out. That's all the longer you can't get remarried. That won't make your unemployed model too happy."

Lurie then took a more serious tone.

"Bill, all your assets are tied up with the ball club. You will have to sell the Indians to pay off Eleanor. I don't see any way around it," he said.

Veeck sat quietly.

"Unlike the rest of the baseball owners, you don't have a brewery or a chewing gum company to diversify your income," Lurie told Veeck. "This is it. An ex-wife with three children - there's no other way. I'm sorry."

"Look at the bright side," Lurie said. "You bought the Indians for $1.5 million. You were offered $2.2 million last year and turned it down. You are not going to be on public assistance. You know the old joke. If marriage is grand, what is a divorce? ... Ten grand."

Veeck sat back in defeat. His world-champion baseball team was being taken away.

On Nov. 21, 1949, Veeck sold the Cleveland Indians for $2.2 million to a group of seven Cleveland businessmen.

"I need the money and a vacation," Veeck told the media why he was selling the team.

CHAPTER 30

Ole Satch's Release Ends Fiery Career

March 27, 1950

Hal Lebovitz ran up the stairs of the Cleveland News newsroom. His heart was racing as always when he had a big story to break. At his desk he inserted a sheet of paper in his typewriter.

"Got a front-page story," Lebovitz hollered to his editor without looking up. "Indians are going to release Satchel!"

Two years earlier, Lebovitz wrote a book on Satchel Paige to capitalize on the Cleveland Indians' World Series season. The 1948 book was just 118 pages with many photos and skipped over any mention of racism Paige had endured.

Now, Lebovitz believed he was writing Paige's baseball obituary.

"Ol' Satchel Paige has drawn his walking papers from the Cleveland Indians and probably is through as a major leaguer," Lebovitz typed.

The peppered-hair sportswriter leaned back in his chair.

"Headline: Satchel Paige's release Brings End to Legendary, Fiery Career," Lebovitz said out loud.

Lebovitz finished the story, handed it to his editor, and headed to Cleveland Municipal Stadium.

When Lebovitz arrived, Hank Greenberg, the Indians' general manager, and shortstop/manager Lou Boudreau were surrounded by a group of reporters.

"In order to make room for new men on our active roster, we believe it advisable to release Paige in view of his questionable physical condition," Greenberg told the reporters.

Lebovitz pulled aside Boudreau for a one-on-one interview.

"What's the reason for dumping Satch?" Lebovitz asked.

Boudreau paused. He knew Lebovitz had become close to Paige while working on the book.

"Hal, honestly, he's a problem child," Boudreau said. "He sets a bad example for the rest of the team. He misses trains and is late for games. He only looks out for himself. We will have a lot of young players up this year. We are giving them a chance. We need to build teamwork. How am I going to do that when Satchel comes strolling in an hour late?"

"Hank said it was because of his 'questionable physical condition,'" Lebovitz asked.

Boudreau shrugged.

"How old is the guy?" Boudreau asked. "Even Veeck wasn't sure. Come on. The man could be 60 years old, for all we know. We have some 20-year-old arms we need to get a look at. The Satchel Paige carnival is over."

At Satchel Paige's home in Kansas City, the phone rang. Paige picked up the phone, and Lebovitz broke the news.

Paige was quiet. He paused.

"Questionable physical condition?" Paige told Lebovitz. "They released me because I'm old? Age is a case of mind over matter. If I don't mind, it don't matter."

Paige hung up.

A string of editors complimented Lebovitz for his scoop. His byline would appear on the front page of the newspaper.

But that rush quickly gave way to a feeling of melancholy.

It finally hit Lebovitz how much he would miss being around

Satchel Paige.

Other sportswriters had joked with Lebovitz that Paige was Veeck's pet player. Now, without an advocate, Paige's playing days were over.

Two days later at his Kansas City home, Satchel Paige received a Western Union telegram from Veeck.

The telegram read: "As soon as I get another big-league club, you'll be back with me."

Paige folded the telegram and placed it in the Bible in his bedroom drawer.

His next step was to pick up the phone and call Abe Saperstein. He told him he was no longer a major league pitcher. Saperstein, who founded the Harlem Globetrotters, worked an occasional side job as Paige's booking agent, for which he received a percentage of Paige's gate revenues. Paige needed to line up barnstorming games to make money.

CHAPTER 31

The Greatest Promoter Of The 20th Century

Abe Saperstein was born in 1902 in East End of London, England, which was home to the poorest slums in the country. He was the eldest of eight children. In the midst of the city's effort to clear out the slums and force residents to relocate, Saperstein's family moved to Chicago in 1907. They lived in what was described as "the poor Jews' quarter" of the city.

Saperstein's father got a job as a tailor, but only after changing his surname to Schneider because the advertisement had stated, "no Jews allowed."

As a young man, Saperstein dropped out of the University of Illinois to support his family.

In 1926, Saperstein formed the New York Harlem Globetrotters and picked the name because he wanted the predominantly all-white audience to know he had a Black team.

In the Globetrotters' first game in Hinckley, Illinois, they made just $8 [$133 in 2023 dollars], which had to be split among the five players and Saperstein.

Bill Veeck was born in 1914 and his father was a sportswriter and the son idolized his father.

When Bill Veeck Jr. was four years old, his father was hired in 1917 as the vice president of Major League Baseball's Chicago Cubs.

The family lived a comfortable upper middle-class life. They lived in Hinsdale, Illinois, an affluent community 16 miles from Chicago. It had a library, theater and country club and golf course.

His father sent Bill Jr. to the Los Alamos Ranch School, a private school in New Mexico with a college curriculum mixed with an active outdoor life.

Veeck left that school without graduating and attended Kenyon College in Ohio where he spent most of his time partying after joining the Beta Theta Pi fraternity.

When his father was diagnosed with cancer, Bill Jr. left college and returned home. The 19-year-old son was at the bedside of his father when he died in 1933.

By age 27, Veeck had worked for the Chicago Cubs, and used all the contacts he made through Major League Baseball to get others to finance his purchase of the minor league Milwaukee Brewers for $40,000 [$850,000 in 2023 dollars].

Veeck had hired the Globetrotters to play before the games of the minor league Milwaukee Brewers, the first team he bought in 1940. From that point on, Veeck and Saperstein became close allies.

In 1951, Hollywood made a movie about the Harlem Globetrotters. The same year, the Globetrotters played before 75,000 fans in West Berlin's Olympic Stadium. Then in 1952, the Globetrotters played before Pope Pius XII. The team reached worldwide fame.

It had also come a long way from Mason City, Iowa 20 years earlier.

During the early days, Globetrotters' tours stopped at hundreds of small towns like Mason City.

On March 12, 1930, Abe Saperstein drove his van into the center of town with the fuel gauge reading a quarter tank. It was 8 p.m., the streets of Mason City were empty, the skies were cloudy and the entire block was dark.

Over two days, Saperstein had driven from Milwaukee to Dubuque, Iowa, and now to Mason City, putting 342 miles on the van. The Globetrotters would play three games over three nights here.

It was the team's first visit to Mason City, and a new city brought many issues. In segregated America, the thorniest issue was finding a place where Black players could eat and sleep.

Blacks had to watch their step in this world.

For example, Jefferson, Iowa, was a "sundown town" where Blacks had to be outside city limits by dusk.

Eight months earlier, the editors of Jefferson's local newspaper wrote an opinion piece about southern lynchings.

"Next time northern folks read of a Negro lynching south of the Mason & Dixon line, let us take it more calmly. They are no worse than we are up north, in fact, as relates to the Negro race, we doubt if they are as bad. At least they do the job more systematically and confine their anger alone to the criminal. Up north here we run amuck."

The closest Black family Saperstein could find able to host the team overnight was just outside Waterloo, about 81 miles from Mason City.

Earlier in the day, Saperstein had called the local newspaper's sportswriters to alert them of the Globetrotters' visit. Their stories parroted as fact Saperstein's glowing reports about his Globetrotters, including that they were based out of Harlem, in New York. Abe Saperstein was actually working out of Chicago, but he kept Harlem in the team name as a cue his team was Black.

Saperstein's on-the-road routine was to arrive at the next event's location a day early to post flyers around town. On this night, he posted more than 100 on business doors and light poles.

In the depth of The Great Depression, he preferred posting the announcements in the downtown district, where it was far more likely those seeing them had jobs.

Saperstein composed the flyers himself. They included the dubious boast that the Globetrotters had 103-5 win-loss record. This conveniently left out some of their defeats to local clubs.

He also arranged for an all-Native American team to play against the Globetrotters in this game. He shamelessly exploited the most extreme stereotypes as part of the draw.

For example, one flyer mentioned that the Native American team was led by Chief Steffes, a well-known Iowa basketball player who had bounced around various semi-pro teams.

The flyer stated Chief Steffes' teammates included players with the stage names Little Horse, Big Eagle and Lone Wolf.

The promotions played on the ignorance of townsfolk with limited exposure to Blacks or Native Americans. Both races were a novelty in most small Midwestern towns, which made a basketball game between the two races a hot ticket.

Mason City was a town of 23,000 with just 350 Black people. Native Americans in Iowa had been relocated to reservations, and no organized tribes lived in the state by 1850. Once a year, Native American tribes came to Mason City for a summer festival. The federal government had only recognized the country's Native Americans as U.S. citizens just seven years earlier.

The Globetrotters won the game, 30-16. Saperstein suited up and played and scored two baskets. But the star of the game was Globetrotter Albert Pullins, a high school star from Chicago. Pullins entertained the crowd with fanciful dribbling, windmill windup passes to teammates, and even connected on a half-court shot. These were basketball feats never witnessed before by the all-white crowd.

The game drew 600 fans, near capacity for the YMCA gym.

Saperstein was one of the greatest promoters of the 20th century.

But he was also one of the more controversial due to his methods.

Besides the Globetrotters, he was also the promoter of the Black baseball team Zulu Cannibal Giants.

Throughout the 1940s, the Zulu Cannibal Giants were a group of Black players who dressed in grass skirts, wore white "war paint" on their faces, played shirtless and barefoot with ankle bracelets, nose rings and earrings, wigs and wielded their custom-made bats that resembled clubs. They also played by stage names such as Nyassas, Limpopo, Wahoo and Impo. Buck O'Neil, one of the greatest Negro League players, played on the Zulu Cannibal Giants. O'Neil, who completed two years of college in the 1930s, was Limpopo. When O'Neil was a child, his father was jailed because the Florida county where they lived needed road workers and would arrest innocent Black men to use as free labor. O'Neil wasn't worried about racial stereotypes. He did what he needed to do to survive.

"Fans will be surprised by the fleetness of these big-footed Africans by the manner in which they steal bases and understand their own crude baseball signals," Georgia's Macon Telegraph newspaper reported in 1949. "Be sure to bring your children out to see Chief Wahoo do his individual show during the baseball game."

Chief Wahoo's act included war cries. Zulu teammates would stage fights with spears and shields during games.

"All of the Zulu clowns are built of giant stature, with exceptionally large muscles, hard-battered faces and large feet," the Johnson City Press of Tennessee wrote in 1948.

White newspapers ran quarter-page ads of the Zulu Cannibal Giants in full attire posing as attacking Zulu warriors.

But by the 1940s, exploiting such racial stereotypes had become the target of increasing criticism and Saperstein found himself under that microscope.

Civil rights activists like Black sportswriter Wendell Smith wrote columns critical of the Zulu Cannibal Giants.

Many of the Black owners in the Negro League voted against hiring Saperstein in 1941 to work public relations for their all-star game because he had a history of "ridiculing Negro baseball" by promoting racist tropes such as the Zulu Cannibal Giants.

And some Black sportswriters saw Saperstein in a negative light. Andrew Young, Black sports editor of the Los Angeles Sentinel, called Saperstein an "exploiter of Negro athletes" in a 1946 editorial.

Abe Saperstein and Bill Veeck first crossed paths in Chicago. In addition to running the Globetrotters, Saperstein also owned the all-Black Chicago American Giants and had other interests in Negro League baseball.

Veeck had worked as the club treasurer for the Chicago Cubs when his father was president of the team. He was fascinated by the Globetrotters.

When he and Saperstein met, a friendship was formed.

Newspaper reporters often characterized them as the Abbott & Costello of sports promoters.

Yet, in one respect, they were very different.

When Bill Veeck left Cleveland, the city's Black newspaper, The Call & Post, paid homage to him on Nov. 26, 1949.

"Before Veeck, there were no Negro players, no Negro vendors, no Negro special policeman, no Negro musicians, no Negro grounds crew members, no Negro employees in the club rooms, or on the public relations staff," Black editor William Walker wrote. "Now, as Bill Veeck leaves, Negroes are integrated into the activities of the Cleveland Indians to a greater extent than any other major league organization. ... He joined more readily in the NAACP drives than do some Negro leaders."

Bill Veeck's views on race had been evolving as he became increasingly exposed to the unfairness Blacks faced. Veeck didn't just sign Doby in 1947 and Satchel Paige in 1948. He befriended them. In 1949, Veeck posed for a NAACP recruiting poster with Paige and Doby. He also became the godfather to Doby's daughter, Christine.

But while Veeck was transitioning into a civil rights activist, Saperstein remained what he had always been – a self-interested mercenary. Still friends, Veeck saw Saperstein in a different light, as a businessman who didn't see the unfairness of the environment he worked in, only profits and gains he could reap.

Saperstein worked as Satchel Paige's agent when Veeck signed Paige in 1948. When Paige became the first Black pitcher in the American League, Saperstein collected $15,000 for arranging the deal.

Bill Veeck and Saperstein hooked up again in 1950, after Veeck had sold the Cleveland Indians. Veeck was out of baseball for the first time in nine years.

When sportswriters would call looking for an easy column, Veeck would tell them he was "unemployed" and "just being a bum."

But nothing could have been further from the truth. Veeck was about to get a courtside view of the integration of another sport – professional basketball. The experience would put a strain on his lifelong friendship with Saperstein.

CHAPTER 32

The Harlem Globetrotters' Empire

Abe Saperstein grew money-making ideas like a starfish grows legs: If one idea fell off, another would grow in its place.

He was a relentless promoter with a stake in almost every venture related to professional Black athletes. At various times, he had been a scout and owner of Negro League teams. Saperstein even launched his own Negro League team in the state of California, although it collapsed after just a few months.

Goose Tatum, one of the more notable Globetrotters due to his comic routines, was discovered by Saperstein in 1942 while scouting Negro League baseball.

Starting in 1926, the Harlem Globetrotters were one of his most successful ventures. They were arguably the best professional basketball team in America and had grown from a small-town gimmick to a big draw in big city arenas.

The Globetrotters traveled the country playing against local non-professional teams that often included former college players. In the early post World War II years, the team also played a role in the survival of a new professional basketball league comprised of all-white teams.

The precursor of today's National Basketball Association was the Basketball Association of America, started in 1946. It became the NBA in 1950 after merging with the National Basketball League, which was founded in 1937.

Aside from the Harlem Globetrotters, at that time professional basketball was not nearly as popular as it would later become.

In 1948, the Harlem Globetrotters had a game with the Basketball Association of America champions, the Minneapolis Lakers. The game was billed as a world championship, and the Globetrotters were on a 102-game winning streak. The Globetrotters were an all-Black team playing the all-white Lakers.

The game was played in Chicago. The Globetrotters had to stay in a segregated hotel on the South Side of Chicago. The rooms were small and the beds were in poor condition.

The all-white Lakers stayed in the luxurious Morrison Hotel that had turned away a Black actress a month earlier. In 1963, the Morrison Hotel was criticized for displaying Black jockey figurines at its entrance for the NAACP convention it was hosting.

The game drew 18,000 people even though it was an exhibition. That was twice the crowd the premiere professional league, the Basketball Association of America, would draw.

The Globetrotters won 61-59 when Ermer Robinson made a 30-foot shot at the buzzer.

On Jan. 1, 1950, the Globetrotters filled New York's Madison Square Garden with 19,000 fans, plus another 10,000 people who were turned away as the game was sold out.

By comparison, the new National Basketball Association was struggling. On April 16, Game 4 of its 1950 championship between Minneapolis and Syracuse drew 10,512 fans.

The NBA survived due to the relationship formed with Abe Saperstein's Harlem Globetrotters. It involved basketball double headers. The first game was played between two all-white NBA teams, and the second game featured the far more popular Harlem Globetrotters. At most of the events, Globetrotter fans would start filing in during the third quarter of the NBA's earlier game.

In 1950, Veeck and Saperstein combined to pull off another basketball tour for the Globetrotters. They would play a series of games against college all stars. The all-star team consisted of college seniors no longer eligible to compete on their school teams. Bill Veeck had helped organize the tour covering 16 cities over 17 days in April.

For Abe Saperstein, the tour meant a manic schedule, but he was a person who didn't believe in taking days off. By then, the Harlem Globetrotters had become an international sensation, and Saperstein was riding high as basketball's most influential power broker.

The Globetrotters' game on April 16 against the college all stars featured Sam Jethroe who tossed-up the jump ball to start the game. Jethroe was the first Black player for Major League Baseball's Boston Braves. Along with Jackie Robinson, Jethroe was one of three Black players who in 1945 were invited to the sham Boston Red Sox tryout.

Bill Veeck was always finding ways to promote Black pioneers.

Veeck and Saperstein were both present for that April 16 Globetrotters' game against the college all stars at the Boston Garden. And so was Walter Brown, the owner of the Boston Celtics.

While the color barrier had fallen in Major League Baseball, the professional basketball leagues were still all-white. That was about to change, and with it the Globetrotters' monopoly on outstanding young Black players.

Saperstein's attitude was that he had a proprietary claim on Black players coming out of college for his Globetrotters.

At that Boston Garden game on April 16 with the college all-star team, the Globetrotter's Nat Sweetwater Clifton had scored 27 points and the Globetrotters won 72-59. Clifton was in his fourth year as a star with the team, but Saperstein had limited him to successive one-year contracts.

Boston Celtics owner Walter Brown wanted Clifton to play for the Celtics. Brown and the Celtics new head coach Red Auerbach were determined to improve the team and were set on signing Black players to help make it happen. While there had been a national movement to integrate baseball, nothing comparable was underway in the less-popular sport of basketball.

Word of discussions between NBA teams and Black basketball players became public knowledge when a March 19 New York News Service article previewing the upcoming NBA draft mentioned the league may soon have its first Black players.

"There may even be a couple of Negro players in the league next year, for the first time," the article stated. "Chuck Cooper, Duquesne's high-jumping, 6-foot-5 center, will be sought by everyone, though there are rumors he will end up touring with the Harlem Globetrotters."

That was the trigger that angered Abe Saperstein the day before that April 16 college all-star game. Chuck Cooper happened to be the lone Black player on the college team. But for this game only, Saperstein moved him onto the Globetrotters' roster.

The seasoned promoter was sending a message to the new NBA and the Celtics owner Walter Brown. The NBA's draft was just nine days away and Saperstein didn't want one of its teams poaching Globetrotter players or snatching a Black college player for the still all-white NBA.

In addition to moving Cooper to the Globetrotters' roster, Saperstein also made a phone call to NBA president Maurice Podoloff. It led to a May 4 meeting in the NBA's New York offices with Saperstein, Podoloff and Walter Brown.

CHAPTER 33

Don't You Know He's A Colored Boy?

On April 25, 1950, in the second round of the National Basketball Association's college draft, the Boston Celtics drafted Chuck Cooper from Duquesne University.

"Don't you know he's a colored boy?" one of the NBA owners asked Boston Celtics owner Walter Brown after he made the pick.

"I don't care if he's striped, plaid or polka dot, so long as he can play," Brown replied.

But Walter Brown now had to face the consequences of crossing Abe Saperstein.

Saperstein had clout with the NBA mainly because of the extra revenue its teams picked up by playing double header games with his Globetrotters.

Professional basketball was not popular at the time. When the Basketball Association of America was launched in 1946, it wasn't to meet a market demand for more basketball. Instead, it was a way by which ice hockey arena owners hoped to boost revenue by hosting basketball games.

In 1949, the Basketball Association of America and the National Basketball League merged to create the National Basketball Association. There were 17 teams the first year, but four departed in the second year with talk of starting a new league. The New York Knicks were a vital team to the NBA's future because of its arena, Madison Square Garden. And the Knicks were threatening to leave the NBA.

And now Saperstein was threatening to boycott NBA arenas if their teams drafted Black players.

That was the backdrop for the May 4 meeting Abe Saperstein

demanded with Walter Brown and NBA commissioner Maurice Podoloff in the NBA's New York office.

Podoloff, 60, was a distinguished attorney and the president of the American Hockey League. He had been appointed head of the Basketball Association of America in 1946 and now oversaw the NBA.

He had asked the Boston Celtics owner to arrive an hour before Saperstein. Brown was accompanied by his new head coach, Red Auerbach.

Basketball may not have been Podoloff's first love (that was hockey), but he was bright and knew the situation had to be defused.

From behind his desk, Podoloff delivered his ruling to Walter Brown.

"Here's how we're going to resolve this," Podoloff began.

"First, you'll be able to keep Chuck Cooper, but you will have to pay Abe. Second, I'm canceling your contract with the Globetrotters' Sweetwater Clifton. We'll let the New York Knicks negotiate a deal with him. That will make the Knicks happy and keep them in the league," Podoloff said.

The Celtics new head coach Auerbach was incensed, but Brown motioned for him to stay quiet.

"So you're going to give in to Abe?" Brown asked.

"Give in?" Podoloff responded. "He's going to walk out of here knowing he lost two of his best players."

"But – " Brown started to respond and was cut off by Podoloff.

"I know. Abe thinks that he and his Globetrotters have a right to all the best Negro basketball players, but that is not realistic," Podoloff said.

He sighed.

"Walter, this league is one lawsuit away from going under. To survive we need the Harlem Globetrotters playing in those second games," Podoloff said. "You want both Sweetwater and this other colored kid? Then you may be playing your last season as the Boston Celtics."

"I need your help here," he declared resignedly.

Brown was silent. After a moment, he nodded.

"Saperstein acts like he invented basketball," Brown groaned.

"Nobody is winning," Podoloff said. "Abe paid us a franchise fee to bring a Chicago team into the NBA next year. But after this, it's not going to happen. Half the league would drop out after he admitted threatening a boycott over colored players."

"And that stays in this room," Podoloff warned Brown and Auerbach. "I have enough headaches to deal with today."

On May 24, a courier delivered a New York Knicks' check to Abe Saperstein's Chicago office for the Globetrotters releasing Sweetwater Clifton.

It happened that Bill Veeck had been camped out in Saperstein's office for several weeks managing details of the now concluded college all-star tour and finalizing other scheduling dates.

Saperstein was out to lunch when the check arrived, so it was accepted and signed for by Veeck's secretary, Wyonella Smith, who was a Black college graduate. She was married to popular Black newspaper columnist Wendell Smith of the Pittsburgh Courier. Wendell Smith was well acquainted with both Veeck and Saperstein.

Wyonella had a "white voice," so when making phone calls scheduling hotel rooms for the Globetrotters, she had to be explicitly clear that the guests would be Black men.

When Saperstein returned, Veeck presented him with the $25,000 check from the New York Knicks for the services of Sweetwater Clifton.

Saperstein realized Veeck had seen the amount of the check.

"Hey, Bill," Saperstein said. "Do me a favor. If anyone asks, a reporter or any of the players, this Knicks' deal was for $5,000."

Veeck did a double take.

"I told Sweetwater I'd split the payment with him for buying out his contract," Saperstein said. "He's just getting $2,500, not $12,500."

Veeck also had heard that Saperstein was paying the Black Globetrotters far less than the white college all-stars on the recently concluded tour.

The Black Globetrotter players learned this only after Nat Sweetwater Clifton asked white all-star player Bob Cousy how much he was paid for the tour. Cousy showed his own check from Saperstein for $3,000 while Clifton was embarrassed to say he was paid just $500.

"Look," Saperstein told Veeck. "No more Globetrotter games in Boston. We're done with the Celtics. And the only reason we are not boycotting the Knicks for the Sweetwater deal is they agreed to give us more games at Madison Square Garden. We made a killing there on New Year's Day."

Veeck nodded but was quiet. He knew Boston's team owner Walter Brown and respected him. Veeck wasn't surprised that Brown wanted to add Black players to the Celtics. Now, Veeck was troubled that his friend and collaborator Abe Saperstein was standing in the way of that.

Saperstein knew Veeck long enough to realize he was unhappy about the Globetrotters' boycott of the Celtics.

In the office the day after the New York Knicks' check arrived, he pulled up a chair and sat alongside his old friend.

"You know nobody has done more for the Negro than me," Saperstein said in a reassuring tone with an earnest look. "Where were all these people – Walter Brown, Red Auerbach – in the 1930s, when the Globetrotters had no money. I remember spending my last dollar getting to the next city to discover we would be playing in a drained-out swimming pool."

"I posted thousands of flyers on post fences advertising our games. Where was Podoloff when I was in Omaha pushing the bus stuck in a snowstorm so we wouldn't miss our next game? That was back when very few in this country cared about basketball unless you brought a show," Saperstein said.

Veeck was quiet.

"You saw what happened to baseball when Jackie joined the Dodgers," Saperstein pleaded. "Within two years, the Negro Leagues were all but done. What am I supposed to do? Just sit back and let the NBA raid all the good colored college players who they've ignored the past 20 years? Let them piggyback on the gate revenues I bring them, and use that money to steal the players that make the Globetrotters so good? Let them put me out of business? I just lost two of my best players!"

Abe Saperstein took a deep breath to compose himself.

"The first time I saw Sweetwater, he was playing for the Rens in front of 50 people at a high school gym. There were no newspapers reporting that game," Saperstein said.

The Renaissance was an all-Black Harlem basketball barnstorming team formed a few years before the Globetrotters' debut. Some claimed they were the inspiration for the Globetrotters concept. Bob Douglas was the Black man who founded the Rens. He had a reputation as a skilled coach and great judge of talent but couldn't measure up to Saperstein as a promoter.

The Rens were losing money, and Douglas had considered folding the team. Instead, Saperstein took it over as the farm club for his Globetrotters. He hired older Rens players to be coaches on those farm clubs.

In Saperstein's mind, he had been a savior of Black basketball. And now, the NBA was threatening all his hard work.

"I created this opportunity for Sweetwater," Saperstein said, looking at Veeck. "You know all those articles about how big his hands are? I called newspaper reporters asking them to come and watch him hold a basketball."

"You know what the Globetrotters' record is coming into this month?" Saperstein asked rhetorically. "We have 3,241 victories and 235 defeats. I tracked that from the beginning. I knew sportswriters love statistics and I gave them one hell of a number."

"Sportswriters do love numbers," Veeck agreed, nodding.

Saperstein was quiet.

"Bill," he said. "Half my family is working for me. This is my livelihood. This is my family's livelihood."

Veeck cleared his throat.

"Abe," he said. "Can I talk now?"

Saperstein nodded.

"I'm not going to tell you how to run your business," Veeck said. "But if I did, I would say stop worrying about winning. Instead, focus on the show your players put on. You're so darn worried about winning every game, you've lost sight of the real reason people come out to watch the Globetrotters."

"They don't care if you lose to the Lakers by two points as long as that little Marques Haynes does his dribbling act. My goodness, I could watch him dribble all day," Veeck said.

"You can't stop what's coming any more than Effa Manley could have stopped major league teams from signing her best Negro League players," Veeck said. "The Negro League owners refused to adapt and now are all going broke."

"But Abe," Veeck said. "I don't know anyone better at adapting in business than you. That's your genius. That's what will save you from that same fate. The National Basketball Association is going to have Negro players. The coloreds are already playing in college, and the pro league will also become integrated."

Saperstein took a deep breath and sat back, realizing Veeck was right.

"Look, I just lost my two best players," Saperstein repeated. He shook his head in resignation.

"I'll go back and play at the Boston Garden next year. But not now. Let's see where this goes and talk about it later," Saperstein said.

In 1953, Saperstein began transitioning the Globetrotters more toward entertainment instead of competition. As part of that act, he hired former player Red Klotz to create the Washington Generals team as a stumbling foil to the Globetrotters. The Generals would fill that role for the next 60 years.

In 1954, Meadowlark Lemon applied for a position on the Globetrotters and was hired. He went on to be a Globetrotters' member for the next 22 years, helping to lead the enterprise into a new era where outstanding individual player skills were exhibited in the context of comedic shenanigans.

CHAPTER 34

Could Satchel Still Pitch In The Bigs?

May 30, 1950

Minot, North Dakota, had always been a seedy little outpost of a town.

Saul Davis fit right in. Given that he was only one of 186 Black people living in the city of 22,000, that said something about his charisma.

Davis had two things going for him in Minot in 1950. Even at the age of 49, he was a great baseball player. And he ran the best damn whorehouse in town.

Like so many Black players during segregation, Davis spent his baseball career barnstorming. For a while, he managed and played for the Zulu Cannibal Giants, a barnstorming Black team whose gimmick was wearing grass skirts with white face paint to mimic African tribesmen. Many Black players refused to demean themselves. Davis didn't care. It was a paying job.

The story in Minot was that Saul Davis came through town during a 1943 barnstorming tour and got so drunk that his team left him behind. The next city large enough to draw a profitable crowd could be days away. Fargo was 270 miles away.

So Davis never left Minot.

Instead, he opened a restaurant that eventually became the center of a profitable prostitution racket.

Davis was an entertaining drunk. He claimed to know musicians Fats Domino and Count Basie, and the town folk believed him. He was connected. In 1925, Davis was the man who discovered 18-year-old Satchel Paige in Birmingham, Alabama. Davis was playing Negro League baseball at the time. And he was friends with Willie Mays, one of the hottest prospects in baseball and destined to be a superstar.

Saul Davis also had a darker side. He had been arrested countless times for crimes including beating his wife, drunk driving and disorderly conduct.

Davis knew Harlem Globetrotter founder Abe Saperstein, who was the promoter for the Zulu Cannibal Giants and had asked Davis to be the player/manager.

Among his Minot friends were several local police officers, county sheriff deputies and the sheriff. He was also friendly with Dee Dee Govan, another Black man who operated a competing house of prostitution down the road, called The Plantation. Govan and Davis made about $15 a week from each prostitute they employed.

Davis' attorney was Paul Campbell. This was unusual because the lawyer was also Minot's city prosecutor and assistant city attorney. But Campbell's city contract allowed him to still keep a limited private practice.

Davis claimed he once was a doorman in Chicago for Al Capone. During Prohibition from 1920 to 1933, the Chicago gangster ran his bootlegging operation out of Minot, using the North Dakota city as a depot for imported alcohol from Canada.

Minot became known as Little Chicago because of the bootlegging and violence it sparked, as well as the highly profitable red-light district located in the Black section of town.

North Dakota's passion for baseball went back before Prohibition to the 19th century. In 1885, Black soldiers assigned to Fort Buford had formed baseball teams.

The sport captured the hearts of many and had become a near-obsession in some places. If a town could find nine men, even if one of them was Black, they fielded a baseball team.

The North Dakota cities were starved for baseball. The state had semi-pro baseball leagues that had thrived since the 1900s. Black players who could help a city's team win were welcomed and even recruited.

North Dakota had unexpectedly become an oasis of integrated baseball in America. Black players were accepted here more than anywhere else in the country. The Black players were a curiosity to the North Dakota's white fans, including children who approached the Black players before games to hear the entertaining vernacular.

It was big news when residents learned in 1950 that Satchel Paige was returning to the state. Bill Veeck was out of baseball for the time being and no other major league teams had expressed interest in signing Paige. He still needed to make a living, so Paige called on his old friend Saul Davis in Minot.

On May 30, Satchel Paige flew into the Minot airport. It wasn't his first tour of North Dakota. That was in 1935, when he led Bismarck's integrated semi-pro team to a national championship.

That team had 11 players, six of them Black. Paige dominated the five-game tournament, which was held in Kansas. He struck out 44 batters in 27 innings, gave up just one run, and won two games.

"I'm not worried about winning the championship for Bismarck," team owner Neil Churchill told newspaper reporters before the 1935 title game. "We'll have Satchel Paige on the mound and you know what that means."

Paige faced the team from Duncan, Oklahoma, which had two white former Major League Baseball players. Pitcher Augie Johns had played for the Detroit Tigers and Joe Hassler played for the Philadelphia Athletics. Both were fringe big-league players who dominated against semi-pro talent that filled the national semi-pro tournament.

"We'll paste Paige's pitches all over the lot tomorrow night," Johns boasted to newspaper reporters the day before the championship game.

Hassler faced Paige four times the next day in the championship game and didn't get a hit while striking out three times.

Playing before 10,000 fans in the championship game, Paige led Bismarck to a 5-2 victory. The Bismarck Tribune ran a full play-by-play account of the championship game in the sports section.

The newspaper's headline read, "Great Negro Athlete Pitches Bismarck To Title." The newspaper also commissioned an artist to draw a half-page tribute to Paige. One caption read, "NO, ELMER – NOT AN ETHOPIAN WAR DANCE. JUST SATCHEL WINDING UP THAT STEEL SPRING IN HIS RIGHT ARM."

The performance enshrined the legend of Satchel Paige in the state of North Dakota. He had become the Paul Bunyan of baseball to many of the state's residents.

From that time on, North Dakota newspapers followed Paige's every baseball move, anticipating when he might return.

That moment had now arrived.

But Paige had savored his taste of the big leagues and believed he deserved that big stage and desperately wanted to get back on it. But that would have to wait.

For now, Paige was the star attraction for a newly formed mixed-race Minot team in a new league that upped the stakes on boasting rights and player salaries.

In 1950, Manitoba, Canada and North Dakota formed the Mandak League. The Brandon Greys from Manitoba, Canada, and the Minot Mallards were among its most heated rivals.

The winner of the season series between the two teams would take home the coveted Barney Mollot Trophy, named after a local

Brandon businessman. At the age of 45, Mollot was instrumental in forming the Brandon Greys.

On May 30, 1950, a Who's Who of North Dakota and Manitoba semi-pro movers-and-shakers were in Minot for the game. The Minot Daily News had sent two reporters and one from the Bismarck Tribune was also on hand.

They came to see Satchel Paige.

At 5 p.m., it was cloudy and a crisp 54 degrees. Experienced fans knew to show up in winter clothing. Two hours before game-time, the grandstands were already packed with the anticipation of a Satchel Paige appearance.

The stadium seated 1,200 people, but on this night more than three times were expected. The overflow crowd was in the standing-room-only sections.

Just a month earlier, President Harry Truman had stopped in Minot, and 8,000 people greeted him at his rally.

The Minot newspaper had questioned whether Paige could outdraw Truman.

Barney Mollot was scheduled to arrive with his team at 6 p.m.

The hour before the game started, side bets were to be made.

"Ole Barney's out for blood with the new league," Frank Williamson, the mayor of Brandon, told Hank Kiehn, the mayor of Minot. "He has recruited colored players from Cuba."

This made Kiehn nervous. He liked to gamble. He lost a bet earlier in the month that made the regional newspapers when the city's population grew less than he predicted. A mayor who bet on census numbers would have big money on the biggest game of the year.

"Cuba?" Kiehn said. "Well, we've got Satchel for three games."

"Just three?" Williamson asked.

"That's all we could afford!" Kiehn shot back. "That Negro makes more than me!"

Kiehn surveyed the growing crowd.

"But he brings them in, eh?" Kiehn said.

Thirty minutes later, the Brandon Greys arrived. They were a hot team which had won their first six games of the season and were ready to face Paige. On this day, 12 of the 15 Brandon Grey players were Black.

Williamson poked Kiehn kiddingly in the ribs.

"Looks like Barney picked up a few more Negroes," Williamson said. "Our bet is still on. $100."

Kiehn nodded.

There was no sign of Paige.

Williamson made his way to the press box and turned to Kiehn.

"We wish you the best of luck, but darn sure hope we win," Williamson said.

At 6:35 p.m., a car pulled into the parking lot. Paige got out dressed in his uniform, followed by Davis, who was unaccompanied. His wife was in the city jail on a prostitution charge.

Paige had a history of skipping out on his scheduled barnstorming games. When he strolled into the stadium for this game, it took the wind from the sails of the opposing Brandon players who were warming up on the baseball diamond.

Ian Lowe, the Brandon Greys' white player/manager, noticed his team's spirit had dropped.

"Hey, come on now. The Indians released him. How much can he have left at that age?" Lowe asked.

Dirk Gibbons, a 22-year-old Black player with the Brandon Greys, shook his head.

"He'll be angry about that," Gibbons said. "You don't want to be on the wrong side of Satchel Paige."

Mesmerized by Paige, the Brandon Greys were no longer playing catch. The packed crowd of 4,000 had lined the fence.

Satchel Paige looked around. It was showtime.

Black barnstorming games and those in the Negro Leagues were far less structured than Major League Baseball, and in many ways more entertaining.

Paige, for example, was known to call-in his outfielders and have them sit down on the infield. He would tell them they wouldn't be needed this inning and not to get up. And then Paige would proceed to strike out the side.

Antics like these drew white and Black crowds and was a big reason so many came to see Paige this day.

Paige took a pack of cigarettes from his pocket and handed it to Davis, and then strolled to the mound.

Paige motioned to his Black teammate, 24-year-old Willie Cathey.

"Young Willie, grab a cigarette from Saul," Paige yelled.

The full attention of 4,000 silent viewers was now focused on Paige.

Cathey took a cigarette and lit it.

"Now, stand next to the plate," Paige commanded.

Cathey looked nervously at Davis, who just smiled. But Cathey wouldn't dare question someone the stature of Paige.

The opposing manager, Ian Lowe, watched Paige.

"What's he doing with the smokes?" Lowe asked teammate Gibbons.

Gibbons ignored Lowe.

Paige looked at the crowd and loudly announced, "OK, now I'm going to throw one of my best pitches – the B pitch – and knock that cigarette out of young Willie's mouth!"

"What in tarnation is a B pitch?" Davis yelled back, playing the straight man to Paige.

"Because it 'be' where I tell it to be," Paige hollered as the crowd laughed.

With Cathey standing motionless at the plate, Paige started his windup. He did a windmill with his right pitching arm and then did a second windmill, and then he stopped.

"Saul," Paige yelled.

"Yes, Satch," Davis responded.

"How far is the nearest hospital?" Paige asked as the crowd laughed.

"Just down the road, Satch! Trinity Hospital. Finest hospital in the state and plenty of room with 30 beds," Davis said.

Paige smiled.

"Don't worry, Willie!" Paige yelled. "Just don't move, son. I won't hit you. How do I know? Because the plate doesn't move, and I never miss it."

Paige did his windup, made a windmill motion once and fired a fastball right at Cathey's head.

Cathey closed his eyes and heard a whizzing sound.

The ball zoomed by and knocked the cigarette out of his mouth.

For a second there was complete silence, and then the crowd roared.

Cathey opened his eyes, relaxed and let out a sigh of relief.

Paige turned his head and glared at the Brandon Greys.

The game began 20 minutes later.

Satchel Paige had been contracted to pitch just three innings in three separate games. And that's all the Minot team would get. Paige learned long ago not to get invested in the politics surrounding his performances.

Just three innings.

The first batter walked to the plate.

The public address system crackled. A short was just discovered as the baseball season kicked off.

"Leading off for the Greys is third baseman Ian Lowe, the Manitoba Senior League defending batting champion," echoed through the stands.

As Lowe dug in, he was wondering: Was Paige really as good as his reviews? Sure, he once led Bismarck to a national championship, but that was 15 years ago. In 1950, Paige was an old man, Lowe thought.

Paige strutted around the mound for a moment and then stood still, sizing up Lowe.

Years ago, on a diamond hugging a cornfield in Davenport, Iowa, Paige had struck out the mighty Rogers Hornsby, Major League Baseball's two-time Most Valuable Player. He could still see the hate in Hornsby's eyes as he whiffed at the final pitch.

He also recalled the respect in the eyes of Stan Musial, who had just been named Major League Baseball's MVP when Paige retired "Stan The Man" on three pitches in Des Moines, Iowa, a few years back.

The list of Paige's white barnstorming victims at the plate included some of the greatest hitters ever to play the game.

The Manitoba Senior League defending batting champ wasn't in the same class.

Yet, when Paige looked at Lowe, he saw a man who didn't buy into the legend of Satchel Paige.

That angered Paige.

Lowe watched as Paige went into his windup. He was struck by Paige's large left foot as it kicked up in the air, appearing almost clown-like.

And then, as if from nowhere, the pitch came in.

Lowe stood and watched it buzz by him. It was faster than anything he'd seen.

The second pitch was just as fast, and midway through his swing Lowe heard the ball pop in the catcher's mitt. Lowe wasn't close to making contact.

When Lowe looked back at the catcher, he noticed he was wearing a hand glove for extra padding.

Lowe stepped out of the batter's box and asked the umpire for time. The umpire granted it.

Two pitches.

Lowe looked at Paige on the mound. Paige stared right through him.

After two pitches, Lowe now had a look of fear.

The third pitch came in just like the first two – hard and straight at his knees. Lowe's swing missed the ball by several inches.

That was it. Three pitches. Lowe's appearance at the plate was over in less than two minutes.

"Number 17," Paige yelled to Lowe, referring to him only by the number on his back as he walked back to the dugout. "Don't feel bad. You'll have something to tell your grandchildren about how Old Satchel struck you out on three pitches."

Lowe's teammates were silent as he returned to the bench.

By the end of his three innings, Paige had struck out seven of the nine batters he faced. One batter hit a weak pop fly to the catcher. The other batter who didn't strike out was late on his swing and hit a ground ball to the first baseman.

Paige left the game with Minot ahead 4-0. They won 4-3. It was a massive feather in the cap of the city of Minot. Paige didn't care. He fulfilled his obligation. He put on a show.

Paige's performance in Minot for his three games was almost perfect. He didn't allow a run in nine innings spread over his three games.

After the final game, Paige went to Saul's Barbeque, owned by Davis on Third Street. It was in the neighborhood where the Blacks lived, many working for the Great Northern Railway company. Enough Blacks lived there for Minot to host one of the few Black churches in the state, the First Baptist.

To the white locals, that section of town was known as "Nigger Town." The townsfolk enjoyed their baseball including their Black players, but otherwise their racial acceptance had its limits. The reason Paige left Bismarck in 1935 after winning the national semi-pro championship was because white residents were upset by rumors he was having affairs with white women.

There were 20 customers in Saul's Barbeque when Paige arrived, including many of the opposing Black players.

Saul Davis was in a good mood. Paige always drew a crowd, which meant extra money for the prostitution racket. Davis kept half the money his prostitutes made from their clients, some of whom were well-known white men in town.

Paige was polite to the wide-eyed players from the Brandon Greys, but sat with Davis at a separate table.

Satchel Paige was usually the life of the party. On road trips with the Cleveland Indians, Paige would leave the forward car they shared and wander to the back of the train, a habit from years spent in the Jim Crow South. Before long, some of the white Cleveland teammates would leave their more comfortable seats and drift towards Paige so they could talk to the entertaining pitcher.

But since his release from the Indians, a cloud was hanging over Paige.

It took two days before the Bismarck Tribune newspaper reached Minot.

The front page of the sports section was a syndicated column "written" by Satchel Paige "as told" to sportswriter Ernest Mehl. It had appeared in more than 200 newspapers.

Davis picked up the newspaper and turned to the sports section.

"Hey, Satch!" Davis yelled. "They got your article? You wrote this?"

Satch nodded.

"What'd I say?" Paige asked.

A young 20-something-white waitress came to the table.

"Is she on the menu?" Paige asked Davis.

Davis surveyed the two other waitresses.

"They all are," Davis said.

"I'm not really into baseball that much," the waitress said. "Are you a baseball player?"

Paige nodded.

"I am a player. I'm not married," Paige responded. "But I am in demand!"

Davis and Paige drank beers for five hours.

At 2 a.m. Paige and Davis were drunk and were the last two in the restaurant.

Paige was no longer wearing the congenial Stepin Fetchit mask he wore in public.

Jackie Robinson's picture was in the Bismarck newspaper after he hit a home run to lift the Brooklyn Dodgers to a 7-6 victory. Robinson was named the Most Valuable Player of the National League the previous year, just his third season in Major League Baseball.

Robinson had become the face of Black baseball. Paige was the circus sideshow attraction.

Paige took the newspaper sports section and crumpled it up.

He looked at Davis, who was three sheets to the wind.

"I was the one who started all the big talk about letting us in the big time! Me!" Paige yelled. "I was the one who opened up the major league parks to the colored teams. I was the one the white boys wanted to barnstorm against. I was the one who should be in the major leagues."

Paige threw the crumpled newspaper to the floor and shook his head.

"Instead, I have to come to North Dakota!" Paige yelled.

Davis jolted up from his intoxicated stupor. He picked up the newspaper from the floor.

"It's not that bad, really," Davis replied, too drunk to realize Paige was in a near rage.

"Saul, it should have been me!" Paige shouted.

Davis saw the photo of Jackie Robinson. He shook his head.

"You're too damn old," Davis shouted at Paige. "And that's the big leagues, Satch! They wouldn't put up with you playing hooky before games and all of the rest of your nonsense. That's why you are here, boy."

Davis nodded to Paige.

"You remember that time you were supposed to pitch for the Monarchs? And instead, you left KC and went to New Orleans?" Saul asked.

A smile slipped past Paige's anger. Yes, he remembered.

"Well, that's why that cracker Branch Rickey didn't take you!" Davis yelled. "You are about as dependable as one of my hookers!"

Davis paused in his drunkenness. He liked that analogy.

"That's what you are, Satchel Paige, nothing but a whore who will pitch for the highest bidder," Davis said. "Just three innings at a time. Like one of my girls who you pay for 15 minutes."

Davis let out a cackle and looked at Paige.

"And tomorrow, you'll pitch in Minnesota for 15 minutes or whatever you signed up for. Three innings. I might head down there with you. I got some girls to pick up," Davis said.

Paige shook his head.

"You have never been there," Paige said.

"Minnesota?" Davis asked. "I go once a month!"

Paige shook his head.

"No, the big leagues. You've never been to the big leagues," Paige said solemnly.

Paige put his beer down and sat in silence. He remembered nearly 70,000 fans in Cleveland.

An hour later, Paige stumbled back to the spare bedroom in Davis' home. He dropped off his belongings there earlier. Now, Paige opened the Bible and looked at Veeck's telegram. He closed it and laid down on the bed.

As the alcohol flowed through his mind, Paige understood this would be the rest of his playing career.

CHAPTER 35

He's Got God-Given Talent But A Devil-May-Care Attitude

May 31, 1950.

Satchel Paige awoke to a knock on the door. Saul Davis was gone. Paige didn't know if Davis even made it home. It was a Black man with a telegram. Paige took it and saw it was from Abe Saperstein.

Paige anxiously ripped it open to read it.

Saperstein wanted him to call him.

Paige had to be in Fergus Falls, Minnesota, to play a team from Moorhead, Minnesota. Paige rarely recalled the town names. They all sounded the same to him. At his next stop, both teams were nicknamed the Red Sox, which confused Paige even more. He wasn't sure which Red Sox team he would be pitching against. The field had a capacity for 1,200 fans.

Before leaving for Fergus Falls, Paige called Saperstein collect.

"Hey, Satch," Saperstein said. "I have a deal set up."

Paige listened.

"Boston. Fenway Park. July 11," Saperstein said. "It's just an exhibition for charity. But there may be some scouts there. The baseball reporters will be there. Keep you in the news. You'll be pitching for the Philadelphia Stars."

Paige's spirits picked up.

"I'll do it," Paige said.

Paige paused.

"Any word on the big leagues?" Paige asked.

Saperstein was quiet.

"Not yet," he said.

Paul Egan, sportswriter for the Boston Daily Record, wrote a column on July 9, 1950, in advance of Paige's Fenway Park appearance.

He wrote: "It's a thoroughly ridiculous state of affairs when Paige barnstorms around the country pitching independent ball while, at the same time, men who could and still cannot carry his glove draw salaries from teams which consider themselves pennant contenders."

On the day of Paige's Fenway Park appearance, he was being escorted by J.L. Wilkinson, formerly the white owner of the Kansas City Monarchs. Wilkinson's Monarchs were the most successful team in Negro League baseball, and often regarded as the league's version of the New York Yankees.

At age 72, Wilkinson was nearly blind. He had to squint to read The Negro Motorists' Green Book, an annual guide that sold for 75 cents and advised Blacks where they could travel, sleep and eat without fear throughout the U.S.

The Green Book's information came from word-of-mouth and showed where the Blacks could find safe havens. It also listed the addresses of Black homeowners willing to take in Black out-of-towners.

Despite his deteriorating eyesight, Wilkinson could see the writing on the wall for the Negro Leagues. He sold his interest in the Monarchs in 1948, the year after Major League Baseball's color barrier was broken.

Now, two years later, he was escorting Satchel Paige during the barnstorming season.

Wilkinson hadn't been out to eat in Boston for a while. He checked the Green Book, and the pair headed to Lonie Lee's Restaurant, about a mile from Fenway Park. There was no worry about Paige getting a cab to the game from there because it was within walking distance.

Another reason Wilkinson was babysitting Satchel Paige was to make sure he didn't eat fried foods, a favorite of the Black pitcher. Paige had suffered for years with ulcers and acid reflux. It got so bad in Paige's last year with the Cleveland Indians that it was difficult for him to stand up straight at times.

But in 1950, Paige was so dedicated to getting back into the major leagues that he had all his teeth pulled to improve his health. And it seemed to work because Paige never felt better.

When Paige and Wilkinson got to Lonie Lee's Restaurant, it was standing room only.

But when the owner noticed Paige, he rushed up to introduce himself, and within a couple minutes Paige and Wilkinson were seated at a table beside the restaurant's only television.

The charity game at Fenway Park was on the same day as the Major League Baseball all-star game in Chicago's Comiskey Park on July 11, 1950. The all-star game was a day game, and the charity game wanted to avoid competing for fans, so it was to be played at 8:45 p.m.

However, the all-star game went into extra innings. And this was the first time the big-league all-star game was televised.

The National League all-star team included Jackie Robinson, who played for Wilkinson on the Monarchs before signing with the Dodgers. The NL team also had Don Newcombe, another Brooklyn Dodger who was the first Black pitcher named to an all-star team.

That rubbed Paige the wrong way. He always felt that honor should have been reserved for him.

The all-star game was in the 10th inning when Paige and Wilkinson were seated.

For the American League, Larry Doby of the Cleveland Indians came up to bat.

Jack Brickhouse, the TV announcer for the game, introduced Doby.

"Doby's hitting .352 with eight homers at the break and having just an incredible season," Brickhouse said as Wilkinson and Paige listened. "He had a double earlier in the game."

Paige's heart sank. Playing in the all-star game was his dream. It was where he felt he belonged, showcased with the other best players in baseball.

And now, Paige just learned the annual game was being broadcast on television for the first time.

An entire nation was seeing the best baseball players live in action on television, and Paige was set to face cut-rate college players dressed as tramps for a charity event.

On the restaurant's TV screen, Paige saw Doby swing and hit a single into left field.

"And Doby gets a base hit!" Brickhouse cheered on the TV. "What a year for the Cleveland Indian outfielder. That's his second hit of this game."

The all-star game was over. Paige was uncharacteristically quiet. Wilkinson regretted that Paige was exposed to the all-star game. As the game played out, he saw the hurt in his long-time friend's eyes.

The two ate in silence.

When the game was over, they headed to the fabled Fenway Park.

The last time Paige was in Fenway Park, he was the winning pitcher as his Cleveland Indians beat the Boston Red Sox 10-6 in extra innings on July 30, nearly a year ago.

That game drew 21,441.

Before the charity game in Fenway Park, Al Schacht was on the field performing his act. Schacht was one of a handful of players who made a living being "baseball clowns" like Max Patkin and Jackie Price. Schacht would wear a tuxedo jacket and top hat over his uniform and perform physical comedy.

As Paige took the mound, the public address announcer said the charity event drew 27,418 fans. That was the appeal of Paige.

Paige was facing the New England Hoboes, which was a collection of local college players and fringe minor league players dressed as homeless men. They wore baggy suits and used black grease on their faces to mimic five o'clock shadows. Another such team was the Georgia Chain Gang where players dressed as jailbirds.

Before the game, the Hoboes sat around a giant pail set up at home plate, pretending to eat soup over the campfire. When Schacht came by to see if he could get a cup, they chased him off, with an actor hired to be a police officer joining in the chase around the field.

Paige understood the role of slapstick entertainment in baseball. But this night, Paige was all business. His dream of returning to the majors was at stake.

He took the mound wearing his old Cleveland Indians uniform, letting everyone know where he came from.

Paige struck out 11 Hoboes in four innings and gave up one run. The game ended in a 3-3 tie.

Paige saved his best "pitch" for after the game. It was a lie he and Wilkinson concocted days before and pitched to newspaper reporters.

Wilkinson believed Paige's only path back to the major leagues was to create the impression there was a demand for his services among the big-league teams.

Fenway Park was the perfect place to plant that seed. It was in the city that was home to the Boston Red Sox and Boston Braves. And both the teams were covered by the Boston Globe, a major newspaper very much aware of the American public's enthusiasm for baseball.

After the game, Wilkinson and Paige were sure to hunt down Boston Globe sportswriter Gene Mack Jr., who covered the Boston Braves, and Globe sportswriter Herb Ralby.

"Great performance!" Mack told Paige as he sat in the dugout after the game.

"I feel better than when I pitched with the Indians," Paige said.

Ralby turned to Wilkinson.

"How about it, Wilkie?" Ralby asked. "Could Satchel still pitch in the bigs?"

Wilkinson nodded.

"We've got two big league teams in contact with us right now!" Wilkinson said.

Ralby's eyes opened wide.

"Who?" he shot back.

Wilkinson shook his head.

"They don't want it out there, or it could create a bidding war," Wilkinson said.

"Come on, Wilkie," Mack said. "Is it the Red Sox and Braves?"

Wilkinson just smiled.

Paige jumped in.

"I know I could help any club in the two leagues as a relief pitcher, and I could start, too," Paige said.

Ralby pulled Wilkinson aside while Paige talked to Mack.

"How old is Ole Satch?" Ralby asked.

Wilkinson smiled.

"Satch is past 45. During the last war, I remember he said he was 38, and that was seven years ago," Wilkinson said.

The Boston sportswriters took the bait.

The next day's Boston Globe headlines were all about Paige.

"Satchel Paige Hero in 3-3 Ball Game"

"'I'm Better Than When I Was Pitching For The Indians,' Claims Satchel Paige"

Mack led his story with, "Satchel Paige, fabulous Negro pitching machine, who anticipates an early return to the major league, helped present one of the greatest entertainment programs in the city's history."

Both articles mentioned that two major league teams wanted to sign the Negro star, but Paige and Wilkinson wouldn't reveal which ones.

Two days later, Boston Braves' owner Louis Perini denied reports his team was interested in signing Paige.

But Wilkinson received a phone call on July 18 from New York Giants general manager Chub Feeney. He wanted to take a look at Paige in two days at a game in Riverhead, New York, when Paige was set to pitch against the Riverhead semi-pro team.

The Giants were sending former major league stars Mel Ott and Carl Hubbell, who had since retired and helped with scouting.

Feeney asked Wilkinson if any other teams were interested in Paige.

"I'm sorry, Chub," Wilkinson said. "They've asked me not to make it public."

Wilkinson hung up the phone and moments later was knocking on Paige's hotel room.

Paige opened it and was just wearing his pajama bottoms.

Wilkinson was wearing a huge smile.

"It worked!" Wilkinson said. "The Giants are coming to scout you Friday against Riverhead."

Paige smiled. He sat on the bed.

Wilkinson and Paige felt it was just a matter of days before the Giants signed Paige.

The New York Giants would be a perfect fit. Just a month earlier, they had signed another Black player, Willie Mays. They were also the second National League team to sign Black players in 1949 after Jackie Robinson debuted with the Brooklyn Dodgers.

In 1950 the Giants' roster included Black players Monte Irvin and Hank Thompson.

And the New York Giants manager was Leo Durocher, who two years earlier had been Jackie Robinson's manager with the Dodgers.

On July 20, Paige took the mound against the Riverhead Falcons in front of a record crowd of 6,155 people.

He pitched three innings, struck out five, and allowed just one hit.

Wilkinson noted that scouts Ott and Hubbell left in the fourth inning after Paige was removed.

Three weeks later, the Giants' brain trust convened to decide Paige's fate.

In the late evening of Aug. 6, Ott, Hubbell, Durocher, and Feeney walked into the office of Giants' owner Horace Stoneham.

The Giants had just beaten the Pittsburgh Pirates in both games of a doubleheader and had now won 15 of their last 16 games. The Giants were only five games behind the first-place Philadelphia Phillies.

These men were to decide whether to sign Satchel Paige.

On July 12, the Giants gave up on 35-year-old pitcher Kirby Higbe, an all-star pitcher just four years earlier. Higbe had lost his stuff and was ineffective. His contract was sold to a minor league team in Minneapolis.

The decision before them now came down to Paige and a rookie named George Spencer.

Spencer was just 23 years old and spent three seasons in the minor leagues. Each year in the minors, he was a little less effective. He had a knack for winning games, however. Spencer had 11 wins and only five losses, which was very good, considering he had a mediocre 4.67 ERA. He didn't strike out batters like Paige.

Stoneham controlled the meeting.

"What'd you guys see in Satchel?" the owner asked Hubbell.

During his 16-year career in baseball, Hubbell was twice voted Most Valuable Player and made nine all-star teams. In the 1934 all-star game, he became a legend after striking out in order Babe Ruth, Lou Gehrig, Jimmie Foxx, Al Simmons and Joe Cronin, considered at that time the greatest hitters in the history of baseball.

His words would carry the most weight.

"Can he pitch?" Hubbell asked. "Heck, yeah. Riverside isn't the big leagues, but they did not come close to getting a hit off him."

Stoneham looked to Ott.

"I called Hank," Ott said, referring to Cleveland Indians' general manager Hank Greenberg. "He said Paige is effective but a giant pain in the butt. Doesn't show up on time, late for games, late for the train. His only loyalty is to himself. And Hank said Satchel was more headaches for Lou Boudreau than it was worth."

The room was silent.

"All that said, I'm with Carl. Satchel still has a great fastball. Even if he's not a long-term investment and will likely be gone by next year. I can guarantee that. It may not even be in the major leagues," Ott said.

Stoneham turned to Feeney, who was Stoneham's nephew and in his first year as general manager at age 39.

"What's he asking for a salary?" the owner asked his nephew.

Feeney shrugged.

"I think he just wants back in," Feeney said. "I don't think it's about money right now with Satchel."

Stoneham finally turned to Durocher, who had been quiet the entire meeting.

Durocher was nicknamed "Leo The Lip" because of his short temper. He argued constantly with umpires and led the National League in being ejected from ball games.

"I like scrappy players. I like hustlers," Durocher said. "And that isn't Paige. He's got God-given talent but a devil-may-care attitude. You know what I say: Nice guys finish last. I want a fighter. I think we should go with this kid, Spencer."

The room went silent.

Stoneham nodded.

"So, we call up Spencer after the upcoming road trip," the owner said.

The conversation was over.

The next day, Wilkinson learned from a newspaper reporter the Giants were passing on Paige. Trying to save face for Paige, over the next several hours he told a string of newspaper reporters the Giants didn't offer enough money.

Al Cartwright, sportswriter for the Wilmington, Delaware newspaper, was the fourth reporter to call Wilkinson.

"Look," Wilkinson said. "The Giants offered Satch $20,000 to sign, but pro-rated for the final two months. So he would get $8,000."

Wilkinson paused.

"Shoot, Satch can make that in three days of barnstorming," Wilkinson said.

But as he walked to Paige's hotel room, Wilkinson dreaded having to break the bad news. He knocked on the door and entered.

Paige took one look at his friend's face and knew.

"The Giants went with the rookie," Wilkinson said.

Paige was silent.

Wilkinson knew Paige well enough to leave him alone. He turned around and walked back to his room.

Satchel Paige was devastated. The anguish overwhelmed him. His

Major League Baseball career was over.

He pulled out his Bible and saw the old telegram from Bill Veeck.

In January, newspapers reported a rumor that Veeck was looking to buy the New York Giants, which Veeck denied. Now in August, a few days after Paige's crushing disappointment, the newspapers reported that Veeck considered himself retired and was living in Arizona for health reasons.

Four days after the big letdown, on Aug. 11, Paige had one of the worst performances of his career in a game in Williamsport, Pennsylvania. He gave up eight hits in just three innings in a 13-4 loss to the Baltimore Elite Giants in a Negro National League game. There were just 1,931 fans at the game, a long way from the 70,000 fans he drew with the Indians.

He told the Williamsport newspaper reporters he was only interested in pitching for a team that could make the World Series.

"I don't figure any other club can pay me enough," Paige said.

Over the next 10 days, Satchel Paige would pitch in Philadelphia, Buffalo, Toronto, Montreal, Columbus, Ohio and Hamilton, Ontario.

On Aug. 17, the New York Giants called up Spencer from the minor leagues. He pitched brilliantly for the rest of the season, appearing in 10 games with a 2.49 ERA in 25 innings pitched.

CHAPTER 36

Now!

May 19, 1951

Black runner Jesse Owens became the emblem of a nation in 1936. He won four gold medals in track and field in the Olympics in Berlin, Germany, with Nazi leader Adolf Hitler watching from the stands. Owens' gold medals in the long jump and 100 and 200-meter dashes and as part of the 400-meter relay team mocked Hitler's belief in a white master race.

But Owens' rewards over the years that followed did not include a satisfying career in the land of the free. Instead, he held various jobs for brief periods and in 1939 filed for bankruptcy. The Olympic champion told the bankruptcy judge, "You can't eat gold medals."

Jesse Owens was hired by Ford Motor Company in 1943 but fired two years later after World War II ended.

In 1946 desperate for work, Owens took a demeaning job with Negro League baseball teams. He was hired to race local fans and horses as a side-show attraction. That lasted two months.

At 38, 15 years after electrifying the nation with his athletic excellence in Berlin, Jesse Owens was now in Chicago struggling to get his public relations firm off the ground.

However, Abe Saperstein had different plans for Owens. Saperstein's Harlem Globetrotters basketball team had struck gold while touring Europe.

Saperstein and Owens had first joined forces in 1946. Hoping to cash in on a lack of professional baseball teams on the West Coast, they formed the West Coast Negro Baseball Association. The effort fizzled in just a few months, the result of poor planning and the money ran out.

Before Owens could talk business with Saperstein on this day, he had to participate in an award ceremony before a Negro League baseball game between the Chicago American Giants and the Birmingham Barons.

In recognition of Bill Veeck's efforts to integrate baseball, he was to receive the South Side Boys Club sportsmanship trophy on "Bill Veeck Day." The South Side Boys Club was a youth foundation that served mostly Black children.

Standing at home plate, Veeck accepted the plaque with a smile and raised the trophy over his head with both hands.

"I owe them more than they owe me," Veeck said into the microphone broadcasting his voice throughout the stadium.

Bill Veeck then limped back to the Baron's dugout to watch the game with Owens and Saperstein.

When Veeck reached the dugout, he heard Saperstein pitching his plan to Owens.

Abe Saperstein had organized a Harlem Globetrotters game in August at West Berlin's Olympic Stadium, the site of Jesse Owens' heroic four-gold medal performance in 1936. Owens would arrive at the stadium in a helicopter, dressed in track clothes, and jog a lap around the track that made him a household name.

"If you think so, Mr. Saperstein," Owens told Saperstein.

Veeck was impressed with Saperstein's helicopter idea.

Meanwhile, Satchel Paige had pitched three scoreless innings and took the mound to start the fourth inning. It would be the last inning he would pitch despite allowing just one hit.

Paige stepped on the mound and looked around.

There were 7,000 fans in Comiskey Park for the first game.

With the Indians just two years ago, Paige had pitched to 45,000 fans in this same park.

But three years after Jackie Robinson broke the color barrier, with the big leagues now integrated, the Negro Leagues no longer attracted large crowds.

A month earlier, Harry Simpson became the 16th Black player to play with a major league team when he signed with the Cleveland Indians. And a few days after this day's game, rising minor league star Willie Mays would get the call from the New York Giants.

The Negro Leagues were dying, and Satchel Paige knew it. The era of barnstorming was also fading.

At the top of the fourth inning, Paige glanced over and caught Bill Veeck's eye. With his final pitch, a smoking fastball at the knees, he then struck out Birmingham catcher Willie Patterson, who didn't even get the bat off his shoulder.

"Look at that guy!" Veeck beamed in the dugout. "He can still fire that fastball. He's got an amazing arm, and there are brains in that noodle of his, too."

After the first game of the day's doubleheader, Owens saw Satchel Paige approach. The past couple years had seen a rift between the two. It traced back to 1949, when Ebony magazine polled sportswriters on who they regarded as the greatest Black athletes of the past 50 years.

Owens topped the poll, followed by heavyweight champion Joe Louis. Jackie Robinson placed third and Satchel Paige came in fourth.

Paige was incensed at not coming out on top. After drawing millions of fans to ballparks over 20 years, he saw an injustice in sportswriters ranking him behind Robinson, who had joined the

Brooklyn Dodgers just 18 months before the poll. He felt humiliated by the 1949 presentation of the sportswriters' award before his team's hometown fans in Cleveland.

Satchel Paige took such slights to heart. His ego still carried the bruise.

"Jess?" Paige asked as he walked up to Owens. "What are you doing here? There aren't any horses to race."

Owens just shook his head.

Paige strutted by Owens, walked up to Veeck, and shook his hand.

"I've got some good news," Veeck announced. "I'm going to buy the St. Louis Browns. And I want you to join me."

Paige was stunned. The news broadsided him.

"Just tell me when!" Paige said.

Paige's eagerness to play for the Browns exposed as disingenuous his earlier comments claiming he had no interest in teams without championship prospects. In 1951, the St. Louis Browns were the worst team in baseball.

Rather than a World Series contender, the team Paige couldn't wait to join was on track to lose more than 100 games that season.

The acquisition was not a done-deal though. For weeks Bill Veeck had been working in secret to get the pieces in place. Fearing some American League owners might interfere if they got word he was looking to get back into baseball, his conversations with financial bankers were strictly confidential and done in the Chicago offices of friend Abe Saperstein.

There were two types of owners in Major League Baseball. Some were just filthy rich, like Tom Yawkey of the Boston Red Sox, New York Yankees owner Del Webb, Walter "Spike" Briggs of the Detroit Tigers and Grace Comiskey with her Chicago White

Sox. These individuals had gained their fortunes outside of baseball.

Others, such as Clark Griffith of the Washington Senators, were self-made men. Griffith was raised in poverty after his father was killed when hunters mistook his father for a deer when Griffith was a young boy. He made his fortune building a Montana cattle raising business bit-by-bit and buying more and more stock in the Senators.

Bill Veeck was not a rich man. What he lacked in deep pockets, he made up as a skilled pitchman. Veeck was among the best at rallying investors into helping him buy his baseball teams. He almost always turned them a profit in the long run.

Now finessing a new group of investors, Veeck was on the verge of making his way back into baseball.

On June 8, 1951, when the news broke that Veeck was buying the Browns, Paige anxiously sent a telegram to Veeck that read: "OK for me to report now to the Browns?"

Three days later, Paige got Veeck's response in a telegram – "Not yet."

Veeck had placed a condition and a July 4 deadline on the St. Louis Browns' deal: He must be the majority owner with 75% of the stock with the old ownership corporation dissolved.

Among other things, the experienced team owner knew he needed to have the final say in all the franchise's player transactions, or it was unlikely he'd be able to sign Paige.

Player acquisitions were one of many potential obstacles to the plan's success. Another was that, unlike Cleveland, the city of St. Louis would not be as receptive to the integration of its Major League Baseball team, or to a showboating Black pitcher.

Seven years earlier, in 1944, the St. Louis Cardinals and Browns were the last big-league teams to end segregated seating.

The same year Doby debuted with Bill Veeck's Indians, the Browns did sign two Black players, but both left after a single season. Willard Brown was 32, and Hank Thompson was 21, both played for the Browns in 1947.

Brown used a teammate's bat to hit his only home run in 1947. When Brown returned to the dugout, he discovered that his teammate had smashed his bat and destroyed it rather than allow it to be used again.

Outside the ballpark, in 1948, racial tensions were heightened when St. Louis became the center of a landmark civil rights case. That year, the U.S. Supreme Court held that local covenants prohibiting the sale of homes to Blacks violated the 14th Amendment's Equal Protection Clause.

St. Louis was the most southerly city with a Major League Baseball franchise and Missouri was the only state with a big league team that had been sympathetic to the Confederacy during the Civil War. In 1950, baseball was still very much an East Coast and Midwest sport.

Veeck's bid to purchase the Browns came down to persuading one individual to sell 8,532 shares of the 275,000 outstanding. Just 18 hours before the July 4 deadline, that share-owner capitulated and the deal was finalized.

On July 5, Veeck sent Paige a telegram. It simply said one word: "Now!"

Paige carefully folded the telegram and placed it in his Bible with the message Veeck sent two years earlier promising they would reunite.

The day after sending the telegram, Veeck was at Sportsman's Park in St. Louis for his first game. To mark his debut, he had a free beer promotion.

The new owner limped around the bleachers with his wooden leg carrying a bucket full of free beer and soft drinks. A fan would approach for an autograph for every other drink he handed out. Veeck signed them all.

It was a doubleheader, and by the seventh inning of the first game, Veeck was down to his final two beers. So he took a seat in the bleachers.

He looked around and saw 13,000 fans—a good first night.

A man approached Veeck and introduced himself.

"Mr. Veeck. I'm Jack Hand, I am a sportswriter," Hand said.

"Call me Bill, Jack," Veeck said. "Where you from?"

"Associated Press," Gaines said.

Veeck was impressed.

"There's a lot of interest to see if you can turn around the Brownies," Hand said. "How well will you do this year?"

"We can't fight our way out of a paper sack," Veeck said with a shrug.

Veeck gave Hand a wink.

"Here's my plan," Veeck said. "I'm going to trade a lot of my players to other teams. We'll louse up the rest of the league with enough Browns that they'll come down to us."

Hand loved Veeck's honesty.

"Next, I'm going to do what it takes to make this team a genuine contender. That can't happen overnight though, so in the meantime we'll add some new attractions that make coming to the ballpark rewarding for our hometown fans."

Veeck looked at Hand.

"Share a beer with me?" Veeck asked.

Hand lit up.

"Thanks, Bill," Hand said.

Veeck popped open a beer and gave it to Hand. He then opened the last beer in the bucket and took a sip.

He turned to Hand.

"You know," he said. "There are fireworks, too!"

Eight days later, Paige signed a contract with the St. Louis Browns.

Major League Baseball's oldest player was back where he knew he belonged.

But that would be just the start of Veeck's plans.

He still felt the sting of the meeting with Effa Manley four years earlier. Manley, then the owner of the Negro League's Newark Eagles, accused him of only wanting a minstrel show by signing just Larry Doby while ignoring at least a half dozen other Black players good enough to play in the big leagues.

Under Bill Veeck, the doors to his new franchise would be wide open to excellent Black players.

He even had a useful facilitator to make it happen – Abe Saperstein. With all his ties to Black sports leagues, Veeck designated Saperstein, who also owned stock in the Browns, his new chief talent scout.

On July 9, the St. Louis Browns signed Roosevelt Evans, a 19-year-old Black high school pitcher out of Detroit. Veeck also invited five Black players from the Mandak League in North Dakota to start negotiations with the Browns' minor league team in Toronto.

And Veeck even had a notion to sign players from Japan. That would be a far more complicated endeavor. The Treaty of San Francisco that officially ended the legal state of war between the U.S. and Japan would not be signed until April 28, 1952.

CHAPTER 37

When The 3-Foot-7-Inch Man Felt Like Babe Ruth

Aug. 19, 1951

In 1961, Eddie Gaedel, a 3-foot-7-inch, 65-pound man, died at age 36. Coming home from a bowling alley on the south side of Chicago, he was beaten and left for dead on the side of the road.

But Gaedel, a heavy drinker, made it home, crawled into bed, and passed away. His mother found her dead son the next morning.

Eddie Gaedel's life was full of humiliation, taunts, and heartbreak.

However, 10 years before his death, there occurred the greatest day of Gaedel's life.

On that day, Bill Veeck opened the front door to his residence at 8 a.m., and there in front of him was Sportsman's Park, home of the St. Louis Browns. Like the troll under the bridge in the famous Norwegian folktale, Veeck lived with his family in an apartment under the stadium.

When the new Browns' team owner looked up, he could see the "Falstaff Beer" banner hanging on the outfield fence. In the ballpark that evening, the company that brewed Falstaff was sponsoring a promotion celebrating the 50th anniversary of Major League Baseball's American League.

The 8 a.m. temperature was already 75 degrees, still warm but a relief from the sweltering heat the night before.

By noon, fans were beginning to file into the stadium for a doubleheader, many of them were Falstaff Beer employees and their relatives.

The St. Louis Browns lost the first game to the Detroit Tigers, 5-2.

During the one-hour break between games, pitcher Satchel Paige played the drums in an eight-piece ensemble with teammates as bandmates.

At first base, a man was balancing bowling pins on his nose and then juggling them.

At second base, an acrobat on a trampoline was doing mid-air flips.

Max Patkin, the clown prince of baseball, was doing the jitterbug on the pitching mound.

Several 1904 Model T cars were driving around the field and fireworks were exploding in the air.

Eddie Gaedel was also present, but Bill Veeck was keeping secret the day's most extraordinary stunt.

In the auxiliary room beneath the stands, Gaedel could hear the raucous sound of 19,000 fans whooping it up amidst the spectacles. He was nervous and having belated second thoughts about performing the proposed stunt in front of all those people.

With him in the room was a seven-foot high papier-mache cake, waiting for Gaedel to climb inside.

St. Louis Browns' public relations director Bob Fishel was with Gaedel in the room and could see the doubt in his eyes.

"Eddie, it's too late to pull out now," Fishel told him. "We have more than $15,000 invested in tonight's show."

Looking more nervous, Gaedel shook his head.

"You remember what Bill told you?" Fishel said with a knowing nod. "Don't swing the bat when you are at the plate."

Gaedel swallowed hard and nodded, not looking at all reassured.

"He said if I didn't go through with it, he was a marksman in the military, and he'd be in the press box with a sniper rifle and shoot me!" Gaedel yelped.

Gaedel looked at Fishel.

"You don't think he's really that crazy?" Gaedel asked.

Fishel just smiled.

"Look around, kid," Fishel said. "The only thing missing is a dancing bear. Instead, he has you. But if you swing at any of the pitches, God help you."

Gaedel puffed his chest out.

"Don't call me kid!" he shot back. "I'm doing it. And I'm going to get on base, and I'll be the most famous pinch hitter baseball has ever seen."

"There you go," Fishel said as he lifted Gaedel, stuck him inside the cake, and rolled it out of the auxiliary room and onto the field.

Five minutes later, Eddie Gaedel popped out of the giant cake and onto the grass. The crowd laughed as Gaedel ran around the diamond twice and disappeared into the dugout.

Veeck watched smiling from the press box. But then there was a pounding on the press box door.

Unlike the hundreds of Falstaff Beer employees at the ballpark this night, Alvin Griesedieck Jr. wasn't wearing a nametag.

Few of the workers remembered Griesedieck's official title, which was assistant sales manager in charge of promotions. At the age of 30, his actual title was "the boss's son."

Griesedieck Sr. was a third-generation brewer who just published a book about his family's business in St. Louis.

Griesedieck Jr. was angry and wanted a word with Veeck.

"What the hell is this? A midget jumping out of a cake? We have more than 500 employees and family members here, Bill. This is a complete embarrassment!" Griesedieck said.

Veeck gave a sheepish shrug.

"You know, Alvin. I'm so sorry. On paper, it seemed so much more entertaining," Veeck said. "Look, stick around for the second game, and I'll personally apologize to your employees after the first inning of the second game. But Max Patkin is here, the clown prince of baseball!"

Griesedieck Jr. waved off Veeck and returned to his seat in a huff.

The carnival on the field was soon cleared, and the second game of the doubleheader was set to begin.

The first batter for the Browns walked to the plate. St. Louis Browns' Frank Saucier stepped up and took three steps to the plate when manager Zach Taylor called him back.

Saucier was puzzled. He shrugged and returned to the dugout.

The P.A. announcer said, "Ladies and gentlemen. We have a pinch hitter for Frank Saucier. Eddie Gaedel will bat."

Gaedel emerged from the dugout wearing a Browns' uniform with the fraction '1/8' as his number. It was the uniform worn by the son of a Browns' official. Gaedel's name and jersey number were listed in that day's game program. He had three bats in his hand and tossed away two of them as he walked to the plate. He took a practice swing with a 17-inch bat weighing 23 ounces.

Umpire Ed Hurley stopped the game.

"Hey. What the hell?" Hurley barked.

Taylor trotted out to meet Hurley at home plate with an official contract and official St. Louis Browns' roster in his hand.

"Ed. It's all legit," Taylor said.

Hurley took the papers and glanced at the contract and roster and then looked at Taylor.

"And the official roster that shows Eddie is on it for this game. He gets the pro-rated $100 for the game," Taylor said.

Hurley again inspected the roster. Two other umpires came over. After reading the contract, Hurley shrugged and put his face mask back on and delivered the verdict.

"Batter up!" Hurley barked.

Detroit Tiger pitcher Bob Cain walked from the mound, got about 10 feet from the plate, and attempted to throw the ball underhanded.

"Cain? What in the hell are you doing?" Hurley asked.

Cain shrugged.

"You want me to throw a regular pitch to somebody's kid? No way! He could get hurt," Cain replied.

"He's not a kid. He's legit. Get back on the mound!" Hurley ordered.

Gaedel swelled with pride. He was officially legit. The umpire just confirmed that.

Catcher Bob Swift laughed so hard he couldn't get down in the catcher's prone position.

Gaedel was offended.

"What are you laughing at? Throw it in there fat, pal, and I'll murder it. Let's go!" Gaedel said, swinging his bat.

Swift turned to Hurley and asked for a time-out. The catcher walked to the pitcher's mound and talked to Cain about how to pitch to Gaedel.

"I have no idea what to do. You think you can throw him a strike?" Swift asked Cain.

"The strike zone is from the letters to his knee, just a few inches. And look at the son of a bitch. He's squatting. The ball is bigger than his strike zone, which is about as big as a baby's bib. If you squat, you'll still be too high. You are going to have to sit," Cain told Swift.

Swift broke out laughing.

"Just do your best," he said, returning to home plate.

While Swift was at the pitcher's mound, Gaedel looked up into the press box. He couldn't see Veeck or anyone on the rooftop that looked like a sniper.

Swift returned to home plate, looked at Gaedel, and sat on his butt.

The crowd caught on to what was going on. With each pitch, the crowd cheered as a ball was called. After the fourth pitch, all balls, Gaedel put his bat down and looked at Swift.

"Next time, throw a strike, cocksucker," Gaedel spat.

"Hey, watch it, Spanky! Does your mother know you talk like that?" Swift shot back.

Gaedel began his walk to first base. Generally, a baseball player could jog the 90 feet to first base in 12 seconds. Gaedel started walking. After 12 seconds, he still had 45 feet to go.

He noticed the crowd was cheering its approval at every step. Gaedel stopped for a moment, tipped his hat to the crowd, and resumed his leisurely stroll. He reached first base in 30 seconds, accompanied by a standing ovation.

The Browns' player Jim Delsing, who was 5-foot-10, came out of the dugout and trotted to first base to pinch-run for Gaedel.

"Good job, Eddie," Delsing said.

Gaedel began his walk back to the dugout. As he strolled off the field, it felt as if the eyes of all 19,000 fans were on him. At that moment, all the taunts and humiliation endured during his life of a 3-foot-7 man were washed away by thousands of people's good-willed amusement.

Today, Eddie Gaedel was a Major League Baseball player.

In the home team's clubhouse after the game, Gaedel was dwarfed by a half dozen reporters surrounding him even though the Browns lost 6-2 and had a lousy record of 37-80.

"I felt like Babe Ruth," Gaedel told the reporters with a huge smile.

St. Louis sportswriter Bob Broeg asked Gaedel what was next.

Gaedel looked up at Broeg.

"This is just the start. He will send me to the plate when the bases are loaded. I want a shot at Bob Feller," Gaedel said.

"Eddie, what do you do for a living?" the sportswriter asked.

Eddie Gaedel paused. He had worked many odd jobs. Just recently, he was employed at a factory that used him for crawling into small, cramped places in machinery.

"I'm a stuntman," Gaedel said.

The next morning, American League president Will Harridge stormed into his office. He had a Monday newspaper in his hand and on the cover was what would become the iconic photo. It was a picture of the 3-foot-7 Gaedel at the plate with a bat poised on his shoulder. It ran in newspapers from coast-to-coast.

Harridge was 68 years old and had been president of the American League for 20 years. His hands were shaking.

"Goddamn it. Goddamn it! How did this happen?" Harridge bellowed. There was complete silence.

"Who approved it?" Harridge demanded. "We are the laughingstock of the entire world right now! These shenanigans made a mockery of the game!"

Earl Hilligan, the bespectacled 44-year-old vice president, stepped forward.

"Apparently, the contract is still waiting for approval," Hilligan said, his voice trembling.

"How can that be?" Harridge asked.

"The newspapers said that Mr. Veeck had been planning this for months," Hilligan said.

Harridge nodded.

"Well, Mr. Veeck didn't submit the contracts until Friday," Hilligan said while reviewing the contract. "The delivery boy dropped off the contracts at 4:45 p.m. That's just 15 minutes before we close for the weekend."

"I know what time we close!" Harridge snapped at Hilligan. "I also know goddamn well that Veeck does, too. That son of a bitch knew we wouldn't be able to review the contract until today. And he scheduled this farce for the weekend."

A secretary raised her hand.

Harridge glared at her.

"Mr. Harridge. Mr. Yawkey has called three times this morning. He said he wants you to call as soon as you get in," the secretary said.

Happy Chandler, the previous commissioner of Major League Baseball, had resigned a few months earlier. Pending a new commissioner, Major League Baseball was run by a four-member committee which included Harridge and Boston Red Sox owner Tom Yawkey.

Harridge sat down stunned. He had a knot in his stomach and was feeling a little light-headed. He feared that he might replace Max Patkin as the clown prince of baseball.

How could he ever explain this to "Mr. Yawkey"?

"Tell me, Earl," Harridge said in a defeated tone. "What did I ever do to Bill Veeck?"

"Mr. Harridge," Hilligan said in a hushed tone. "What do you suggest we do?"

Harridge snapped out of his spell of self-pity for the moment.

"Well, we sure as hell aren't approving the contract," Harridge said. "It's null and void. As far as Major League Baseball is concerned, this Eddie Gaedel character never existed. You get that memo out to the official scorer pronto."

Hilligan, who was a former sportswriter, grimaced.

"It's not that easy, sir," Hilligan said. "There is more to the incident than just Eddie Gaedel. The pitcher has a base on balls assigned to him in the box score, and the pinch runner also entered the game. I don't see how we can remove Eddie Gaedel from the box score when his base-on-balls and removal for a pinch runner also would have to be removed."

Harridge just nodded.

"Earl," Harridge said, with a long pause. "I don't care. Keep all the statistics the same. Just that goddamn midget is not to appear in any official box score that comes from this office! We'll apply the 'best interests of the game' standard as our rationale."

Harridge looked around at the rest of his employees.

"I'm going into my office to talk to Mr. Yawkey," Harridge said. "When I get done, we need to meet to address his concerns."

Harridge walked into his office and closed the door. He glanced at a chair he kept in his office that used to belong to former commissioner Kenesaw Mountain Landis. Harridge was an admirer of Landis. Baseball's Hall of Fame had repeatedly asked for Landis' chair for its own hallowed display, but Harridge wasn't giving it up.

Now, he understood why Landis tried to keep Veeck out of the league in 1943.

Two hours later, Harridge nullified Gaedel's contract and struck him from the official record book. Harridge then signed a letter of reprimand and had it mailed to Bill Veeck.

Two days later, Harridge received Veeck's response.

Veeck demanded that the New York Yankees' 5-foot-6 shortstop Phil Rizzuto be immediately suspended from baseball for being too short.

Veeck ended his letter, "I am baffled by all these new rules."

On Aug. 22, three days after Gaedel's infamous at-bat, Boston Globe sportswriter Victor Jones sat at his desk and started to write his column for the next day.

"He's been described as a midget," Jones wrote about Gaedel. "I prefer to say that he's a member of the human race who happens to not be as tall as some other members of the human race. He was sent into the game to get on base. And he got on base via a walk. That's the way Ted Williams often gets on base. Mr. Harridge barred Gaedel on the general grounds that he was not in the best interests of the game. Has anyone ever proved that Will Harridge was in the best interest of the game?"

CHAPTER 38

Grandstand Managers Night

Aug. 24, 1951

Bill Veeck sat at his kitchen table wearing his sports shirt and slacks. He had sandals on as he ate his breakfast with the morning newspaper. His wife, Mary Frances, was also at the table.

"No rain today, Mary. Great. And 82 degrees," Veeck muttered to his wife. "Thank God it's not the 90s like the past few days. We may sell out today after all."

"A sell out?" Mary responded. "You may want to check on the attendants for the day care. The fans love dropping off their kids and picking them up later. But with all these fans coming, you'll need a few more hands to watch over all the children."

Veeck rose and walked to the front door. Opening it, he viewed Sportsman's Park stadium. Veeck's family lived in an apartment under the stands of his baseball stadium.

Veeck tried to remember if he had someone picking up the rocking chair prop for this night's promotion. It was called, "Grandstand Managers Night," a gimmick that included the regular Browns manager sitting in a rocker on the dugout roof.

The plan was for 1,100 fans in the section right behind the home team dugout to serve in the role of team manager. They would make key strategic decisions such as when to pinch hit or remove the pitcher. Each fan was given a placard with the word "YES" on one side and "NO" on the other side. Veeck's director of promotions Bob Fishel would be in front of this section with a dozen pre-printed signs asking "Yes/No" managerial questions.

Fishel would flash a placard asking the fans a strategic question and the fans would answer by displaying either the "Yes" or "No" side of their cards. The majority ruled. Fishel would relay the response via radio to the dugout. While this was going on, the real manager Zach Taylor would relax in a rocking chair in street clothes atop the dugout "taking the night off."

Veeck had booked the legendary baseball manager Connie Mack to sit with the 1,100 fan managers. Mack, however, was 88 years old and becoming increasingly senile. Mack started managing in 1894 and continued for 53 years before retiring in 1950. There were persistent rumors that Mack had dementia and spent most of his last year in baseball asleep in the dugout. And when attentive, he would call for players who had been retired for decades to pinch hit.

Before the game, Veeck had received and ignored a telegram from the American League office advising that Philadelphia Athletics general manager Arthur Ehlers was protesting that night's promotion stating that it made a joke of the league.

An hour before the game, Veeck met with fans Charles Hughes and Clark Mitze. They submitted the best entries in the essay explaining why they should be major league managers. The American League office sent Veeck a telegram that the official Major League Baseball contracts he had submitted were rejected. They were not allowed to be on the field.

Veeck had an assistant holding a pair of two-foot trophies that had inscribed on them, "One of the best coaches ever banned from the coaching lines - from the St. Louis Browns, Aug. 24, 1951."

"I'm sorry, you can't be in the dugout," Veeck told Hughes and Mitze as they were given their trophies. "I try not to break the rules but merely to test their elasticity."

Veeck then approached the field with a megaphone.

"Ladies and gentlemen! Today, you are managing the team!" Veeck's voice boomed out.

The crowd erupted in cheers as the 1,100 fans waved their YES/NO placards wildly.

"But we won't have you go it alone. I've got the great Connie Mack to help you!" Veeck said.

The crowd let out louder cheers.

Veeck looked to Fishel, who walked Mack by the hand to his seat in the stands.

Veeck continued with the megaphone: "Connie coached for 50 years and has 3,731 career wins."

Veeck paused for that number to sink in.

"Folks, that's like if you coached a team for 20 seasons, won every game, and went 154-0 every year," Veeck said.

A confused Mack looked around as if he didn't know where he was.

A man patted Mack on the shoulder.

"Mr. Mack! It's an honor to sit next to you!" the man said.

Mack turned around and feebly shook the man's hand and nodded.

"Coach Mack! How do we beat the Athletics?" another man shouted from several rows.

Mack turned around and nodded.

"Athletics?" Mack mumbled to himself. He shook his head.

"I'm the coach of the Athletics!" Mack said, who managed that team from 1901 to 1950 before retiring.

The first pitch was thrown a few minutes later.

In the first inning, St. Louis Browns pitcher Ned Garver gave up a three-run home run, and the Browns trailed 3-0.

Sherm Lollar, the catcher for the Browns, called timeout and ran to the pitcher's mound.

"Ned. What's going on?" Lollar asked.

"The jackass Fishel just asked the fans, 'Should we warm someone up?' They are all waving 'YES' signs," Garver said. "This 'fans are the manager' spectacle is a joke!"

Lollar smiled.

"Actually, coach Taylor had me on the bench. The fans voted me in," Lollar said.

Garver looked surprised.

"Shoot. I have 14 wins. That's more than anyone on the team. Who'd they want to pitch other than me?" Garver asked.

Lollar didn't answer. He had another pressing concern.

Sherm and Connie Lollar met in 1946 where she was a bookkeeper and he was playing for Bill Veeck's Cleveland Indians. Sherm was traded twice and when he landed in St. Louis with the Browns, the Lollars got married on July 10, 1949. The Lollars held the ceremony after Sherm's St. Louis Browns game against the Cleveland Indians. Sherm had a base hit in the day game and then got married later that night.

Sherm and his wife had an agreement – she was not to attend his games as it made him very nervous.

But this promotion was too much fun for Connie Lollar to stay away. She sweet talked her husband into letting her attend.

"Ned," Sherm Lollar said. "Look in the third row where the fan managers are sitting."

"OK. Who am I looking for? I only see your wife, Connie. And there's also Connie Mack," Garver said.

"Wait, I never see your wife at games," Garver said.

"Yeah," Lollar responded. "I told her I don't like it when she comes to the games. But with this stupid grandstand fan night - she really wanted to come."

Garver nodded.

"I was wondering why I never see your wife at the games. You guys are inseparable off the field. She's your biggest fan," Garver said.

"She is my biggest fan and the best wife any mug could have," Lollar said. "But I get worried about looking bad in front of her. I get so nervous, and it messes me up. And now, the fans voted me in, and she's all excited. If I stink up the field, I'll let everyone down."

Garver smiled and gave an envious grin.

"Sherm, if I ever am lucky enough to meet a woman with that kind of hold on me …." Garver said.

Just then, Umpire Bill Summers approached the two and interrupted Garver.

"Gentlemen, would it be acceptable to you if we resumed playing baseball again," Summers asked facetiously.

"Bill, he's all nervous that his wife insisted she come to the game," Garver said.

Summers turned around.

"Where is she?" the umpire asked.

"She's in the third row of the grandstand in the white dress. She's got the Yes card in her lap," Garver said.

Connie Lollar sat in the stands smiling, surrounded by the mob of fans waving their cards to answer another question.

"Lovely woman. Now, can we start playing baseball again?" the umpire asked.

Lollar nodded and turned around to look at the fans.

There were runners on first and third base. The fans were asked if they wanted to play the infield back to try and get a groundball double play or pull the infielders in to try to throw the runner on third out at home on a ground ball.

Fishel held up a sign that read, "PLAY INFIELD IN," and the fans waved their Yes and No signs.

Lollar tried to count them in his head.

Fishel then used his walkie-talkie to tell St. Louis Brown infielder John Berardino to relay the message to Lollar. Regular manager Zach Taylor sat in a rocking chair on the roof of the dugout, smoking a pipe as it was his official day off.

"They will want us to play back for the double play!" Lollar said.

"Bullshit! We are already down three runs in the first inning. We can't give up another run," Garver shot back.

"I'm the catcher. I set the defense. I'm doing what the fans said," Lollar said with a smile.

"That's just because they put you in the lineup, Sherm," Garver said.

Lollar winked, blew a mock kiss to Garver, and motioned for the infielders to play back. The next batter hit a hard ground ball to second base, and it turned into a double play. The fans called the proper defense.

At that moment, Philadelphia Athletics' manager Jimmy Dykes came running out of the dugout like his hair was on fire. He ran up to umpire Summers.

"Bill! This game has to be declared a forfeit! The fans are taking too long to make their decision. This is a disgrace. It's your job to enforce the rules!" Dykes bellowed as he stood toe-to-toe with the umpire.

"There's nothing in the rules, Jimmy, about a time limit on a manager's decision. If there were, I'd forfeit half the games you manage," Summers shot back.

"You are enjoying this charade!" Dykes shouted at Summers.

"Gee. Jimmy. Fans questioning a manager's every call?" Summers shot back sarcastically. "Instead of worrying about the fans, you better get back to managing. The Browns are the worst team in baseball. You lose to the worst team in baseball with their manager sitting in a rocking chair on top of the dugout, smoking a pipe. Maybe Philly will have a few grandstand manager nights, too?"

Dykes took two steps and then kicked dirt over home plate and stormed back to the dugout. Summers was annoyed that he had to bend over and clear off home plate. Usually, he'd eject a manager for such a stunt. But Summers wanted Dykes to have to sit through the game.

"Jackass," Summers muttered as he cleaned off the plate.

In the third inning, the game was tied 3-3 as Lollar came up to hit.

Dykes remembered that Lollar was a last-minute replacement as picked by the fans to play. They had to change the official lineups that were exchanged before the game.

"Hey. Lollar! Your own manager knew Batts was a better catcher," Dykes yelled to Lollar, referring to the Browns' other catcher Matt Batts. "The nitwit fans put you into the lineup!"

Connie Lollar was upset hearing Dykes mocking her husband.

She took her YES sign and started waving it at her husband. Lollar turned around and looked at his wife. He swallowed and tried not to acknowledge his biggest fan. He looked at Dykes and just shook his head at the manager.

Summers stepped away from the plate and looked at Dykes.

"Hey, Jimmy. Knock it off. His wife is in the stands watching," Summers said.

"Ha! I was wondering how he got in the lineup! His old lady voted him in!" Dykes yelled back.

Two pitches later, Lollar swung and connected.

The ball shot upwards into the sky. Sherm Lollar briefly watched it. He lit up as the ball disappeared into the left-field bleachers. Lollar hit his eighth home run of the season.

As he ran around the bases, the fans held up their YES placards and cheered.

Lollar stepped on home plate and gave a look to Dykes, and then looked into the stands for Connie. His wife had been swallowed up by the cheering fans who were on their feet.

The crowd of managers sensed they could win a game for the hapless Browns.

It was the ninth inning. The St. Louis Browns, the worst team in baseball, were three outs away from winning a game managed by the fans. The Browns led 5-3.

Garver took the mound for the final inning. He couldn't help but look to the stands. He saw Fishel holding up a sign to the fans that read, "Should we jerk the bum?"

A section of fans waving NO cards showed the vote solidly in his favor.

Garver retired the last three batters in a row, striking out the final

Athletics player to end the game.

After the game, St. Louis Post-Dispatch reporter Bob Broeg interviewed Connie Mack.

"Connie, do you think Veeck is making a joke of the league?" Broeg asked.

Fishel was Mack's chaperone for the day and listened nervously to Broeg's question.

Mack turned slowly and smiled at the sportswriter.

"No," Mack said. "They had the infield play back in the second inning and got the double play. That's all managing is, really. Just trusting your hunches."

Fishel was incredibly relieved by Connie's moment of lucidity.

Broeg went across the field and got to the steps of the dugout, where Athletics' manager Dykes was standing.

"Jimmy, the worst team in baseball just beat you, and they were managed by the fans," Broeg told Dykes.

"Ah, bullshit," a still fuming Dykes said. "The fans didn't beat me. Ned Garver did. He's going to win 20 games this year for the worst team in the league."

"Jimmy, what did you think of Grandstand Managers Night?" Broeg asked.

"It's a disgrace to the game. I feel sorry for Zack Taylor to have to degrade himself," Dykes said.

St. Louis Browns manager Zach Taylor was still sitting in his rocking chair in street clothes, enjoying the victory. He saw Veeck approaching.

"Hey, boss. Do I still have a job?" Taylor asked Veeck.

Veeck chuckled and nodded toward the field.

At that moment fireworks went off behind Dykes and the sportswriter. Both were startled. Broeg and Dykes turned around. In the middle of the outfield, a pyrotechnics sign was on fire, and it spelled out: "Thanks grandstand managers for a swell job. Zack manages tomorrow."

CHAPTER 39

Veeck Hires Confederate-Bred Rogers Hornsby As Manager

March 28, 1952

It was 81 degrees at noon, and Bill Veeck stood along the fence of Olive Memorial Stadium in Burbank, California. A warm breeze rustled through his sports shirt. The warmth reminded him why he loved spring training. After spending most of his life in the Midwest, summer-style temperatures in March lifted his spirits.

He looked up and saw Fred Lieb approaching. Veeck instantly smiled.

The 63-year-old Lieb started his sports writing career in 1909, writing profiles on players for Baseball magazine. Along the way, he formed friendships with some of the game's biggest names, including Lou Gehrig and Babe Ruth.

In 1931, Lieb led a barnstorming tour to Japan and Hawaii that featured some of the era's big-name players. The hugely profitable venture helped liberate Lieb from daily sportswriter duties, allowing him to launch a syndicated baseball-only column that ultimately appeared in more than 100 newspapers nationwide.

Fred Lieb became his generation's most influential baseball writer and covered every World Series game from 1911 through 1951. But his real gift was enticing his sources to open up to him. He had a disarming demeanor with a thin mustache and deeply receding hairline that gave him the look of a college professor.

Perhaps that is why Rogers Hornsby and Tris Speaker confided in Lieb that they were members of the Ku Klux Klan. That admission didn't sit well with the veteran baseball writer, but he wasn't the type to admonish players with whom he had developed relationships while covering their careers.

Lieb had also known Bill Veeck's father, Bill Veeck Sr., who had been a sportswriter before becoming the Chicago Cubs' general manager.

Veeck Jr. was fond of Lieb and hadn't seen him since the previous World Series six months earlier.

"Let me guess," Veeck said when Lieb came within earshot. "You are writing a book on this year's St. Louis Browns miracle championship season?"

Lieb snickered.

"I don't write fiction," Lieb responded.

They shook hands.

"Actually, I do have an idea I'm pitching to my publisher," Lieb said. "It's a book about comedians and pranksters in baseball."

Veeck's eyes lit up.

"Well, you've come to the right man," Veeck said.

"I do have a question," Lieb said. "It is the most burning question among us sportswriters this spring."

Veeck was now curious.

"What inspired you to hire Rogers Hornsby?" Lieb asked. "It's the most bizarre partnership in baseball I've ever seen."

Lieb wasn't the only one to question the move. The Black newspapers were much more aware of Hornsby's checkered background.

Four days after Hornsby was hired by Veeck, Black sportswriter Wendell Smith questioned the move in an article.

Smith cited Hornsby's long history of giving no praise to Black ballplayers, whether it be Larry Doby or Monte Irvin, another promising Black player who started with the New York Giants in 1949.

And now Hornsby would be managing the free-spirited Satchel Paige.

Smith described the Veeck-Hornsby marriage with these words: "… a Texas-born, Confederate-bred Rogers Hornsby, who will, we are reliably informed, manage the St. Louis Browns, owned by Chicago-born, Yankee-bred Bill Veeck …"

Smith quoted Hornsby after Jackie Robinson broke the color barrier in 1947, saying Hornsby howled like a Texas coyote.

"Negro ballplayers and white ballplayers will never get along," Smith quoted Hornsby as saying. "It is socially impossible for them to do so. Negro players should stay in their own leagues. I'm sure they will be happier there. Not only that, but I don't think there are any good enough to make the majors."

Smith reported that when Hornsby managed in the Pacific Coast League in 1951, his team was the only one without a Black player.

"The stench of racial prejudice has hovered over Hornsby through the years," Smith wrote in his article. "Perhaps Veeck is not familiar with Mr. Hornsby's record. If he does not have a clear understanding with Hornsby on this matter of Negro players, Veeck may wake up some morning and find his club and well-laid plans torn asunder."

Now, even the white Lieb was questioning the move.

Veeck responded to Lieb's question.

"He worked for us as a hitting instructor with the Indians three years ago," Veeck said. "I didn't have much interaction with him."

"But everything Hornsby touches turns toxic," Lieb pointed out.

When Hornsby's son died in a military training accident in 1949,

Hornsby's wife barred him from attending the funeral.

His other son, Bill, had recently retired from baseball with a dismal .200 batting average.

Rogers Hornsby told a reporter, "I'm glad Billy learned early that he wasn't a real player. … Imagine how I would have felt, seeing the Hornsby name down in the batting averages with the pitchers."

Shaking his head, Lieb summed it up.

"I can't think of a thing you two have in common," Lieb said.

Veeck put up his hand.

"We have one essential thing in common," Veeck said. "We both want to win. Promotions don't work so well when you lose 102 games."

Lieb nodded in agreement.

Veeck paused his conversation with Lieb.

Just then, Satchel Paige walked onto the field.

Veeck perked up.

"Hey, Satch! Come on over here," Veeck called out.

Veeck turned to Lieb.

"We signed Satchel Paige last year in mid-season. This year, we get him the full year," Veeck said.

Paige strolled over.

"Satch. This is Mr. Lieb. He writes for The Sporting News," Veeck said.

Paige nodded with an infectious smile.

"Satchel. The word is that you are five years older than your listed age. Word is you're 45," Lieb said.

Paige pretended to be confused.

"Like I've been telling you guys for years, I'm 39," Paige said.

Veeck interjected.

"We will have a 'Guess Satchel Paige's Age' promotion. The closest guess gets a free turkey dinner," Veeck said.

Lieb looked to Veeck.

"You know his age?" Lieb asked, hoping to get the answer to the sportswriters' persistent water-cooler chat question.

"Me and Satch drove down to Mobile and got a copy of his birth certificate in 1948 when we signed him in Cleveland," Veeck said.

"You going to share his age?" Lieb asked.

Veeck smiled.

"We'll reveal it during the promotion," he said.

Lieb turned to Paige.

"Satchel. Looking back, you ever regret not being able to play during your prime in the majors?" Lieb asked.

"I never look back," Paige said. "Something might be gaining on me."

Paige nodded to Veeck.

"I'm going to go warm up now, Bill!" Paige said as he jogged off to the pitching mound.

Lieb put his pencil and notebook away in his pocket. It signaled to Veeck that they were now off-the-record.

"Hornsby won't pitch Satchel with the game on the line," Lieb said.

Veeck laughed and shook his head.

"Satch is our best pitcher. The fans love him," Veeck said.

"Hornsby doesn't respect Negroes or Jews. He told me when he played for the Cubs, he was a member of the Ku Klux Klan. He's a Texas boy," Lieb said.

Veeck's smile disappeared.

"Well, Hornsby will like Satch once he has the most wins on the team," Veeck said.

Lieb shrugged.

"Hey, I never did get a chance to talk to you about that Sporting News editorial," Lieb said.

In 1948, The Sporting News Publisher J. G. Taylor Spink wrote that Veeck went too far by signing Paige due to his age. Spink wrote that if Satch were white, Veeck would never have given Paige a chance to play for the Indians.

"I agreed with it," Veeck said.

Lieb was stunned.

"It's 100% true," Veeck said. "If Satch were white, I never would have signed him. That's because if Satch were white, he would have been in the big leagues 25 years ago."

Lieb laughed.

"Hey," Lieb said. "Mr. Spink wanted me to tell you he got your telegrams."

Veeck smiled. After every one of Paige's six victories that year, Veeck sent Spink a telegram that said simply: "Paige, winning pitcher."

Veeck had more to tell Lieb about Paige.

"And, this year, he's going to play the snare drum during the seventh-inning stretch. He's a natural. That man is full of surprises," Veeck said admiringly.

"Your players will play songs for the fans during the seventh-inning stretch? What other antics do you have up your sleeve this year? You know, baseball doesn't like them," Lieb said.

Veeck waved off Lieb.

"You mean the owners and commissioner don't like them. You know the fans love them. They pay my salary, not the league," Veeck said.

CHAPTER 40

The Air Had Been Sucked Out Of The Room

March 31, 1952

The train carrying both the Pittsburgh Pirates and the St. Louis Browns had just arrived in Corpus Christi, Texas. Players were making their way down the train steps and toward the station's cab stand to catch a ride to Schepps Palms Field, seven miles away. In four hours the next exhibition game between the two teams would begin.

The two teams were making a post-spring training sweep through Texas and giving baseball fans a chance to see major league players. At that time, St. Louis was the most southernly city with a major league franchise.

Branch Rickey was sitting on a station bench waiting for a cab. In 1950, five years after signing Jackie Robinson to the Brooklyn Dodgers, Rickey moved on to Pittsburgh to become the general manager.

Rickey picked up a three-day old issue of the Corpus Christi Caller-Times newspaper that had been left behind on the bench. It reported the municipality had banned Blacks from using city golf courses and cited opposition to the decision by Dr. H. Boyd Hall of the local NAACP.

A letter from the city's Parks and Recreation Board chairman advised the ban was temporary, pending further consideration of "what arrangements could be made consistent with the laws of the state and consistent with the common good."

Rickey saw Satchel Paige coming down the steps from the train. The two had smoothed over the hard feelings Paige still felt for not being selected as the major league's first Black player.

"Are you pitching tonight, Satch?" Rickey asked.

"The game doesn't start until I arrive," Paige responded, flashing his trademark smile.

"Well, good luck," Rickey said.

"When will you be signing Negroes for Pittsburgh?" Paige asked.

"Not yet," Rickey said. "We just traded for Curt Roberts last year. He's still in the minors but may get the nod next year."

Rickey spotted a cab arriving and stood up. He shook Paige's hand before walking over to get in a taxi.

Paige sat back on the bench. He had been in Corpus Christi before while playing in the Negro Leagues. Six years earlier, at a field called Fireman's Park that had giant potholes in the infield, he pitched for the Kansas City Monarchs against the St. Louis Cubs. The crowd was almost all Black fans, but the best seats remained empty and reserved for whites.

Paige found himself in Corpus Christi again after the 1949 baseball season when he put together an all-star barnstorming team that included white teammates of his from the Cleveland Indians.

Paige knew the biggest challenge of a trip to the city was getting from the train station to the ballpark. With few exceptions, the white cab drivers refused to take fares from Black customers.

One of the more subtle aspects of the racism that was endemic in America at that time and the many discriminatory laws, rules and conventions it imposed, was how it made living a normal life all but impossible for Blacks.

Most white Americans were oblivious to these burdens and had little understanding or appreciation of how they blighted the lives of millions of their fellow countrymen.

In 1952, taxi cabs were the most common way for ballplayers to get to the ballpark when they were out of town. Paige's teammates may not have realized that he may not be able to find a cab driver willing to transport a Black man. The alternative was for Paige to walk the seven miles for a game scheduled to begin in four hours.

Decades later, a white man named Max Womack described how he learned of this particular injustice and the shame it left with him.

In 1946, at a cab stand in Nashville's train station, Womack got behind a Black Army lieutenant who had already been waiting several minutes for a taxi. When one pulled up, and the Black veteran didn't step forward, Womack said to the cab driver, "He's ahead of me."

The cab driver said he wouldn't accept the Black man as a fare. A little later, a battered sedan with a cardboard "Taxi" sign and a Black driver arrived and the Black lieutenant had found a ride.

Womack said he never forgot the humiliation on the Black officer's face and his own feelings of shame and helplessness.

In the Corpus Christi of 1952, Satchel Paige walked over to where several taxi cabs were waiting for fares outside the station. The cabbies knew the train schedules and a half dozen were lined up.

"You going to Schepps?" Paige asked one driver. The cabbie just shook his head.

Paige moved to the next in line.

"Need a lift to the ballpark," he said.

"Already got a fare," was the response. Paige continued down the line and received similar refusals from every one of the half dozen drivers waiting for a fare.

Black players were expected to walk if they couldn't get a ride. It was 83 degrees and getting hotter. Paige looked around and shook his head.

He walked back to the train, found a seat in the section reserved for Blacks in the back of the car and took a nap.

Ten days later, and three days before the start of the regular season, Browns' manager Rogers Hornsby sat in Bill Veeck's office at the stadium back in St. Louis. It was the first time the manager and owner had talked since Veeck left the spring training camp in March.

Hornsby handed Veeck several forms he had filled out.

"This is the list of fines I imposed," Hornsby said.

Veeck took the papers and reviewed them.

"There's a $100 fine for Satchel," Veeck said. "What's that about?"

Hornsby straightened up. He knew Veeck had a soft spot for the Black pitcher.

"In Texas, he skipped a game," Hornsby said. "I can't have that on my team. Especially this colored goofball you stuck me with. The coloreds can't be depended on to show up."

"Did he give a reason?" Veeck pressed.

Hornsby didn't like being questioned. Paige told him at the time that no cab driver would take him to the park. Hornsby snarled at Paige, "What do you expect me to do? Lead you around by the hand?"

Hornsby looked at Veeck.

"Some excuse about not being able to get a taxi to take him," Hornsby said. "That boy has his own airplane, right? Should have flown that to the game!"

Hornsby laughed at his joke.

Veeck sat back. He knew enough from the time he had spent in

Texas to realize that Paige's explanation was not an excuse, but the face of something ugly.

Veeck nodded.

"And these other fines?" Veeck asked. "The ball boys?"

The St. Louis Browns had employed young teenagers to chase down foul balls and retrieve them to be used again in games.

"The goddamn ball boys aren't doing their job. They only recovered about half the foul balls," Hornsby shot back. "I think they are keeping some and selling them on the side."

Veeck nodded again.

The meeting was over. Hornsby got up and walked out. Veeck dropped the papers detailing the fines into the waste basket.

A month later, and nine games into the new season, the St. Louis Browns' record was 7-2. Hornsby had miraculously turned a laughingstock franchise that lost 102 games the previous year into a winner.

But he had yet to pitch Satchel Paige in a game.

Paige played his first game on April 26 when he pitched two innings in relief and didn't give up a run in a 5-0 loss in Chicago against the White Sox.

In the next game, April 27, Hornsby called on Paige again.

The starting pitcher Ned Garver entered the fifth inning with a 3-0 lead but gave up four runs on five hits and a walk with still one out needed to get out of the jam.

Hornsby came to the mound and motioned for Paige to go in. Paige did his customary stroll from the bullpen.

Paige looked around with runners on first and second. He looked at the batter, Jim Busby.

"Young man," Paige called out to Busby. "I call this pitch the midnight dodger. Because it will be midnight before you realize what hit you."

Paige went through his exaggerated windmill motion twice and threw the pitch. And Busby got a piece of it, and it bounced right back to Paige.

Busby wasn't even out of the batter's box, and Paige had the ball in his mitt. He looked at Busby and started walking toward his catcher, Sherm Lollar.

With Busby hustling to first base and Paige still walking in the opposite direction toward home plate, Lollar thought Paige maybe believed he caught the ball in mid-air and made the final out.

But Busby knew it was a bouncer and was running hard. The confused Lollar just stared as Paige kept walking until … suddenly Paige whipped an under-arm shot to the first baseman without even looking, throwing Busby out and retiring the side. The no-look rocket to first base left Lollar stunned.

Paige was wearing his million-dollar smile, but it disappeared at the sight of a furious Rogers Hornsby waiting for him in the dugout.

"This isn't one of your jigaboo barnstorming games!" Hornsby raged. "I played on this field with Babe Ruth and Lou Gehrig. Show some respect!"

"I'm just here to pitch," Paige said. "I know how to do that. If you remember, coach, in one of those jigaboo barnstorming games I struck you out two times. You didn't get a piece of a single pitch and blamed it on being a night game with new lights."

Hornsby responded with a menacing smile.

"You just can't control that mouth, can you, boy?" Hornsby said. "Keep it up. That's all you'll be doing – barnstorming. You keep those Negro antics off the mound!"

"You're the manager," Paige conceded.

After facing just one batter, Hornsby replaced Paige with a pinch hitter.

On June 3, the Browns played the Washington Senators on the road. The game was tied 2-2 in the 12th inning when Hornsby finally sent Paige to the mound.

Paige pitched the next six innings without giving up a run. With two outs in the top of the 17th inning, it was Paige's turn at the plate. This time, Hornsby had no one left on the bench to pinch-hit.

Paige ripped a base hit that allowed teammate Joe DeMaestri to score and gave the Browns the lead. It was Paige's third hit of the game.

Paige pitched the final inning and got the victory and improved his record to 5-1.

The game lasted more than four hours. The team's record improved to 21-26. It wasn't great, but the Browns were no longer a laughingstock.

The Browns' players celebrated on the field and then they filed into the locker room. Spirits were high all around as players Sherm Lollar and Ned Garver hooted and hollered and patted Paige on the back.

Hornsby had skipped the on-field celebration with his players and now was coming out of the shower in the midst of the locker room celebration. The players went silent at the sight of their detested manager. Hornsby didn't say a word.

On Paige's greatest day as a St. Louis Brown, Hornsby passed him by without making eye contact and went into the manager's office and shut the door.

The celebration was over. The air had been sucked out of the room as Hornsby crushed his team's spirit.

CHAPTER 41

I'd Rather Lose Without You Than Win With You

June 10, 1952

Gayle Talbot, a 50-year-old sports columnist for the Associated Press, cradled a beer in the bar of the luxurious Omni Parker House Hotel. With him was 76-year-old Melville Webb, a recently retired Boston Globe sportswriter who felt out of place by the posh surroundings.

"Why did you invite me here?" Webb asked. "You know I'm retired. We never drank here."

Talbot smiled and leaned forward.

"I got a tip. Veeck is firing Hornsby," Talbot said.

Webb shook his head.

"Veeck isn't that nuts. He just signed Hornsby to a three-year deal," Webb said.

"I heard it right from the horse's mouth," Talbot said.

"If that horse is Veeck, you better make sure it passes the post-race drug test," Webb snorted.

Then Webb smiled.

"That may be the only horse that Hornsby hasn't bet on!" Webb said as both he and Talbot erupted in laughter. Hornsby had a reputation for betting and losing a lot of money on the horses. A former friend sued Hornsby in court in 1927 claiming Hornsby owed him $70,000, the equivalent of $1.2 million in 2023 dollars. Hornsby made $30,000 in 1927 as one of baseball's top paid players.

"Seriously," Talbot said. "It would be nearly impossible to imagine two more opposite personalities."

Webb tried to get a waitress to take his order. Then he leaned over to say something in private.

"Hey, I just saw this in the newspaper yesterday," Webb said. "Hornsby's wife filed for divorce. She's claiming he won't pay her a reasonable monthly allowance. Wait until she hears he just lost his job!"

Talbot paused as the gossip sunk in.

"Hornsby is honestly the biggest horse's ass I ever met," Talbot said. "He's just always biting the head off of reporters no matter what question they asked. His wife has my complete sympathy."

A mile away, the St. Louis Browns' train was pulling into the Boston train station.

St. Louis Browns' traveling secretary Bill Durney, a chubby man in a tweed jacket with a background in radio public relations, was trying to track down Hornsby.

Durney spotted Hornsby as he exited the train.

"Mr. Hornsby," Durney called out.

Hornsby turned and immediately cringed.

"Mr. Veeck has asked to meet with you at the Omni Parker House Hotel," Durney said. "Shall I call you a cab?"

"It's not even a mile away!" Hornsby snapped. "I'll walk. Wouldn't do you any harm to get out and exercise."

Durney was used to Hornsby's abuse. He knew former athletes didn't respect reporters or people from the business side of baseball.

"Let me guess," Hornsby said. "Did he sign some more midgets?"

Just then, St. Louis Brown's outfielder Earl Rapp walked by.

"Those midgets would have a better chance of getting on base than Rapp," Hornsby said while Rapp deflated hearing the insult from the team's manager.

Hornsby looked at Durney.

"Have someone take my bags to the hotel, and I'll go meet with Veeck," he snapped. "If I have to meet with the owner every time this team has a three-game losing streak …."

A short time later, Hornsby walked into Veeck's hotel room and shut the door behind him. Hornsby was scowling and not in a good mood. Bill Veeck was sitting at a desk with that day's newspaper in his hands when Hornsby sat down. Veeck laid the newspaper down in front of him.

"What? You are going to tell me your latest promotion - resurrect Eddie Collins before the game, have him pop out of a damn cake, and put him at second base?" Hornsby said with an adversarial tone. Collins was a Hall of Fame second baseman who died the previous year.

There was an uncomfortable silence. Veeck wasn't smiling.

"You don't like my managing," Hornsby said, noticing this wasn't the usual lecture on tips Veeck would give him.

"I was told that baseball came first with you. That was all you cared about," Veeck said.

"You still sore I didn't protest that umpire's call Saturday in New York? I'm the manager. Not you," Hornsby shot back.

Veeck shook his head.

"You blew that. But it's not the issue," Veeck said. "Satchel. Why don't you pitch him more? You keep him in the bullpen, mostly in blowout games. He was our best draw last year. The fans loved him. If you don't pitch him, I can't promote him, and I don't know when he will pitch."

Veeck looked at Hornsby.

"Hell, on Friday, you waited until the ninth inning to bring him in against Washington, and that was because you didn't have any pitchers left. Satch has only given up a run in his last 22 innings, and yet he sits," Veeck said.

Hornsby smirked.

"I just do what I need to win. If I thought a colored player would help me win, I'd play him. We lost to the Yankees last night. They got that kid Mickey Mantle. Mize. Rizzuto. Why don't you walk your peg-leg butt to their dugout and see if Casey Stengel would swap rosters with me? Give him the colored player while you're at it," Hornsby growled.

Hornsby stared right at Veeck.

"I told you I'd improve your team when you hired me. You want to bring the circus to town, and I don't care. Just keep it outside of the lines when I'm managing. We started the season winning seven out of our first nine games. You didn't win your seventh game last year until mid-May. You had midgets batting, and you had that fairy Max Patkin as a third-base coach last year. Patkin is a disgrace. You lost more than 100 games. We will probably win 30 more games this year, and that's because of me. It's the same damn rotten players, Bill. The only thing that changed was me."

Veeck paused.

"Win 30 more games," Veeck said, seemingly talking to himself.

Veeck nodded approvingly.

"I hope we do. But you won't be here to see it. I'm firing you," Veeck said.

Hornsby was stunned.

"You are firing me when we are just 51 games into the season? I got a three-year contract for $100,000. You are going to pay me not to coach for the next three years?" Hornsby asked incredulously.

Veeck nodded.

"I've made bigger financial mistakes. I got divorced and had to sell my team. I still like my ex-wife more than you, and she cost me my world champion Indians."

Hornsby shook his head in disgust and got up.

"Rajah, we both have a World Series ring. And mine is a heck of a lot more recent. I love winning. I've won wherever I've gone. Winning is the best promotion. But God's honest truth? You know what?" Veeck asked.

Veeck had Hornsby's attention because he had never referred to Hornsby before by his "Rajah" nickname.

"I'd rather lose without you than win with you," Veeck said.

Hornsby had no response.

He turned around and left.

Leaving the hotel, Hornsby ran into a waiting Talbot.

"Rajah, is it true?" Talbot asked.

Hornsby stopped.

"How'd you find out?" Hornsby snapped.

Talbot was silent.

"I'm not going to go for any of his screwy ideas," Hornsby said. "When you work for a screwball, you have to expect screwball tactics."

Hornsby paused. He nodded.

"And you can tell the world that Veeck is a screwball," Hornsby said. "Veeck is just publicity crazy. He wants to get his name in the newspapers all the time. And that's what he did today!"

Hornsby exited the hotel, and Talbot left to file his scoop.

Durney was entering the hotel just as Hornsby got into a cab. Durney ran into Talbot.

"Hey, your boss just fired Rajah!" Talbot said as he bolted to the exit.

Durney went right to Veeck's room.

"You fired Rajah?" Durney said.

Veeck sat back and lit a cigarette.

"I made a mistake," Veeck admitted. "Hornsby knows more about baseball and less about people than any man alive. Satch has given up just one run in the last 22 innings, and that redneck won't pitch him more than an inning or two."

"We are losing games because he won't use Satch," Veeck said, shaking his head. "And he's the only damn thing we have to promote on this team."

"You see his extra windmill arm motion on his delivery?" Veeck asked. "He doesn't have to do that. He's putting on a show. This man is a born entertainer. And Hornsby won't pitch him. We'd get 30,000 to see Satch pitch."

Durney stood in silence.

"Well, I know the players will support the move," Durney said.

Veeck paused. A thought was going through his head. Durney had seen that look before.

"Bill. Get a pad and a pencil. The players are about to award me a trophy for firing Hornsby," Veeck said. "It's a night game. And you got about four hours to get the trophy made."

When Veeck walked into the dugout at Fenway Park six hours later he was met by the St. Louis Browns players and six newspaper reporters.

St. Louis Browns pitcher Ned Garver approached Veeck and handed him a 24-inch silver trophy. Garver took out a card and began to read from it.

"This is from us players in thanks for getting rid of Rogers Hornsby. To Bill Veeck, for the greatest play since the Declaration of Independence," Garver said.

Veeck stepped back with an awkward look on his face.

"Wait, Ned. Are you reading that right?" Veeck asked.

Garver looked puzzled.

"That's what I wrote down," Garver said.

Veeck looked awkward.

"But that's not what is on the trophy, Ned," Veeck said.

Garver walked over and looked at the trophy.

Garver nodded.

"Sorry," the pitcher said. "To Bill Veeck, for the greatest play since the Emancipation Proclamation."

The dozen other St. Louis players cheered and patted Veeck on the back, and reporters moved in to interview players.

Talbot asked St. Louis pitcher Gene Bearden, "What did you think of the firing of Hornsby?"

Bearden didn't hesitate.

"He doesn't have a friend in the world. And he doesn't deserve one," Bearden said.

Paige approached Veeck.

"Bill. This Emancipation Proclamation line. Does that mean I'm free to pitch my way?" Paige asked.

Veeck was beaming.

"Free at last, Satch. And I wouldn't be happy if you didn't let it all hang loose," Veeck said.

Paige smiled. His groove was back.

CHAPTER 42

The 45-Pound Catfish

June 20, 1952

Bill Veeck's father began his career as a sportswriter for the Chicago American newspaper. The articles that Bill Veeck Sr. wrote criticizing the Chicago Cubs became so tiresome to Cubs owner William Wrigley that he hired the elder Veeck to be the vice president of his baseball team.

It was a classic "OK, wise guy. You think you can do better?" type of hire.

Bill Veeck Jr. learned at an early age the influence of newspapers.

Decades later, Bill Veeck Jr. came to talk to a group of newspaper publishers with one mission – get Satchel Paige selected to the current season's American League all-star team.

The event was the National Newspaper Publishers Association's 1952 annual conference, held at the Kiel Auditorium in St. Louis. The speaking invitation provided direct access to many of the most influential people in the newspaper business. At the podium, Veeck stood before the editors, publishers and executives wearing his trademark open sports shirt with no tie.

Veeck told the publishers that he had sent a letter to New York Yankees' manager Casey Stengel urging him to select Paige for the all-star team. Because the Yankees won the previous year's World Series, it was Stengel's job this year to pick the all-stars for the American League team.

Veeck implored the publishers to join his campaign to make Paige an official all-star. He asked the newspaper executives to urge their readers to also write Stengel to select Paige.

"If I had to have a pitcher to win one game in a World Series, it would be Ole Satch," Veeck told the publishers. "If push comes to shove, you can take all my [St. Louis] Brownies away from me but leave me Satchel Paige."

"Paige deserves a place on the team," Veeck told the audience. "It would be a great honor to a great athlete and to the Negro people."

John Johnson, the Black sports editor of the Black newspaper the Kansas City Call, sat in attendance and swelled with pride that Veeck would advocate for a Black player.

"This man," Johnson thought, "loves Satchel Paige."

Society may not have been on Veeck's side, Johnson thought. Johnson knew that the Browns had given a tryout to a Black pitcher named Willie Harris earlier in 1952. Harris was from Chicago and Veeck invited him to St. Louis for a workout.

But Harris was not allowed to stay in any of the St. Louis hotels and the only place he was welcomed to eat was the Union Station train depot.

Veeck went from the conference to the ballpark for that night's June 20 game against the Washington Senators. Veeck was greeted by the sight of Satchel Paige lounging on a canvas recliner placed in the pitcher's bullpen.

Much had changed in the few days since Veeck fired manager Rogers Hornsby. Veeck purchased a luxurious body-contour lounge recliner for Paige and stuck it in the bullpen, something Hornsby would never have allowed. The recliner came with a canvas top with the word "Satch" displayed on each side.

In the eighth inning, Paige got the call to enter the game from his new manager, Marty Marion.

Paige did his customary stroll to the bullpen as the 8,000 fans applauded.

Paige got to the mound, and Marion gave him the ball.

"The last guy got fired for not trusting you," Marion said. "Don't make me look like a fool. This game is yours."

Paige took the ball and did his warmups. There was a runner on second base.

He looked at the first batter, Washington Senator Pete Runnels. He smiled.

"I'm bringing a slow pitch that I call Stepin Pitchit!" Paige yelled, a reference to the Black actor Stepin Fetchit. "But I am telling you that you won't, Stepin Hitit!"

Runnels laced a shot into right field and knocked in the runner from second base to tie the game 4-4.

Paige took the ball back and was furious.

Mel Hoderlein, the next batter, popped out to end the inning.

Paige got back to the bench and looked at Marion.

"You keep me in, coach," Paige said. "I won't give up any runs."

Marion did keep Paige in the game. And for another nine innings, Satchel Paige didn't give up a run.

In the top of the 18th inning, Marion approached Paige.

"Satch," Marion said. "You did your job. And then some. You gave me 10 innings of shutout ball. I'm bringing in George to pinch-hit for you. It's midnight. We need to score a run."

Paige nodded. He understood. He pitched 10 shutout innings.

At 1:04 a.m., the game was called with a tie score due to a curfew.

On June 27, the Browns beat the Detroit Tigers. Paige was one of the first players to leave the stadium after the final out.

Paige grew up in poverty in Mobile, Alabama. And in those days, fishing was both a personal passion and a way to feed his family.

Paige loved the serenity of a good fishing hole and he had a knack for finding them. It wasn't long after his arrival in St. Louis when he found his spot.

It was just off State Route 79, on the banks of the Mississippi River near a sleepy, one-street town of 4,400 people called Louisiana, Missouri.

It was sufficiently isolated that Paige didn't have to worry about trouble from white people offended a Black man was infringing on their fishing spot.

Paige rarely felt better than he did driving to his fishing hole. He had just pitched two shutout innings to record his ninth save of the season in a 2-1 win over the Detroit Tigers. The thorn in his side that was Rogers Hornsby was just a memory. He chuckled at the newspaper headlines that replayed in his mind when Hornsby was fired. His favorite was, "Players Hated Rogers Hornsby"... "Not A Friend In The World"...

It was almost midnight when Paige reached his spot, located on the Missouri side of the Mississippi River, just a few hundred yards from the Champ Clark Bridge. The water levels were rising after rains washed food into the rivers. The fish would be biting.

With his loaded pistol on his hip underneath his shirt, Paige cast his fly-fishing line into the river and stood on the shore. The moon was out, and its reflection bounced off the slow-moving river.

Paige was holding the pole in one hand and felt a slight tug. Just as his other hand reached for the pole, it was nearly jerked out of his hand. Paige felt like he was being dragged into the Mississippi River and had to lean back with all his might. It felt like his line may have hooked onto a boat, but the river was clear.

Paige watched his pole bend into a "U" shape by the pull at the other end of the line.

Paige felt himself slowly being pulled into the river.

Back at his St. Louis residence late the next morning, Paige answered a knock at his door. A photographer from United Press International introduced himself.

Paige led the photographer into his bathroom, and there in the tub filled with water was a 45-pound catfish.

"My God!" the photographer exclaimed. "That looks like a small shark!"

Paige smiled.

"I call it 'Moby,'" Paige said.

Paige posed for a photo and then spent that afternoon cleaning up the charcoal grill on his patio. Satchel Paige was planning to serve Moby to teammates at a Sunday night dinner just two days after reeling in the catfish.

On June 29, the evening of the get-together, Paige was still in his baseball uniform. There had been an incredible come-from-behind victory earlier that Sunday, earning Paige his sixth victory. The Browns had defeated the Detroit Tigers, 3-2.

Paige's six wins and nine saves made him the top reliever in the American League. His closest competitor was Fritsch Dorish of the Chicago White Sox, who had four saves. Paige's all-star game resume was getting more impressive by the game.

Teammates began to arrive for dinner. The guests included catcher Clint Courtney, manager Marty Marion, and pitcher Bob Cain, who had pitched to Eddie Gaedel with the Tigers a year earlier but was now a teammate. Pitchers Ned Garver and Gene Bearden also were present. Both had played with Paige while on Bill Veeck's

Indians. The hero of the day's game, Dick Kryhoski, was also seated.

Bill Veeck was the last one to show.

When Veeck entered, he was overwhelmed by the smell of the seasoning Paige had used to drench Moby. It made Veeck's eyes water and he almost sneezed.

"What is that smell?" Veeck said, waving his hand in front of his nose.

"You aren't from the South," said Courtney, a Louisiana native. "That's how you cook catfish!"

Veeck smiled at the sight of Courtney and Paige sitting together. During spring training, Veeck never would have imagined the two hanging out after a game. The only thing they had in common was having been born into poverty. Courtney told teammates he was so poor growing up in the deep South, his shoes were so worn out he could step on a dime and tell whether it was heads or tails.

The Browns traded for Courtney at the start of the season. The reports on him were so positive they traded their starting catcher Sherm Lollar. The New York Yankees were willing to part ways with Courtney because he constantly got in fights on the field due to his rough style of play. In one instance, he knocked out an opposing second baseman's two front teeth with a rough slide.

Rogers Hornsby had coached Courtney in the minor leagues and had a big influence on the 25-year-old catcher. Courtney was one of the few players Hornsby liked.

Courtney shared another trait with Hornsby. Both were racists. Courtney approached Veeck in the first days of spring training and said he would refuse to be Paige's catcher. Courtney wouldn't play with a Black teammate.

But Veeck asked Courtney to warm up Paige for a spring training game. Courtney reluctantly agreed. The irrepressible Paige got Courtney to laugh after making a comment about a teammate and by the end of the week, they were eating dinner together.

That's what Veeck had hoped for and envisioned. He didn't think it was possible for someone not to like Satchel Paige if you just got to know him.

Paige had finished preparing his monster catfish. He had a cornmeal breading - his grandmother's recipe - and had grilled it until it was perfectly tender and moist inside.

Kryhoski was the first to try Paige's main dish at the dinner table. He stabbed into his catfish and put it into his mouth. He chewed it and nodded.

"Hey, Bill," manager Marion said. "You think Kryhoski deserves a bonus for his clutch hit? Two outs in the bottom of the ninth, and he hits a two-run homer to win it!"

The table cheered.

Veeck was silent.

"Don't let it give you a big head, Dick," Veeck said. "That hat you wear is the biggest in the American League. Your head is so big, I had to pay an extra $2 to have a hat specially made. I was going to take that out of your salary. But I'll pick up that tab now!"

The dining players laughed.

Veeck looked to Paige.

"Well, Satch, we find out tomorrow who makes the all-star game," Veeck said. "No matter what, you've proven you deserve to be on the team!"

"Heck yeah!" Courtney said.

Paige smiled. He had tried to put it out of his mind, but it wasn't working.

In the National League, Black pitcher Don Newcombe of the Brooklyn Dodgers had already made three all-star teams. But no Black pitcher had yet been picked as an American League all-star.

Satchel Paige felt being the first Black American League all-star pitcher would cement his reputation as the greatest ever. Without it, he feared his accomplishments in the Negro Leagues and barnstorming would be forgotten. Among other shortcomings, the poorly organized Negro Leagues suffered abysmal record keeping.

In comparison, Major League Baseball usually had two separate official scorekeepers at every game. Although his time was running out, everything he accomplished at the major league level was written in stone.

"Hey, Satch," Courtney said. "My dad is going to come to see me play next week. He is going to whoop me when he finds out I'm friends with a Negro. But I'm pretty sure we can take him!"

Paige shook his head.

"I'm not a fighter, Scrappy," Paige said, using the nickname he invented for Courtney. "I have other people handle that for me."

Paige startled his teammates by getting up and walking over to the phone. He flipped through an address book and dialed a number.

The room drew silent as Paige dialed. Paige had a short conversation.

"Scrappy," Paige said. "This man would like to talk to you."

Clint Courtney was confused and a bit intimidated.

He got up and walked over to Paige, who handed him the phone.

"Hello?" Courtney said.

He listened. Courtney then lit up.

"Hey, guys!" Courtney shouted. "It's Joe Louis!"

Paige had met Louis, the recently retired heavyweight boxing champion, four years earlier while pitching for the Indians, and they exchanged phone numbers and kept in touch.

Paige learned Courtney was a big boxing fan.

After his house cleared out, Paige didn't sleep a wink that night. He'd learn the next day if he was going to be an all-star.

CHAPTER 43

How The Hell Old Are You?

June 30, 1952

Early on a Monday morning, Casey Stengel arrived at his office at Yankee Stadium.

This was the day when he would announce the player selections for the American League all-star game. Once selected, the player would be forever labeled an "all-star."

In a regular season game five days earlier, the St. Louis Browns had beaten the Yankees 10-9. The visiting Browns were sitting on a one-run lead at the top of the ninth inning when Satchel Paige was brought in as a relief pitcher. He didn't give up a walk or a hit and got the final outs to get the save.

That loss didn't sit well with Stengel, the New York Yankees' manager. His Yankees were in the middle of a pennant race and had just a 2.5-game lead in first place.

Stengel sat down at his desk and opened the daily newspaper. His reading was interrupted by a knock, and the team's secretary walked in with a bag full of mail addressed to the manager.

Stengel already knew what the letters said. The sack held more than 100 letters sent by fans from across the country, all urging him to select Satchel Paige for this year's American League all-star team.

Stengel scanned a few of the letters, but stopped after opening the 10th letter that read, "Bill Veeck said …"

He shook his head.

"Son of a bitch Veeck," Stengel muttered.

In St. Louis later that same day, Browns' batboy Bill Purdy entered the team's clubhouse looking for Satchel Paige. Spotting the player, Purdy announced that Bill Veeck wanted to see Paige in his office.

"He said immediately, Satch," said the 14-year-old batboy in a serious tone. "I think it's important."

Paige entered Veeck's office in street clothes as it was hours before that day's game.

Veeck was sitting behind his desk with a newspaper.

"This sportswriter wrote, 'At age 48, 52, 56 or 60 – Satchel will let you take your pick - is breezing strikes past American League batters,'" Veeck read out loud.

Paige shot Veeck a quizzical look.

"If I'm in the big boss man's office, that means one of two things: I'm either traded, or you're missing silverware," Paige said with a nervous laugh.

Was Paige traded? He braced for the bad news.

"Neither," Veeck said. "I got a telegram today from the New York Yankees. Casey Stengel has named you to the all-star game in a week."

Paige went uncharacteristically silent.

Veeck continued, "Satch, you will be teammates with Mickey Mantle and Yogi Berra. And Larry and Minnie are going to be on the team."

Larry Doby was still a member of the Cleveland Indians along with new Black teammate Minnie Minoso.

Veeck rose from his desk and handed Paige the telegram.

"Remember when we talked about having three Negroes on the same big-league team in my last year in Cleveland and how we thought that seemed impossible?" Veeck said. "Now, we will have those three Negroes on the same all-star team."

Veeck was beaming but noticed Paige was not speaking.

Paige stood silently for several seconds.

"Minnie and Larry will be there?" Paige asked in a soft voice.

Veeck knew Jackie Robinson would also be on the National League all-star team but knew better than to bring that sore subject up to Paige.

Veeck nodded with a big smile.

"They can never say that the Negroes don't belong now. I was thinking of promotions for this and –" Veeck stopped mid-sentence.

He noticed Paige was biting his lip, trying to hold back the tears.

Bill Veeck had never seen Paige so emotional. Satch always came across as bulletproof and able to take everything in stride.

Veeck motioned for Paige to take his chair behind the desk.

Paige moved slowly and took a seat. He tried to say something but was too choked up.

It took almost a full minute for Paige to compose himself, but he finally looked up at Veeck, who sat on the edge of his desk waiting for Paige to speak.

In a soft, quiet tone, Paige said something Veeck had never heard before.

"When I played for the Craws in Pittsburgh, the field couldn't hold a thousand fans. It was up on a hill surrounded by the ugliest factories and empty fields," Paige said, just above a whisper.

He looked up at Veeck.

"But when the Pirates were playing the same day, I could hear the fans at Forbes cheering down the road," Paige said, referring to Major League Baseball's Pittsburgh Pirates.

"Those should have been my cheers because I was better than all of them," Paige said. "I played in Des Moines, North Dakota, South Dakota; no amount of money would fix what was taken from me."

Paige took a deep breath.

"Back when Joe DiMaggio was a kid, I don't know, maybe 17 years ago, I got to face him," Paige said. "You could tell he was going to be something special. I had a bunch of local kids who were from the high school team. And we were playing a top white minor league team. Joe couldn't touch me the first three times he batted. Then, in his last at-bat, he hit the ball up the middle, and it hit my glove, and he got a hit, and they won the game," Paige said.

Paige paused as he replayed the hit in his mind.

"I can still see that ball coming off my glove now. I should have had him. After the game, this kid DiMaggio had a big smile," Paige said. "And his teammates were cheering him, and I could hear them say, 'You got a hit off of Old Satch.' And a Yankee scout came to me and said, 'I'm going to tell the front office. We know we have a keeper. He can hit off Old Satch.'"

Paige sat in the memory for a moment.

He looked to Veeck.

"Never in my life had I wanted anything more than to be able to pitch against the best hitters in baseball when I knew I could dominate them," Paige said.

"And it was the emptiest feeling in the world to know it would never happen. That I would be stuck to pitching in cut-rate side shows for $80 a game," Paige said.

Paige recalled a 1935 article in the Kansas City Star about him.

"Satchel has a fastball which looks like a shooting star," the newspapers exclaimed. "Big league scouts have longingly wished for some method to transform Satchel's color to get him into the majors."

Paige slumped in the chair.

"You know, the money's all gone. Cars. Women. Guns. The Satchel Paige lifestyle isn't cheap," Paige said.

Paige was a well-known spender. One time in 1948, when Paige was on the Indians, a salesman came into the locker room selling wool undershirts for $7.50 [$100 in 2023 dollars]. His good friend and teammate Gene Bearden jumped in between Paige and the salesman.

"Don't you buy it!" Bearden snapped at Paige. "I'm telling you now, don't you buy it. That's too much money! If you buy it, you and I are through!"

Paige bought it.

Time magazine reported that Paige made $36,000 in 1948 and spent it on a white Lincoln, a red Cadillac, a red Jeep, a station wagon and more than 20 shotguns.

The money was gone. The Negro League and barnstorming accomplishments would eventually be lost because they were never documented like the history of Major League Baseball.

"All I've really wanted was to be recognized for being the best pitcher baseball has ever seen," Paige said.

"I'm pitching in a real big-league all-star game," Paige told Veeck. "But they can't take this from me. Satchel Paige – all-star."

A year earlier in 1951, Joe DiMaggio had retired after 16 years with the New York Yankees after suffering through the worst season of his career at the age of 36.

Veeck looked at Paige.

"Wait. They called you Old Satch when DiMaggio was a kid? How the hell old are you?" Veeck asked.

Paige burst out laughing.

Paige stood up, and Veeck limped over to hug Satchel.

Paige persevered. He made it into the majors. He was the first Black pitcher to make the American League all-star team. He was 45. Or somewhere about there.

CHAPTER 44

You Know How It Is With A Bad Penny

Sept. 29, 1953

Grace Comiskey was a woman in a man's world, the only female owner in baseball in 1953. She inherited her Chicago White Sox baseball team after the death of her husband in 1939. She fought off the First National Bank of Chicago, the trustee of her husband's estate because there was no specific clause in John Comiskey's will that his wife would take over the team. She won in court. She had learned to fight for a seat at the baseball table.

And this night, she would have to do it again. And she was comfortable in that role. This time, it would be at the American League team owner's meeting at the Hotel Commodore in New York.

The official baseball decisions would be announced later in the night at the Hotel Commodore. That hotel was stuffed with minor league managers looking for major league jobs, newspaper reporters, and baseball executives trying to network.

The most pressing item on the agenda was the fate of Bill Veeck's St. Louis Browns. St. Louis was one of a handful of cities with two major league franchises, the Cardinals and the Browns.

Veeck recognized from the start that St. Louis was not big enough to host two baseball teams. He thought his Browns could push out the Cardinals.

Veeck thought he had won out when St. Louis Cardinals' owner Fred Saigh pled guilty to tax evasion charges in January 1953 and was sentenced to 15 months in prison. The Cardinals were put up for sale. A deal was made for the Cardinals to move to Houston, leaving St. Louis to the Browns. But at the last minute, August Busch Jr. came in and bought the Cardinals and kept them in St.

Louis, bankrolled by his beer empire.

Veeck was left with the short straw. His Browns were losing money, and he had to relocate the franchise to a better market. Veeck wanted Baltimore. Most Major League Baseball owners agreed, with one caveat: Veeck had to relinquish his ownership and get out of baseball.

During the 1953 owner's meeting, backroom discussions related to the Browns' fate were humming all over. The most important one was a mile from the Hotel Commodore at the Gramercy Park Hotel bar.

And that was why Grace Comiskey had just been summoned to appear before the network of wealthy white owners who ran the American League and were known as the "sportsmen."

Grace Comiskey had a heart attack three years earlier that left her weakened. She walked slowly into Gramercy Park Hotel bar in Manhattan.

Charlie Schwefel, the Gramercy Park Hotel owner, met Comiskey at the front of the bar and escorted her to a remote booth.

This was a meeting of industry titans.

At the exclusive booth sat Tom Yawkey, owner of the Boston Red Sox, Del Webb, co-owner of the New York Yankees, and Philadelphia Athletics owner Roy McGillicudy, son of legendary manager Connie Mack and known as Roy Mack. The youngest member of the group was 31-year-old Walter "Spike" Briggs Jr., the son of Walter Briggs Sr., the Detroit Tigers owner who had passed away the year before. All these men were connected to each other in various ways. For example, Spike Briggs' father had bought the Detroit Tigers after William Yawkey, the man who adopted Tom Yawkey, decided to sell the team in 1908.

Webb was a construction tycoon who made his first million with military contracts during World War II. Webb's construction company built the Poston War Relocation Center in Arizona. This barbed-wire concentration camp housed 17,000 Japanese-Americans who were uprooted from their homes and relocated to the camp during the war.

Yawkey and Webb were the two wealthiest and most influential baseball team owners. They were also the leaders of the anti-Bill Veeck faction.

Notably, six years after Jackie Robinson broke the major league color barrier, none of the franchises represented at the table had ever had a Black player on their roster.

Webb also had a relationship with the late mobster Bugsy Siegel, who six years earlier hired Webb as a general contractor to build the Flamingo Hotel and Casino in Las Vegas.

Webb liked to tell the story about how Siegel confessed to him during a private meeting that he had killed more than a dozen people. Webb was horrified.

"Don't worry," Siegel told Webb. "We only kill each other."

Webb originally called the meeting to convince the "sportsmen" to side with him. Webb had organized a group to buy the Browns and move them to California.

But Baltimore won out as the Browns' next landing spot, as long as the deal could be finalized without Veeck.

Grace Comiskey was also a problem on another baseball matter. The soon-to-be new owners of the relocated Browns to Baltimore wanted to hire general manager Frank Lane away from Comiskey's White Sox. His contract with the White Sox ran two more years.

Lane had an excellent reputation in the league as a shrewd trader.

The Yawkey-Webb coalition's goal was to sweet-talk Grace Comiskey into releasing Lane from his contract so he could go to the soon-to-be named Baltimore Orioles as a token of appreciation to the new ownership for agreeing to jettison Veeck.

Grace moved into the booth and sat at the end seat. She was winded and had to momentarily catch her breath.

The male owners noticed Comiskey was struggling. Before they could say anything, Comiskey spoke up.

"I know what you're thinking," Comiskey said. "What will happen to the White Sox if my health worsens?"

"Let's cut the crap. We know my son is a complete screwup," Comiskey said of her son Chuck. "But he's my son. My health isn't great. But I'm leaving majority ownership to my daughter. So, a Comiskey woman will still be running the show. Trust me on that."

Yawkey smiled and set down his drink.

"Well, we wouldn't want it any other way, Grace," he said. "We called you here to talk about Frank Lane. It would be a nice gesture to the new franchise if you allowed Mr. Lane to help the Orioles get a moribund franchise back on its feet. Veeck left that franchise in shambles."

Comiskey quickly shot him down.

"I'm not in the nice gesture business, Tom," Comiskey said. "I'm in the winning baseball games business. And if you thought I would give up the architect of the White Sox's revival, that would make as much sense as trading Babe Ruth."

Yawkey sensed the conversation had turned personal. It was well known Yawkey preferred to be called, "Mr. Yawkey" and his Red Sox were haunted by trading Ruth to the Yankees in 1920.

Comiskey was incensed that they would even make such a pitch and was convinced they would never have tried such a stunt with a man.

"Hey, I just thought of a nice gesture," Comiskey said. "How about the Yankees and Red Sox share their television and radio revenue with the teams from the smaller cities? I bet you the new Baltimore owners would love that."

Webb shook his head. The meeting was disintegrating. Revenue sharing had been a persistent point of contention between team owners and Veeck, who for years had been a smaller-city franchise owner preaching from that soapbox.

"I think you and Bill Veeck would be the only owners in favor of that," Webb said. "And after today ..."

"So Veeck is going to be out?" Comiskey asked bluntly.

"The game is changing," Yawkey said.

"Yes, it's becoming more colored," Comiskey said. "That's really what this is about. I look around this table, and I see four owners without a single Negro on their roster."

Comiskey looked at the new Detroit Tigers owner Briggs, the youngest member of the Yawkey-Webb cabal and the new owner of the Detroit Tigers.

"Spike. We hired a scout just for the Negro Leagues, and we just traded for the colored Minnie Minoso, a two-time all-star," Comiskey said. "Times are changing."

Yawkey shook his head.

"No, don't throw the Negro issue at us. This is not about the Negro ballplayer. It is about Bill Veeck," Yawkey said, his voice rising. "His fans hung him in effigy just last week because it was rumored he was leaving St. Louis."

Yawkey took a sip of his cocktail.

"We no longer hold a monopoly on the fans' interest, Grace. We aren't the only game in town. I've got these Boston Celtics now, and this Red Auerbach is as sharp as a basketball man you will find."

The Boston Celtics were in their fifth season in Boston in 1950 when they drafted Chuck Cooper, making him the first Black player in the National Basketball Association. This put more pressure on the Red Sox to play a Black player, something they had yet to do.

Yawkey took another sip from his drink.

"We aren't the only game in town anymore. The National Football League is becoming more popular. We have competition." Yawkey said.

He looked at Comiskey.

"Can we trust Bill Veeck? Can we trust this circus man not to embarrass us with his outrageous stunts? Christ! We are still seeing photos of that goddamn midget!" Yawkey said in disgust.

Webb spoke up.

"Grace, Veeck came to New York City and spoke to a group when he was with the Indians," Webb said. "He told them with newspaper reporters around that Joe DiMaggio was drastically underpaid and worth $100,000."

Webb was still furious another owner publicly commented on the Yankees' payroll.

"That's four times what we were paying him. And we ended up paying him that $100,000 due to the pressure from the fans. That's Veeck! He wouldn't let us televise Yankees games unless the Browns got a cut of the revenue," he said.

There was an uncomfortable silence.

Comiskey looked around at the table. The decision to kick Veeck out was a done deal. Comiskey slowly rose from her seat.

"Well, gentleman, I've lost my appetite," Comiskey nodded.

She got up and left the table.

Mack waited until Comiskey was out of earshot.

"We have bigger problems than Veeck," Mack said. "The goddamn players and their pensions will put us out of business."

Yawkey shrugged.

"Pensions are troubling. But Veeck is something we can solve tonight," he said.

Three hours later, Veeck sat in his Hotel Commodore room with his attorney Kenneth Teasedale.

"Bill, the Browns' ownership group has advised me to tell you they want to sell to the Baltimore group for $2.5 million. That's the only way to save the franchise and for us to turn at least a small profit for the investors. That's what the ownership group wants to do," Teasedale said.

The attorney paused.

"You're the majority stock owner. It's your call," Teasedale said, obviously disheartened.

Veeck nodded.

"I see," he said.

Veeck sat back in his chair and sighed.

He knew people like his assistant general manager Rudie Schaffer had put a second mortgage on his home to help the Browns meet payroll.

Veeck knew he was beaten.

"You know, Ken, I didn't like the American League owners when I came into the league, and I don't like them going out of it," Veeck said. "Clearly, the feeling is mutual."

Five hours later, the sale of the St. Louis Browns was announced at the Hotel Commodore, and the franchise was moving to Baltimore without Veeck.

Reporters rushed up to Veeck at Hotel Commodore for comment.

"As of now, I am out of baseball," a distraught Veeck told the reporters. "But you know how it is with a bad penny. I may turn up somewhere or somehow."

Sportswriter Bob Maisel of the Baltimore Sun talked to a baseball executive for a story he was writing on Veeck's ouster. The executive told Maisel he would only comment off the record. Maisel agreed.

"I'm fond of the guy," the executive said about Veeck. "But, I feel about Veeck something like I feel about elephants. I love elephants, but I wouldn't want to own one. They're nice to be around now and then, but if you had one in the house, it might create just a little more excitement than I can take."

The executive looked at Maisel.

"Does that answer your question about having Bill run your ball club?" he said.

CHAPTER 45

Negroes In The Factory, Not On The Team

Hustin Lewis said he felt like "a big hand" swept him up and hurled him like a missile out a fourth-floor window of the Briggs Manufacturing building.

William Sparlock watched his co-workers rise in the air "as though off some ghostly springboard" and hit their heads on the ceiling. When he saw the flames, he tried to run but the floor he stood on collapsed and caved in.

Lewis and Sparlock lived long enough to tell newspaper reporters some details of the day of the greatest catastrophe in Detroit's industrial history.

But within 10 days, both men died in the hospital, only their words surviving.

The Briggs Manufacturing Company building exploded at 8:05 a.m. on a Saturday, April 23, 1927. The explosion caused the deaths of 21 people and injured hundreds of others.

Seventy drums of paint, each containing 55 gallons, were engulfed in flames instantly and shot off like cannons.

The fire spread so quickly that workers reported that the paint nozzles they held instantly burst into flames, severely burning their hands. An entire section of the five-story building collapsed with rubble piling 30 feet high.

The Associated Press reported the deaths:

"THE DEAD

Detroit, April 25 - The revised list of the dead in the Briggs Manufacturing Company fire Saturday:

James Gillan, 23, negro

Harry Mason, 43

James Woodall, 42

Andrew Wilkinson, 32, negro

William Henderson, 21, negro

Joseph Gooditch, 46

Ovid Shaw, 21, negro

Boze Hixon, 30, negro

Unidentified negro

Harvey Thompson, 27, negro

Sonny Treadwell, 28, negro"

Eight of the first 11 reported deaths were Black people. Newspaper reporters on the scene said the faces of the dead Black factory workers turned white from the flash burn of the explosions.

The building belonged to Walter Briggs, Sr., who was then part-owner of the Detroit Tigers baseball team. Although Briggs wouldn't allow Blacks to play for his baseball team, they did work in his factory. They worked in the most dangerous jobs for the lowest pay.

Similar conditions prevailed throughout the city's iconic auto manufacturing plants. Blacks were tolerated at best and were limited to the riskiest and most grueling jobs.

In the years after World War I, southern Blacks flocked to northern cities, including Detroit, drawn by promises of a new life working in factory jobs.

The migration persisted as labor shortages that originated during World War I were aggravated by ever-tightening immigration restrictions beginning in the early 1920s.

Briggs Manufacturing stood out in that industry as a lousy place to work, for whites as well as Blacks. Long after 1914, the year Henry Ford famously increased the pay in his flagship auto assembly plants to $5 a day, many Briggs employees were still making just $1 per day or less.

Only about 3% of U.S. autoworkers in the early 1920s were Black. Yet in 1927, the vast majority of those who perished in the Briggs Manufacturing Company fire were Black.

Black auto workers were placed almost exclusively in foundry or paint room jobs. In the foundries they worked with molten metals, pouring super-heated substances into molds. The temperatures were so high it was said it turned the faces of the few white foundry workers black, covered as they were with sweat, dirt and oil. In the paint rooms, workers had no way to avoid breathing toxic fumes.

The Briggs fire was attributed to a spark igniting vaporized paint, probably from static electricity. While a government investigation did not hold Briggs accountable, within three months sweeping new state regulations were imposed on auto plant ventilation and fire risks.

Walter Briggs' company offered to pay all the medical expenses incurred due to the notorious 1927 explosion.

Two years before the fire, the company generated $11 million in profits [$193 million in 2023 dollars], producing components for 500,000 Ford Motor Company automobiles. At the age of 48, Walter Briggs Sr. was one of the nation's wealthiest men.

But that was just a start for a man who now rubbed elbows with industrial titans no less prominent than Henry Ford.

Briggs wanted a legacy.

He gave his name to his only son, Walter Briggs Jr., who was known as "Spike."

In 1938, the elder Briggs renamed the ballpark where the Tigers played, "Briggs Stadium," and spent $700,000 to add 22,000 more seats.

The expansion made Briggs Stadium the nation's second largest baseball stadium, topped only by New York's Yankee Stadium, which was known then as "the Cathedral of Baseball."

The elder Briggs had plans to leave the stadium to his son.

"I have arranged for my son Spike to take over the park when I pass along," the father told the Detroit Free Press in 1937. "He has some youngsters, and when he moves on, we intend that they shall take over the park. Since it is our intention that the stadium shall remain in possession of the Briggs family for a long time to come, we deem it fitting that it should be known as Briggs Stadium."

Spike was groomed accordingly to carry on his father's legacy.

A few months after the 1927 Briggs factory explosion, the 15-year-old Spike was competing in horse shows. He attended Connecticut's Canterbury School, a boarding school where future president John F. Kennedy and the grandson of William Randolph Hearst would later attend. Spike graduated from Georgetown University in 1934.

Briggs Jr. enlisted in the military during World War II. By June of 1942, he was a second lieutenant in the Army Air Force and eventually was promoted to a major serving in the Office of the Assistant Chief of Air Staff in Washington, D.C.

Bill Veeck joined the military in 1943, serving as a private in the U.S. Marine Corps. While helping to man an anti-aircraft gun in the Northern Solomon islands, Veeck's leg was crushed by one of the huge gun's recoil. Veeck eventually had his leg amputated after 36 different operations failed to save it.

After the war, Spike Briggs was assigned to various high-ranking positions at his father's companies – Briggs Manufacturing and the Detroit Tigers. He gained a reputation as a hard drinker, and for rubbing shoulders with the rich and famous. Newspaper stories described him having cocktails with other pro sports executives in Miami Beach, where his family had a second home. Back in Michigan, pictures in the local newspapers showed him on an exclusive suburban Detroit golf course with Bing Crosby.

Newspaper reporters described Spike as brash, blunt, ill-tempered and excessively outspoken.

Spike's official involvement with the Tigers began in 1935, when at the age of 24 he became an assistant team secretary and treasurer. The next year, an Evansville Press headline read, "Spike Briggs Is Groomed To Run Tiger Ball Club."

By 1940, Spike was performing publicity duties, and was appointed vice president of a minor league team in Beaumont, Texas.

In 1945, he boasted to a sportswriter about what seemed to be a relatively trivial accomplishment as a baseball executive for the Tigers. Briggs Jr. described timing how long it took to empty Briggs Stadium after a game. It took less than eight minutes, reportedly making it the fastest exit time in the league. In 1951, Spike was named president of the minor league team, the Buffalo Bisons.

But no one doubted that his father was calling the shots. Under Briggs Sr.'s control, the Detroit Tigers made it to the World Series in 1934, 1935, 1940 and 1945.

The important sounding but in fact, superficial assignments suggested that Spike's father didn't have much confidence in his son.

"It's a harsh fact that regardless of the titles he held with the Tigers

- from assistant secretary-treasurer to vice president during the years his father lived - Spike had little real authority or voice in running the organization," Detroit Free Press sportswriter Tommy Devine wrote.

In 1952, Walter Briggs Sr. died. If Spike had ever really been picked to be the father's sole heir for the Tigers, he wasn't when it mattered. The father bequeathed equal shares in the trust that owned the team to his son and four daughters.

In 1953, Spike sold the family's interest in Briggs Manufacturing Company to Chrysler Corporation for $62 million [the equivalent of $707 million in 2023]. He told the newspapers he did it "to devote full time to the Tigers."

The baseball team and stadium were all that remained of the Briggs' legacy.

CHAPTER 46

Veeck Goes Down, Again

Nine days after Walter Briggs Sr. died Jan. 17, 1952, his son Spike assumed control of the Detroit Tigers. Under Spike Briggs' control, the Tigers floundered.

That year, the Tigers lost 104 games, by far the worst performance in their 50-plus-year history. In the 1953 season, the Tigers lost 94 games. And in 1954, they lost 86 games. Spike had strung together three of the worst seasons in team history.

In September 1955, Briggs offered his sisters $2.5 million to buy them out and take sole ownership of the Tigers.

The sisters refused their brother's offer and then convinced Detroit Bank & Trust, the Briggs trust's executor, that with their brother in charge, the baseball team was no longer a sound investment and should be sold.

Spike was in a panic. The celebrity lifestyle and media attention he had enjoyed for so long while his father was still alive was in jeopardy. Negotiations leading to a sale were already underway.

Spike Briggs decided to hold a press conference on the team's impending sale at the Detroit Athletic Club, which had still not admitted a Black member 69 years after it was founded. Spike and his father had been long-time members.

On Jan. 18, 1956, about a half dozen newspaper reporters filed into the Detroit Athletic Club's ballroom. One of the reporters was Joe Falls from the Associated Press.

Falls was a hard-nosed reporter from Brooklyn who had a knack for controversy. Most sportswriters were sports fans who felt lucky to be covering teams and games they loved. Falls, just 29 years old, didn't fawn over rich and powerful sources like most newspaper reporters. Falls knew he had the power to influence public opinion as a sportswriter in the 1950s, something even millionaires feared.

Spike Briggs stood before the reporters and broke the news that the Detroit Tigers would be for sale due to tax reasons.

"But there is no rush," Spike said.

While other reporters took the Tigers' owner at his word, Falls smelled blood in the water.

"How bad could the tax problems be that a family with your wealth couldn't overcome?" Falls asked.

Spike knew enough to be wary of Falls, who arrived in Detroit in 1953. Falls had broken stories on the Tigers that only top executives were privy. It annoyed Spike Briggs, but he couldn't deny that Falls had secured excellent sources.

"We have decided baseball isn't a good investment for the trust," Spike said.

"You mean your sisters," Fall said. "The rumor is that you and your sisters no longer talk after they refused your offer to buy the team from them."

Spike tried to hide his anger.

"This isn't about my family," Spike shot back. "We are all in agreement the team must be sold."

"Your father said he wanted to leave the team to you," Falls asked. "Why didn't he?"

For an instant, Spike froze. He didn't want to admit that at some point, his father concluded that his son wasn't capable of carrying on the Briggs' legacy.

"That wasn't Dad's way," Spike said. "He wanted to treat us all alike."

That wasn't the only lie Spike told this day.

"Any offers yet?" Falls asked.

"We don't want to sell out to some money-mad people who will milk the franchise dry in two or three years, make a big profit, and then pull out, leaving a depleted ballpark and nine old men on the field," Spike said. "That can happen, you know."

Falls smiled. That sounded like a reference to Veeck's situation in St. Louis in 1953.

"Would you sell to Bill Veeck?" Falls asked.

"Several of those who have inquired into the sale of the club have mentioned Veeck's name," Briggs said. "It seems odd to me that he should be mentioned by several groups and not just one."

Falls nodded.

"Will the condition of the sale be that you be kept as the Tigers president?" he asked.

"I say chances are nine out of ten I won't be around," Spike said. "Some people think I can stay with the franchise. Why, I've even heard talk that we'll sell only to someone who will retain me. That's ridiculous."

Spike paused.

"I hope to stay in baseball," he told the reporters. "I've already been contacted by other clubs."

Those were more lies. Spike would only sell to a buyer if they agreed to keep him on as a top executive. And no teams had contacted him. Who would want a petulant former team owner whose four-year resume included three of the worst seasons in team history?

On July 2, Bill Veeck was joined at the Detroit office of attorney Richard Van Dusen by some trusted colleagues who would belong to a potential syndicate that would purchase the Tigers. One key player was Jerold Hoffberger from Baltimore, president of the National Brewing Company. Hoffberger had been involved with Veeck when he purchased the Cleveland Indians and St. Louis Browns.

The moneyman was John Hilson, a New York investment broker who had also partnered with Veeck on the purchase of the Indians and Browns.

The gang was back together this time on a bid for the Detroit Tigers.

Van Dusen began the meeting. He had reviewed the team's financial records that had been made available to prospective purchasers.

"Since the old man died, the team has been horrible on the field," Van Dusen said. "Yet, their attendance this year is sixth best out of 16 teams. This fan base is ready for a winner again. They just need a competent owner."

"The best news is we made the best offer – and it's not even close," Van Dusen said, smiling. "We came in at $5.25 million. The next best is $5 million. There are only four finalists. None of the others have anyone with experience running a ball club. Just bankers, radio executives, the owner of the NHL's Toronto Maple Leafs, plus Bing Crosby and Clark Gable."

Van Dusen looked at Veeck.

"The biggest obstacle will be you, Bill," Van Dusen said. "Spike doesn't like you. The nut didn't fall far from the tree with that one. You already know Walter Sr. was no Bill Veeck fan, to put it mildly."

Van Dusen asked Veeck if he read the veiled reference Spike had made at the press conference regarding the "money-mad people" who skim the cream and leave the town with "nine old men on the field."

Veeck nodded and connected the negative characterization to his inevitable plan to bring back Satchel Paige.

"Satch won't like being called old," Veeck said with a slight smile.

"Just how the hell old is he?" Van Dusen asked.

"I'm saving that answer for my first promotion when the Tigers sign him!" Veeck answered with a grin.

At the time, Paige was pitching for a minor league team in Miami owned by Veeck.

"He's got 11 wins for us with a 1.86 ERA," Veeck said. "That man can pitch forever."

Then Veeck lost his grin.

"You're right though, I may be what kills this deal," he said.

Veeck saved the biggest news for last.

"Spike has agreed to meet with me privately and talk. The meeting is next week," Veeck said.

The newspaper coverage of Veeck focused on his promotional stunts. One newspaper reporter used it to knock Veeck's appropriateness as an owner of the Tigers.

The most vocal newspaper critic of Veeck was the powerful H.G. Salsinger, the 70-year-old sports editor of The Detroit News. Salsinger had been covering the Detroit Tigers since 1909, a year after the Model T debuted. Salsinger knew the Briggs family intimately and was among the nation's most respected baseball writers.

Salsinger was no fan of allowing Blacks in the major leagues. In a May 8, 1945 column, he used the same dodgy and patronizing argument those against integration had contrived, the Black players were financially better off remaining in their own segregated leagues.

By 1956 that claim was demonstrably false. Doby, for example, had been paid $1,800 in 1942 to play for the Newark Eagles, a Negro League team. By 1951, his fifth season with the Cleveland Indians, he earned $25,000. Black catcher Roy Campanella made $4,500 a year playing for the Baltimore Elite Giants in the Negro Leagues. By his second year with Major League Baseball's Brooklyn Dodgers in 1949 he was getting $12,500.

Two years after that 1945 column, Salsinger attacked Bill Veeck's signing of Larry Doby, which broke the American League's color barrier. With no mention of Rogers Hornsby's Ku Klux Klan associations, Salsinger repeated Hornsby's claim that if Doby were white he wouldn't be good enough to play in the white minor leagues, much less in Major League Baseball.

But by 1956, the old "Blacks aren't good enough for the major leagues" excuse was being disproven every day in stadiums across the country.

That year was Larry Doby's 10th season in the big leagues. He had made the all-star game six years in a row and two years earlier finished second in the American League's Most Valuable Player voting.

Salsinger got one thing right in that first column, though, when he noted that the only Black player who could make more money by barnstorming was Satchel Paige.

"Ole Satchel Paige, for instance, has made more than twice as much money pitching for Negro clubs as he could ever have made pitching for a white team, and Paige can be favorably compared with any white pitcher of the last 25 years and more," Salsinger wrote. "He could never be subjected to the rules and regulations governing white players. Old Satch does what he pleases and goes where he pleases. An incurable nomad, he is ever on the move. He jumps contracts, recognizes no training rules or jurisdiction of any kind."

Obviously, Salsinger was no fan of Veeck, Doby or Paige and in 1956 he used all his influence in an effort to stop Bill Veeck from getting back into baseball.

One Salsinger column began with the headline, "No Veeck Circus." Salsinger sang praises for Walter Briggs, Sr., saying he gave baseball "dignity, sincerity, enthusiasm and affection."

"Mr. Briggs was a solid enthusiast (of baseball) and Veeck's bizarre antics angered and disgusted him and made him more resolved that all activities of his club must be confined exclusively to baseball without any features borrowed from the midways of county fairs," Salsinger wrote.

Though unspoken in the public forum of white newspaper publishing, the real issue and objection to Veeck was the likelihood he would bring Black players to the Tigers.

Salsinger and others in Detroit's mainstream publications were largely silent on that matter, but that was not the case in Black newspapers. While the Detroit Free Press might bury a short item about a Tigers farm team signing a Black player, a prominent Black newspaper trumpeted it under the headline, "Sixth Tan Player Enters Tiger Farm-Den."

And by this time Detroit's Black community and newspapers were becoming more impatient with the Briggs' family increasingly notorious failure to put a Black player onto the parent club's roster.

Those Black fans had no doubts about what that failure represented. In Detroit, the Tigers' stance was widely supported with crude slogans like, "No Jigs For Briggs."

South of the Mason-Dixon line, similar sentiments were in open view, and not just in baseball. In March, Delta State Teachers College in Cleveland, Mississippi withdrew from the NAIA National Basketball Championship when tournament officials refused to grant them "protection" from playing against teams with Black players.

In July, Louisiana Gov. Earl Long signed a law prohibiting mixed-race athletic events in his state.

So not surprisingly, amid the drama of who would become the next owner of the Detroit Tigers, Black fans unambiguously championed Bill Veeck.

Veeck figured his upcoming one-on-one meeting with Spike Briggs would make clear if the highest bidder really would become the next Tigers owner.

Spike insisted on meeting in the ritzy dining room of Detroit's Statler Hotel, one of the city's most expensive and luxurious destinations.

When Veeck arrived, he was met in the lobby by Ernest Steck, the hotel's general manager.

"You must be Mr. Veeck," Steck said, noticing that Veeck was wearing a sports shirt with no tie. "Mr. Briggs asked me to watch for you."

Veeck nodded.

"I forgot my tie … back in Arizona," Veeck said.

Actually, Veeck was dressed no differently than when he sat in the bleachers with fans back in Cleveland. Which meant he was the only man in the Statler Hotel dining room not wearing a tie.

Bill Veeck was no fan of fine dining, and even less of a fan of

Spike Briggs. Looking at the younger man, Veeck saw a spoiled brat raised in luxury and privilege, who had a knack for screwing up everything he got involved in.

"Would you like a drink?" Spike asked.

"Let's see how the conversation goes," Veeck said. "I'll let you know."

Spike laid his card on the table.

"We won't sell to a buyer who doesn't take me on as the general manager," Spike announced. "You want to own the Tigers? You are looking at your next general manager."

Veeck shook his head.

"When I buy a team, I'm the one running the show," Veeck said.

Spike shook his head.

"I'm a lot like Dad. If I'm going to run a team, then I want to run it my way," Spike said.

Veeck gave Spike a hard look.

"And where has that gotten you?" Veeck asked. "Your sisters won't talk to you. The Tigers haven't come close to becoming a winning club since you took over. These fans are dying for a winner. You can't deliver one. You aren't your father. He knew that."

There was a long silence. Spike wasn't accustomed to people setting him straight.

"We submitted the highest bid," Veeck declared. "The process was clear. I'll take my chances that your sisters want the extra money."

Spike sighed and Veeck got up.

"I guess I won't be having that drink," Veeck said.

On July 15, Bill Veeck was awakened early by a phone call from his attorney Van Dusen.

"Bill," Van Dusen said. "Bad news."

Days after the bid "deadline" on the Tigers' sale had passed, the second-highest bidder was invited to make another offer. They beat Veeck's offer by $250,000 and agreed to take on Spike as the general manager.

"They can't do that!" Veeck said, the news hitting him like a cold shower. "The bid process was clear. We all only get one shot."

There was silence.

"You're the lawyer, Richard," Veeck said. "Do we have a lawsuit?"

"Technically, yes," the attorney answered. "But with a family as connected as the Briggs, we'd have little chance of winning in their backyard."

On July 16, Spike Briggs announced the family was selling the Tigers to radio executives Fred Knorr and John Fetzer for $5.5 million, a Major League Baseball record. Spike also told the newspaper reporters that he would be retained as the team's general manager.

Knorr was a neighbor and a close friend of Spike's.

"Spike will be our executive vice president and chief of operations," Knorr told more than 50 newspaper reporters attending a press conference. "Spike will run the club."

"We're going to run this club without promotional gimmicks. The late Mr. Briggs would have wanted it that way. Spike plays a very important role in our plans. Spike's going to be with us a long time, we hope," Knorr said.

Most of the newspapers mourned Veeck's loss.

The Connecticut newspapers' Journal sports editor Frank Corkin Jr. wrote a column the next day with a headline, "Veeck Gets Knocked Down – Again."

"You knew he wouldn't get it when he submitted his offer," Corkin wrote. "Few men in any sport have been publicly slapped as hard as the American League owners whacked Bill Veeck. ... Veeck rubbed some of the old-timers the wrong way. That was his mistake. They paid him back in St. Louis and they've just slapped him down again. Let him pop up somewhere else in the American League and they'll clobber him there. Just how these ivory tower untouchables determined that Veeck is harmful for this game, which is as commercial as any business you can think of ... is beyond my limits of reasoning."

On July 31, a Black weekly newspaper, the Jackson, Mississippi Advocate, reported: "Thousands of Detroit baseball fans were openly disappointed this week as liberal-minded Bill Veeck lost his uphill struggle to become the new owner of the Detroit Baseball Company...Detroit's Negro population, at odds with the Tigers for several years over the club's inability to field a Negro player at Briggs Stadium, followed the sale transaction very closely."

CHAPTER 47

Cows Are A Noble Animal

Feb. 9, 1959

Bob Burnes, a sportswriter for the St. Louis Globe-Democrat, was anxious to get to the KMOX radio station building. He had been a fixture on the station as the "sports guy" ever since his 30-minute show premiered in 1948. His voice was better than his pen, and after 11 years on the radio, he grew to learn what got a reaction out of his listeners. And at the top of that list was Bill Veeck.

Six years had passed since the Browns left St. Louis, and Veeck had been out of baseball the whole time.

But Burnes knew Veeck would still pull in the listeners.

On this day, he planned to dedicate the entire broadcast to Veeck.

"Greetings, KMOX listeners," Burnes said in his introduction to his 6:30 p.m. show. "Today, we will talk about our old friend Bill Veeck. He's back in the news because he just bought the Chicago White Sox today."

"As you may recall, Veeck argued violently with Boston and New York. How it was all accomplished, with Veeck bowing out, no one will ever say. But one thing is certain. New York and Boston were the leaders in the move to derail him."

Burnes, who did not like Veeck, paused.

"So many times, no one really says what they are truly thinking in public. In the Veeck situation, those who dislike Veeck kept it close to the vest, although we held out the hope that somebody in the American League would have the courage to say, 'I voted to throw the bum out in 1953, and I still feel the same way.'"

Burnes paused.

"But no one did," he said.

The radio host reported Dorothy Comiskey Rigney, daughter of the late Chicago White Sox owner Grace Comiskey, sold the majority stake in the team she inherited to Bill Veeck.

Bill Veeck was back in baseball, to the delight of fans and the ire of stodgy team owners.

That was confirmed three months later, along with the return of another baseball icon, 3-foot-7 Eddie Gaedel.

Thirty minutes before the May 26 night game between the Cleveland Indians and Chicago White Sox, a helicopter hovered over Comiskey Park. Veeck had stolen the idea of using a helicopter as a prop from his old friend Abe Saperstein. Veeck's promotional stunt was to pay tribute to his double play combination of second baseman Nellie Fox and shortstop Luis Aparicio. Both were 5-foot-9 future Hall of Famers who were among the shorter players on the field.

When the helicopter promptly landed at second base, out jumped four dwarfs who were painted green and dressed like Martians from outer space. They were all brandishing toy ray guns and were led by one-time pinch-hitter, 3-foot-7-inch Eddie Gaedel.

The four "Martians" stormed the White Sox dugout and grabbed Fox and Aparicio and guided them to home plate.

"I'd say, 'Take us to your leader,' but I know him already," Gaedel told Nellie Fox.

The Martians gave the two players their own toy ray guns, hustled back to the helicopter, and were on their way.

Less than two weeks later on Sunday, June 7, the Chicago White Sox hosted the Boston Red Sox at Comiskey Park for a double header. Red Sox owner Tom Yawkey made the trip with his team to watch them play and then meet with American League chairman of the board Will Harridge, whose office was in Chicago.

Earlier in the year, Yawkey's longtime drinking buddy and former Red Sox star Joe Cronin had been named president of the American League. Cronin's first act was to move the American League headquarters to Boston. But the Chairman of the Board Office, headed now by Will Harridge, remained in Chicago.

Whenever the Red Sox were in Chicago, Harridge and Yawkey would meet.

The White Sox won the first game, 9-4, before 26,000 fans, and Yawkey was sitting in a private box above the grandstands. During the between game intermission, Veeck came to meet Yawkey and the two men shook hands.

"Bill, welcome back," Yawkey said.

Despite their differences over baseball team management and promotions, the two men had always maintained a civil relationship.

Veeck greeted his fellow team owner and then announced, "I got a surprise for you. Take a look at the field."

The Comiskey Park staff was leading six cows onto the middle infield. The cows were brought to a halt. Then, three Boston Red Sox and three Chicago White Sox players walked onto the field, and each player was directed to a small stool beside each cow.

Yawkey was perplexed.

"What are cows doing on the field?" Yawkey asked. "Or dare I ask?"

Veeck was beaming.

"It's a cow-milking contest!" Veeck said. "The winning team gets $500."

Yawkey looked down on the field.

"Who are the Red Sox players?" Yawkey asked.

"Busby, Geiger and Runnels," Veeck said.

Yawkey shook his head.

"You know, Geiger is an old farm boy. He's from Illinois," Yawkey said.

"A ringer!" Veeck protested gleefully.

Chicago was hindered when the cow being milked by White Sox Nellie Fox kicked over the pail twice.

Sure enough, the Red Sox team, led by Geiger's efforts, won the contest handily.

"Cows on a baseball field," Yawkey said, shaking his head. "You never cease to amaze me, Bill."

"They are a noble animal," Veeck replied.

Yawkey shrugged and changed the subject.

"Bill, I think I'm going to watch the second game from the Bard's Room," Yawkey said.

The Bard's Room was a private, exclusive bar underneath the grandstands accessible for 40 years only to celebrities. It had mahogany paneling and looked like an upscale cabin with a fireplace and the head of a 10-point buck displayed in the middle of the bar.

Veeck nodded.

"I'll meet you there in a few," Veeck said. "I turned it into my personal office."

Yawkey took a few steps and then paused.

"Bill," Yawkey asked. "We're not going to be served by midgets, are we?"

CHAPTER 48

After 26 Years, A Black Man Plays For Tom Yawkey

July 21, 1959

There was no hint this day would mark a historic moment in baseball history.

The previous night, the Red Sox had played an exhibition fundraiser for cancer against the Milwaukee Braves, formerly the Boston Braves. The Boston Globe made no mention of Elijah "Pumpsie" Green.

The following day, July 21, the Red Sox traveled to Chicago to play the White Sox at Comiskey Park.

Leading off for the Red Sox in the eighth inning, Vic Wertz hit a single.

Green came into the game to pinch run for Wertz, which marked the first appearance of a Black player for the Boston Red Sox. Until this moment, the Red Sox had been the last segregated Major League Baseball team. A Black player had now appeared on the roster and on the field for every one of the 16 teams in the American and National League.

The milestone came 12 years after Larry Doby broke the color barrier in the American League.

Doby, now 34 years old, was playing for the Chicago White Sox and in the twilight of his career. He watched Green's debut from the Chicago White Sox dugout, idled by a sore groin. He was having more and more trouble staying healthy.

When Doby glanced down the line of players on the White Sox bench, he saw Al Smith, a Black teammate he had played with on the 1953 Indians. Next was Earl Battey, a Black backup catcher in his fifth season with the White Sox. Black outfielder Harry

Simpson was also present, who was also a teammate of Doby's on the Indians.

Simpson had been traded four times in his eight years. His teammates called him, "Suitcase."

Doby's old team, the Cleveland Indians, was coached by Joe Gordon. It was Gordon who played catch with Doby in 1947 when Doby's other teammates were determined to humiliate him and freeze him out during the pre-game warmups. Now, 12 years later, Gordon was the manager and had four Black players on his Cleveland team.

Doby realized he had personally witnessed baseball slowly and irrevocably changing. And Bill Veeck's fingerprints were all over the advances.

Segregation's final curtain in baseball had just been yanked down. The Boston Red Sox were the last team in baseball to have a Black player take the field.

And for the first time, Blacks were hired as hot dog and beer vendors at Boston's Fenway Park, something Veeck had done 12 years earlier in Cleveland.

Bill Veeck had outlasted Boston Red Sox owner Tom Yawkey in the decade-long racial tug-of-war.

The larger struggle for equality was far from over, however. Black players 13 years into integration still lived separately from white players. They went to different restaurants, hung out at different clubs, and had their own slang that only the Black players recognized.

When in 1959 a Sports Illustrated reporter overheard a Black player use the word "mullion" and asked what that meant, the Black player shot back, "Ask someone else, not me. I'm not going to tell you." The term "mullion" referred to an unattractive woman.

This was the world Pumpsie Green had now entered.

The circumstances of Green's call-up to the Red Sox on this day were suspicious. Green had generated much negative publicity for the Red Sox when he had a good spring training by hitting .327 and tying for the team lead in home runs with four. The Boston sportswriters voted him the best rookie during spring training, but he was still demoted to the minor leagues in Minneapolis when camp broke.

The manager for the Red Sox during spring training was Mike "Pinky" Higgins, who had told a Boston sportswriter a few years earlier, "There'll be no niggers on this ball club as long as I have anything to say about it."

But Higgins had been fired July 3 after the Red Sox lost and fell to 31-42.

Boston Evening American sportswriter Huck Finnegan embarrassed the Red Sox nationally with an April story on Green's treatment a day after he was demoted. The article claimed the Red Sox had done everything possible to break Green's spirit.

"Why kid around?" Finnegan wrote. "Pumpsie was a dead duck from the start."

The Red Sox held spring training in Scottsdale, Arizona, which was still segregated in 1959. While the white Red Sox players stayed in the Safari Hotel in Scottsdale, Green was driven 17 miles away to the Frontier Motel in Phoenix that allowed Blacks. Scottsdale was a sundown town, meaning that only white people were allowed to stay in the city when the sun set.

Green was driven to and from practice during the spring training games but was left alone and isolated in his hotel room. Black players who pioneered integration said living alone in segregated hotels was the biggest challenge.

When newspaper reporters questioned the Red Sox management why they still held spring training in a city with segregated housing, they said that the hotel was full of so many tourists and race wasn't an issue.

For the final spring training games, Green was told to play with the Chicago Cubs, who were in Phoenix playing their spring training games. The Red Sox didn't bother with the 17-mile one-way trips anymore.

Within hours of the demotion of Green, the Boston NAACP had requested a hearing before the Massachusetts Commission Against Discrimination on charges of racial discrimination.

Yawkey was invited to attend. Instead, the Red Sox management sent a letter denying the charges and stating that the claim the demotion was due to bias "had no foundation in fact."

The Red Sox's claim was disputed by Walter Carrington, a 28-year-old Black man, a Harvard Law School graduate and the youngest person to ever serve on the Massachusetts Commission Against Discrimination. Carrington published a report in April on the hiring practices of the Red Sox. He investigated the franchise for the Massachusetts Commission Against Discrimination. Carrington wanted the Red Sox charged with violating the state's Fair Employment Law. His report found that the Red Sox - "with one brief exception" - had never hired a Black person anywhere in the organization, even in the most menial positions, such as an usher, vendor or groundskeeper.

After Green's demotion in April, team officials had agreed he needed to spend the entire season in the minor leagues for "seasoning."

Carrington had been a persistent thorn in Yawkey's side over his failure to promote a Black player to the Red Sox. Carrington had threatened to take the Boston Red Sox to court over the matter, something the Red Sox feared because it could set a league-wide precedent of courts interfering with baseball operations.

Boston Red Sox management refused to sign any document mandating Green be promoted. But on May 26, they agreed that they would only use hotels that accepted Black ballplayers during spring training.

But now, Green was called up to the major league team on July 21. The Red Sox didn't even fly his wife Marie and 2-year-old son Jerry in for the game from California to watch Pumpsie make history. Green called his wife after the game. The Red Sox gave such short notice on the promotion that Green didn't have a chance to call his wife before the game. Green was playing in Minneapolis in the minor leagues while his wife was at their California home. Green was surprised that his wife had learned about the promotion before he could tell her over the phone. A friend heard about it on the radio and told Green's wife.

The local Boston newspapers were given no notice, and their offices were 1,000 miles away. The Boston newspapers, for the most part, had championed the integration of the last remaining team in baseball to play a Black person and would not be able to witness the historic event in person. They would have to rely on the wire service for the game. Only the Boston Globe had their beat writer Roger Birtwell on hand. The Red Sox were starting the first day of a 14-game road trip.

It would be two-plus weeks before the local media could see Green play first-hand. The Red Sox had found a way to bury the historic event.

When asked what changed before the game, Red Sox's new manager Billy Jurges simply told the reporters, "I needed an infielder."

CHAPTER 49

We Both Love Beating The Yankees

July 21, 1959

Boston Red Sox owner Tom Yawkey arrived an hour before the night game in the owner's box at Comiskey Park, where he was a guest of Bill Veeck.

He was both impressed and irritated that his rival was in the hunt for a World Series so soon after taking the White Sox helm. In the 11 years since losing that 1948 playoff game to Veeck's Indians, the Red Sox had not won a pennant.

Now in 1959, that persistent ache of a lack of a championship was compounded by the current success of a long-time pain in the butt adversary. Bill Veeck was back in baseball for the first time in six years, with a team that was the overwhelming favorite to win the American League pennant and make the World Series.

The two men were in the owner's box chatting before the game.

The White Sox were 51-39 in Veeck's first year as owner and tied for first place with the Cleveland Indians.

"I have to congratulate you," Yawkey told Veeck. "Beating the Yankees, even. The White Sox haven't won the pennant in 40 years, and now it seems you are in the cat bird's seat."

Yawkey took a puff of his cigar.

"And I see you brought your Negro friend Larry Doby back around," Yawkey said.

Doby had been struggling as a Detroit Tiger when Veeck signed him on May 13. Doby was no longer an all-star and was hitting just .241 as a reserve for the White Sox.

"Larry is going to finish his career here. I don't want him going out in Detroit," Veeck said, revealing his disdain for the Tigers legacy of "No Jigs For Briggs" days under the racism of previous owner Walter Briggs Sr. "He's had a great career. He should go out under an owner who appreciates him."

Yawkey looked out on the field. He noticed another Black player on the White Sox.

"And you brought over Negro Al Smith from when you were with the Indians. Those people seem to follow you around like tin cans on a string like you are some Pied Piper of Negro players," Yawkey said with a laugh.

Veeck pulled out a pin and showed it to Yawkey. It said, "I'm a Smith, I'm with Al."

"On August 26th, when you guys come back into town, I'm having an 'Al Smith Night.' We're going to honor Al. For this promotion, anyone named Smith, Smythe, Schmidt, or Smithe gets in for free," Veeck said.

Yawkey smirked.

"It's a pity I won't be able to attend. That's St. Anthony's Feast in Boston. You know the Italians, if I missed that," Yawkey said.

"You know Bill, we have our own Negro player now," Yawkey said. "Pumpsie Green. I'm told he's going to debut today."

Veeck smiled.

"Really? Boston's pro hockey team has one, too. Amazing how the Bruins were able to find a Negro hockey player before the Red Sox could find a Negro baseball player," Veeck said.

"We were waiting for a major star," Yawkey shot back.

Veeck was annoyed that Yawkey would be so disingenuous. Veeck knew the real story. He wasn't some toothless governmental commission on racism.

"You passed on Willie Mays and Jackie Robinson," Veeck said. "And the star you've been waiting on is Pumpsie Green? With that track record, I would fire all my scouts."

Veeck suspected Yawkey was trying to undermine Boston's first Black baseball player. What better way to demonstrate the Black player couldn't play at a major league level than to sign a mediocre prospect and make him your franchise's first Black player?

"Well, Bill, after you left the league and sold the Indians, we did try to trade for Doby," Yawkey said. "We even offered Dom DiMaggio."

Veeck knew that the trade proposal was insincere folly. No baseball executive would trade a star in his prime like Doby for a fading veteran. Joe DiMaggio's brother Dom was 35 years old in 1952 when the first trade was offered. In 1953, DiMaggio only had three at-bats the following year and was out of baseball.

"Pumpsie will take the heat off," Veeck said. "At least you don't have to be worried about being taken to court now that Green is playing."

Veeck regretted the words as soon as he said them. They were true, but he had violated his duty as a gracious host. Yawkey had always been courteous and welcoming to Veeck when he was in Boston.

Yawkey took a puff of his cigar.

"I've managed to own the same team for almost three decades. I've always been a respectable member of my community. I'm the vice president of the American League," Yawkey said. "And you are like a bad penny."

Yawkey's tone revealed his anger.

"A brilliant man once told me that about you as a warning, Bill. Damned if he wasn't right," Yawkey said, harkening back on the conversation he had more than 25 years earlier with then-commissioner Kenesaw Mountain Landis.

Veeck smiled.

"Another great man once said, 'I like your interest in sports ball, chiefest of all baseball particularly. It's our game – the American game.' Do you know who said that?" Veeck asked.

Yawkey nodded.

"Walt Whitman. I studied him at Yale," he said.

"Do you know why he was right?" Veeck asked.

Yawkey sensed a conciliatory tone in Veeck's voice.

"Why?" Yawkey asked, taking the bait.

"Two men like us, what could we ever share in common? You graduated from an Ivy League school. I'm a college dropout. You inherited your millions by age 25. I worked in the Cubs' ticket office at that age," Veeck said.

Veeck paused and looked at Yawkey.

"And you don't really like me," Veeck said.

Yawkey chuckled and nodded. He appreciated the moment of honesty between the two adversaries.

"And I don't envision any Tom Yawkey fan appreciation nights at Comiskey after you're done celebrating your Negro of the Week," Yawkey said.

Veeck smiled.

"No. But we do share one thing. And we owe our thanks to baseball for that, for it most certainly will be the only thing we will ever have in common," Veeck said, smiling.

"We both love beating the Yankees," Veeck said.

Yawkey burst into laughter.

"Amen to that, Bill. Amen to that," Yawkey said as he took another puff from his cigar.

Yawkey looked around.

"Do you have an ashtray?" Yawkey asked.

Veeck stuck out his wooden leg, in which was a small hole surrounded by burn marks and ash smudges. This clearly wasn't the first time Veeck's wooden leg had been used as an ashtray. And in this instance, it was also serving as an olive branch. Yawkey smirked and shook his head but abided with the spirit of the offer and flicked his cigar in it.

The White Sox won the game, 2-1.

CHAPTER 50

World Series Bonus For An Absent Teammate

Aug. 1, 1959

On a warm Saturday morning Bill Veeck called the Chicago White Sox brain trust into his office. Manager Al Lopez had demanded the meeting, forcing Veeck's hand.

The outcome would determine Larry Doby's future in major league baseball.

With the 1959 season well along, the White Sox were in first place with a one-game lead over Doby's and Veeck's old team, the Cleveland Indians.

And Doby's presence on his current team had become too big of a distraction for the White Sox's new owner - Bill Veeck - to ignore.

Lopez didn't like Larry Doby and made no effort to hide it. Lopez had traded Doby away twice when the manager and player had landed on the same team.

Larry Doby claimed it was racism. Others weren't so sure. Over the years, the major leagues' second Black player had acquired a reputation among his white teammates for being "thin-skinned" and a sullen loner. It didn't matter that, to the extent it was true, Doby often had good reasons for both.

Veeck worried he may have been partially responsible for Lopez's grudge, which likely traced back to incidents at the very start of Larry Doby's major league career.

In 1947, Veeck was the Cleveland Indians' owner and Lopez was on the team. Veeck had signed Doby that year and Doby became the first Black player to ever play in the American League. While Lopez was never a Doby fan, at first there were no signs of outright hostility.

That season, Indians' manager Lou Boudreau humiliated Al Lopez in a game, in a way that put Larry Doby on the spot.

On Sept. 14, Lopez was at-bat with two strikes. In an extremely unusual move, Lou Boudreau pulled the player out of the game in mid-count. This was extraordinary, something almost never done in the major leagues unless a significant injury had occurred that prevented a batter from continuing.

The action meant a humiliated Lopez had to walk back to the dugout in front of 22,300 fans, making way for someone else to finish the at-bat. Larry Doby was the mid-at-bat pinch hitter. Doby struck out on the next pitch, and under the rules it was counted on the scorecard as a strikeout attributed to Lopez.

Lou Boudreau was then acting as a player/manager for the Indians, and Veeck was not satisfied with Boudreau's managerial decisions. Veeck wanted Boudreau to step down as manager but still play shortstop. Boudreau refused, so Veeck made plans to trade him to the St. Louis Browns when the season ended.

At the same time, Al Lopez decided his next stop in his baseball career was to be a manager. Veeck asked him to hold off managing another team, promising to make him the Indians manager when Boudreau was gone.

All those plans collapsed in face of a "rebellion" by Cleveland fans, who idolized Boudreau. Veeck had to walk-back his plans to trade-away the player/manager. This made Lopez the odd man out, relegating him to a minor league coaching job the following season.

No one can say for sure whether Boudreau's humiliation of Lopez at the plate that day in 1947 was related to what occurred much later. And it also doesn't explain why Lopez made Larry Doby a focus of his ire. The rookie was just doing what his manager ordered.

But either way, it appeared Doby now had an enemy for life, for which he would pay a heavy price.

Boudreau moved on from the Indians in 1951, and Lopez finally got the manager position he had sought on the team under different ownership. Under his stewardship the Indians finished in second place for three years in a row. The team finally broke through in 1954, winning an American League-record 111 games, the American League pennant, and a trip to the World Series

The New York Giants, their National League opponent, had won 14 fewer games. The Cleveland Indians were by any measure one of the greatest teams ever, and to their fans winning the World Series seemed inevitable. The gamblers had made the Indians 17-to-10 favorites to win it all.

Those hopes were cruelly dashed, and Larry Doby rightly got a share of the blame. The Giants humiliated the Indians by winning four games in a sweep.

In the regular season, Larry Doby hit 32 homers and 126 RBIs, finishing second that year in the voting for the American League's Most Valuable Player. But in the World Series, the best he could do was two singles in 14 trips to the plate, a dismal .142 batting average. But that wasn't the only disappointment.

In the eighth inning of the first game, New York Giants center fielder Willie Mays immortalized himself with what is still considered the greatest fielding play in the history of the game. With two men on base and the score tied 2-2, the Indians' Vic Wertz smashed a ball 425 feet into deep center field. Mays made an over-the-shoulder catch at the warning track in a play that is forever known by historians and fans as "The Catch."

Larry Doby was on second base when Wertz had come to the plate. Had he tagged-up after Mays improbably snagged that fly-ball, he would have been able to score from second base with ease and give the Indians the lead. That was the proper baserunning move. Instead, Doby mistakenly took off running the instant Wertz hit the ball. When Mays caught the ball, Doby had to turn around and scramble back to second base. Doby didn't score that inning. The Giants went on to win the game in extra innings and sweep the World Series in four games.

The disappointment appeared to have unhinged Al Lopez on the subject of Larry Doby. Or at least that's how it appeared during the 1955 all-star game the following year. Lopez and Doby were both selected for the American League team, which featured perhaps the most inexplicable strategic decision by a manager in the history of baseball.

In the eighth inning, with Doby available to pinch hit, Lopez instead allowed pitcher Whitey Ford - among the worst hitters in the game - to bat for himself.

Among other things this flew in the face of the spirit and tradition of the annual all-star game, which by definition features rosters filled by the best hitters and pitchers in baseball, all of whom want their moment in the sun before a nationwide audience.

Leaving Whitey Ford in the game when a big-hitter like Doby was sitting on the bench, along with a number of all-star pitchers eager to take the mound, was simply bizarre. Of course, Ford struck out, and the National League team won the game 6-5 in extra innings. Doby silently fumed on the bench at the snub.

The judgement of fans and of sportswriters covering the game were summed up by South Bend Tribune sportswriter Joe Doyle in an article published the next day.

"Manager Al Lopez was broiling on coals hotter than Hades," Doyle wrote. "Why in the name of Babe Ruth did he let Whitey Ford bat for himself in the eighth inning when Larry Doby was just itching to get in there and swing?"

The answer was, Al Lopez had become unhinged on the subject of Larry Doby.

Five years later, manager Lopez and player Doby once again found themselves on the same team: Bill Veeck's Chicago White Sox, which was powering towards a 1959 American League pennant-win.

Doby was clearly past his prime, and of course manager Al Lopez wanted him gone.

Veeck hesitated to pull the trigger, and instead referred the decision to a vote of the top brass. The decision-makers would be Veeck, Al Lopez, general manager Hank Greenberg, and White Sox co-owner Chuck Comiskey.

Veeck was the only person to vote to keep Doby on the team.

Bill Veeck dreaded what came next: Informing Doby that he was no longer in Major League Baseball. For the first time in the Black pioneer's career, he was being sent down to the minor leagues.

When Larry Doby arrived at Comiskey Park for an afternoon game the next day, Al Lopez called to him.

"Doby!" Lopez barked. "Veeck wants to see you in his office."

The player knew what was coming.

In the office Veeck was sitting behind his desk. Doby sat on the other side, waiting for his boss and patron to break the news.

"I know it's bad news, Bill," he said. "I know Lopez never wanted me on the team."

Veeck shrugged sadly.

"We're in first place by two games, and we need another pitcher. I was out voted," Veeck said. "This team is going to go to the World

Series. I wanted you to have that experience one more time with me."

"Do you remember my first game?" Doby asked after a long pause.

Veeck nodded.

"You used to say someday they'd put up a statue of me." Doby reminisced. "You still believe that now?"

"More than ever. You outlasted even the Boston Red Sox, Larry - you were still around when they finally hired a Negro player," Veeck said. "For what you endured, you deserve more than a statue. And I've always felt guilty. I should have known what I was bringing you into back then, but I had no idea. As usual I was looking at it as another promotion. I didn't prepare you because I wasn't prepared. I was naive. And for that you paid a dear price."

Veeck's voice trembled. "You deserved better."

Doby was quiet.

"You mind if I sit here a while?" he asked after a moment.

Veeck walked over to his office door, closed it, and returned to his desk.

The two friends sat together in silence for the next 20 minutes, waiting for the other players to clear the clubhouse. When they had, Doby walked through it one final time, fearing these were his final moments as a major league ball player.

Seven weeks later, on Sept. 22, the Chicago White Sox beat the Indians, clinched the American League pennant, and secured a trip to the World Series, its first in 40 years.

The locker room saw a wild celebration that left the players soaked in beer. When the cheers finally began to subside, Lopez went into his office for 20 minutes of interviews with sportswriters.

When he came out, Lopez noticed the players were just finishing a meeting. Players-only meetings were frowned upon by managers, because they sometimes inferred he had lost control of the team. Often times, players-only meetings led to player rebellions against the manager.

Lopez knew that couldn't explain a meeting by a team that had just earned the right to play in the World Series.

He approached a group that included Sherm Lollar, Nellie Fox, Luis Aparicio, Billy Pierce, Earl Battey, and Al Smith. Battey and Smith were the two Black players left on the team after Doby's departure.

"What's going on?" Lopez asked.

"The players had a vote," Smith said. "We're giving Larry half the bonus each of us gets for making the World Series."

Lopez was shocked. Half the bonus was $3,647 per player, or $38,000 in 2023 dollars.

"Doby is not even on the team," the bewildered manager protested. "He played, what, 20 games? Might as well have been none. He didn't do anything."

Smith was still soaked in the celebratory beer. He had grabbed a towel and was turning toward the shower, but stopped and looked back at Lopez, who the players called "skipper."

"Skip," Smith said to Lopez, "You didn't have a vote."

In 1947, Larry Doby's introduction to Major League Baseball was met by angry teammates who literally turned their back and refused to shake his hand. A dozen years later, he was leaving the game with a large bonus coming out of his teammates' own pockets, in appreciation of all he had contributed and endured.

CHAPTER 51

Is That A Mortar In The Clubhouse?

May 1, 1960

Bill Veeck had waited four days for this moment. Hearing the crack of the bat thumping a ball, he sprang to action.

Veeck made his way to the auxiliary room in the press box.

Chicago White Sox outfielder Al Smith had swung and launched the baseball into deep center field in the third inning in a game against the Detroit Tigers. It appeared to be the team's first homer in four games.

Veeck limped through the press box, picking up the pace with each step. Veeck heard the crowd roar, confirming Smith's drive had cleared the fences. He entered the auxiliary room where his new electronic scoreboard controller's box was kept.

Veeck opened the door.

"Don't you dare!" he blurted, causing the scoreboard operator Ed Short to freeze in a panic.

Veeck had reserved for himself the privilege of unveiling the first official display of what had been dubbed by newspapers as The Monster.

Veeck strode over to the controller's box, saw the switch marked "home run," and flipped it on.

Immediately, Roman candle fireworks shot out from the new enormous electronic scoreboard and lit the sky. Veeck sat and watched as the crowd went quiet as the deafening roar of fireworks exploded in mid-air.

The fireworks lasted 32 seconds. That was longer than it took Smith to circle the bases, completing his home run trot with one eye fixated on the fireworks display. The strong smell of sulfur permeated the field.

Veeck was like a child on Christmas morning as he savored what the newspapers had called his "new toy" for the first time. And the hair on the back of his neck was standing up.

The Chicago White Sox owner had always been a visionary in promoting baseball. His latest idea had been inspired while watching Jimmy Cagney's 1948 movie "The Time of Your Life." One of the characters wins at an arcade game, which causes bells and whistles to go off with fireworks.

An idea was born. Why can't baseball have electronic scoreboards that do the same thing?

In 1960, the White Sox christened their 130-foot-wide scoreboard dubbed "The Monster" for $340,000 [$3.7 million in 2023 dollars.]

Opponents hated the scoreboard. After a White Sox homer triggered a round of fireworks on May 10, Detroit Tigers manager Jimmy Dykes grumbled to reporters, "Is this Disney Land?" Dykes said he would ask the American League to ban the scoreboard.

Veeck was at control of his electronic scoreboard when the Yankees came to Chicago on May 20.

He had a gleam in his eye when Ted Kluszewski came to the plate to hit. The 1960 White Sox was not a team of home run hitters, except for the 6-foot-2 slugger. Kluszewski was an ox of a man who played college football at Indiana and briefly considered playing pro football. He struggled at times with his weight. The baseball program fans purchased said he weighed 225 pounds. But this season, he was creeping more around 260 pounds. He insisted on wearing a jersey with cut-off sleeves to show off his muscular arms.

The electronic scoreboard didn't just light fuses, it also blared sound effects customized for certain players and situations. When Kluszewski would hit a double and lumber to second base, he was accompanied by the sound of a stampeding herd of steers.

But the home-run fireworks show was really what Veeck had been itching to flick on.

A week earlier, the scoreboard operator had prematurely triggered the fireworks for what he thought was a Minnie Minoso home run. But it turned out to be a fly ball caught at the warning track.

"That just cost me $100!" Veeck vented to the scoreboard operator, referring to the cost of the explosives every time it was triggered.

In the first inning of this game, Kluszewski hit a deep shot to left field but was just short of going over the fence for a home run. Veeck's itchy trigger finger was poised just above the "home run" switch but was withdrawn when the ball was caught for an out.

The eager team owner finally had his moment in the third inning, when Kluszewski ripped a home run over the right field fence. Veeck gleefully flipped the "home run" switch, and the fireworks filled the air.

Baseball had an unwritten code: players didn't show up a pitcher after hitting a home run. Yankees legend Mickey Mantle once explained how he honored that code after hitting a homer by circling the bases with his head down.

Veeck had always thumbed his nose at baseball's rules of etiquette. And now he was doing so electronically.

In the eighth inning, the Yankees brought in pitcher Ryne Duren, who had the reputation as the hardest-throwing pitcher in the major leagues.

"I would not admire hitting against Ryne Duren," Yankees' manager Casey Stengel once said. "Because if he ever hit you in the head, you might be in the past tense."

Chicago White Sox catcher Sherm Lollar was on deck when White Sox manager Al Lopez called him back.

"Watch yourself," Lopez warned. "They brought him in for a reason. Duren's going to throw at you."

"You think so?" Lollar asked.

"I would," Lopez said with a knowing nod.

Lollar was worried. He walked to the plate and looked at Yankee catcher Yogi Berra.

"Yogi," Lollar said. "You know I don't control that scoreboard, right?"

The first pitch was a fastball aimed at Lollar, who turned away and was nailed in the back by the ball.

Lollar fell to the ground as a sharp pain stabbed him. Lollar had been hit dozens of times. Three years earlier, he had been hit by a pitch 16 times in one season. The pain usually subsided within a few seconds. This time, a searing pain in his mid-section prevented him from getting up. He cringed while trying to move his right shoulder as a pain that felt like an electrical shock flowed through him.

Grimacing in pain, Lollar looked up at the auxiliary room where Veeck was sitting.

Veeck looked down at his catcher sprawled on the ground near home plate. He pushed the button, and a "screaming lady" sound effect echoed through the park to acknowledge the horror of one of his players being hit by a pitch.

On May 30, the Indians came to Chicago with outfielder Jimmy Piersall.

The final out of the game came when Chicago's Kluszewski swatted a long fly ball to center field. Piersall caught the ball, and then spun around and hurled the ball at the giant scoreboard.

He was on target, striking the scoreboard and smashing one bulb on a string of lights that displayed messages typed by the operator. Someone from the bullpen tossed Piersall another ball, which he also threw at the scoreboard. He hit the scoreboard a second time but didn't cause damage.

White Sox general manager Hank Greenberg was sitting next to Veeck in the press box when the two balls caromed off the scoreboard.

Veeck was furious, which shocked Greenberg. He couldn't recall previously seeing the owner angry.

Veeck rose and stormed into his office, picked up the phone, and called the Indians' clubhouse.

"Let me speak to Piersall!" Veeck demanded of the voice on the other end.

Moments later, Piersall was on the phone.

"Listen, young man! What do you think you are doing hitting my scoreboard?" Veeck asked.

"Mr. Veeck!" Piersall shouted back. "Someone threw an orange and hit me in the back. I was mad! So, I threw the baseball at your stupid scoreboard."

Piersall paused.

"That scoreboard is a joke!" Piersall yelled. "It's the biggest joke in baseball, as far as I'm concerned!"

"You damage my scoreboard, and I'll put you on a rocket and launch you into orbit!" Veeck shouted back.

There was a moment of silence.

"Your scoreboard should go off just once a game," Piersall said. "All those damn bombs bursting over my head. It's nerve-wracking!"

Veeck was quiet.

"Jim. You are a heck of a player. A damn fine fielder and I am quite fond of you," Veeck said. "But you do not throw anything at my scoreboard. You'll regret it!"

Veeck hung up.

When Veeck returned to the press box, a half dozen reporters were waiting for him.

"What if Piersall hits your scoreboard again?" the reporters asked Veeck.

"I'm going to do something drastic," Veeck said, still fuming.

"Like what?" the reporters asked.

"You just watch that Sox-O-Gram tomorrow if he acts up," Veeck said. The Sox-O-Gram was the section of the scoreboard where Veeck could write electronic messages where the letters are lit up by individual light bulbs.

"I can put any message I want to on that, and I've already got one in mind," Veeck said. "If he thinks I am joking, just let him try aiming at that scoreboard again ..."

Veeck didn't complete his sentence but left the threat unfinished.

Piersall was the first batter in the next day's game. The newspaper reporters were anxious to see the next act in the scoreboard showdown. Some sportswriters had bet that Veeck had ordered his pitchers to throw at Piersall and hit him for revenge.

Instead, pitcher Billy Pierce unleashed a fastball. Piersall swung and connected, and the ball shot off his bat and landed 390 feet away in the left field bleachers. Piersall had hit a home run.

Veeck was sitting in the auxiliary room running the scoreboard when Piersall homered. He looked at the "groan" switch and flicked it on.

A large groan emitted, and Piersall was momentarily stunned, shook his head in disbelief, and continued running around the bases.

As Piersall touched home plate, he tipped his cap to Veeck in the auxiliary room.

Veeck responded by typing a message that was displayed on the Sox-O-Gram for the entire crowd to see: "Nice one, Jimmy."

That spat was over.

On June 17, the hated New York Yankees came to town. Veeck made a habit of running the scoreboard against the Yankees.

In the second inning, New York's Clete Boyer slammed a pitch from Billy Pierce into the bleachers in left field for a home run. Veeck shook his head and flipped the "groan" switch, and the scoreboard released the sound of a "groan."

After Boyer circled the bases, he jogged back to the dugout.

Moments later, Greenberg tapped Veeck on the shoulder.

"Look at that!" Greenberg said.

Yankees manager Casey Stengel and about a half dozen Yankees jumped onto the field just in front of the dugout, and they all danced the jig while holding two lit sparklers in their hands.

The crowd picked up on it and cheered wildly.

The Yankees were mocking Veeck's new toy.

When Mickey Mantle clubbed a home run in the eighth inning that landed 20 rows into the right field bleachers, the Yankee outfielder put his head down and completed his home-run trot. Like many of the Yankees, Mantle found the electronic scoreboard tacky.

After Mantle circled the bases, the Yankees repeated their sparkler dance. But this time, the Yankee pitchers in the bullpen also joined in.

Veeck was stewing over the opposing team's display when Bob Fishel entered the auxiliary room and sauntered up to Veeck.

Fishel was the public relations man with the Yankees but also had previously served with Veeck with the St. Louis Browns and helped pull off the Grandstand Managers Night and the Eddie Gaedel stunts.

Fishel didn't say a word, but instead just flashed a cat-that-ate-the-canary smile at his old boss.

"I thought I smelled a rat! I knew it!" Veeck blurted out, instantly recognizing the mastermind behind the hilarious dig at him. "Everyone knows Casey Stengel has the imagination of a cardboard box!"

Fishel grinned.

"I finally got one over on you!" he said.

The next day, newspapers around the country ran photos of Mickey Mantle holding two sparklers in his hand as he stood on the steps of the dugout.

A line had been drawn in the sand, and Bill Veeck would cross it the next time he visited New York.

A month later, on July 23, the White Sox traveled to New York for a Saturday game against the Yankees.

In 1944, Yankees' assistant coach Ralph Houk fought in the Battle of the Bulge during World War II. For his service, he received a Silver Star, Purple Heart, Oak Leaf Cluster and the Bronze Star. Houk was still nicknamed "The Major" due to his military rank.

An hour before the start of the game, while the Yankees were taking batting practice, Houk glanced over to the White Sox dugout.

"What?" Houk thought. Something caught his attention.

Houk did a double take. He took a few steps in the direction of the dugout.

"Is that a mortar in the dugout?" Houk asked himself.

A closer look confirmed it. The White Sox had a military-type mortar sitting in their dugout.

Houk bounced across the field and flagged down Yankees manager Casey Stengel.

"Casey," Houk said with a look of bewilderment. "Why would the White Sox have a mortar in the dugout?"

Stengel shrugged his shoulders.

"A mortar?" Stengel asked.

Stengel looked at Houk. He knew better than to question The Major's military knowledge.

Stengel went into the dugout to use the phone to call the head of the Yankees' security.

Twenty minutes later, New York City fire chief Edward Cavanagh was on the field with a half dozen firefighters and two New York City police officers.

They walked into the dugout where Veeck had been told to meet them. Veeck was standing next to the mortar.

"I have the proper insurance," Veeck said.

In case something went wrong, he pulled out a Lloyds of London insurance policy covering the stadium.

The fire chief inspected the policy.

"Look, Mr. Veeck, no fireworks allowed in the city of New York," the fire chief said. "And certainly, no mortars in Yankee Stadium, either."

Cavanagh paused.

"A mortar with a 30-inch cylinder? What are you going to do? Fight a war?" he asked Veeck.

"They started it," Veeck said.

Cavanagh motioned, and the firefighters lifted the mortar out of the dugout and carried it away.

Houk, Stengel, Fishel, and the New York Yankees' players watched with amazement as the firefighters carried away the mortar.

Stengel turned to Houk and Fishel.

"I tell you what," Stengel said. "That son-of-a-bitch Veeck. His roof isn't nailed on right."

Stengel looked to Fishel.

"Bob, you worked with him. How nuts is he?" Stengel asked.

Fishel looked around and scanned the field.

"You guys haven't seen a midget, have you?" he asked.

The White Sox won the game 5-3. But, after the game, newspaper reporters surrounded Veeck and were more interested in the mortar.

"It was my plan, if we hit a home run, to launch fireworks out of the mortar," Veeck told reporters after the game, with nonchalance as if he were giving away free miniature bats. "But we didn't hit a home run. Singles and doubles proved adequate."

CHAPTER 52

The Drum Major Instinct

April 9, 1968

Martin Luther King Jr. knew his fate.

Months before he was assassinated, he had asked family members to play his sermon, "The Drum Major Instinct," at his funeral so that he could be a part of his own eulogy.

When the day of that funeral tragically arrived, the Ebenezer Baptist Church where it was held was filled to capacity with celebrities and politicians, including a half dozen candidates in the upcoming presidential election.

Thousands more surrounded the church, the vast majority were Black. Most were impeccably dressed in their best suits, hats and Sunday dresses. People were packed so closely together, it was difficult to raise their hands on a hot, humid Atlanta morning. Only those just outside the church could hear King's recorded voice giving the sermon he had requested as his eulogy.

Many had climbed telephone and light poles to get a glimpse of the horse-drawn wagon that would carry the casket in the procession that followed. An estimated 100,000 people lined the four-mile route to Morehouse College, King's alma mater.

Bill Veeck was one of the handful of white people standing outside the church, and also one of the few men not wearing a tie. Next to him, was sportswriter Wendell Smith, the Black man who recommended Jackie Robinson to Brooklyn Dodgers general manager Branch Rickey.

Now, 21 years after Robinson broke the color barrier, in deference to King's death and funeral, Major League Baseball had decided to postpone the opening day of its 1968 season for two days.

Smith and Veeck had a long-standing professional relationship. Over the years, it had been strained by Veeck's perception that Smith's writing was lionizing Jackie Robinson's contribution to the integration of baseball at the expense of Larry Doby.

Smith wrote Robinson's story in a book released in 1948 that was followed by a 1950 movie on Robinson, in which the baseball player portrayed himself. Brooklyn Dodgers general manager Branch Rickey had paid Smith $50 a week to travel with Robinson in 1948 and ghostwrite his experiences for newspapers.

Meanwhile, in Veeck's mind, Larry Doby endured the same racism as Robinson and didn't have any of the celebrity status that was showered on Robinson. It was a slight that tugged at Veeck's conscience and accompanying guilt that he didn't do as much to promote Doby as Rickey had done to support Robinson.

Veeck had canceled Larry Doby's promotions in 1947 because he didn't want added pressure on Doby. But in hindsight, Robinson was now known as the hero of integration while Doby's sacrifices were largely forgotten.

"You know," Veeck said, breaking the silence after the funeral ended. "Satchel told me this day was coming. He told me three years ago, 'They gonna get that man ... and when they do, we are gonna lose something good.'"

Smith nodded, appreciating that Veeck had nailed his impersonation of Paige's voice.

"Ole Satchmo," Smith said. "Leroy Paige, the pitcher, is one of the few individuals living in this world today who isn't conscious of the fact that a long time ago, someone invented that unique device popularly known as a clock."

Veeck smiled.

"He danced to his own tune," Veeck said.

Smith looked at Veeck.

"Satch's not here, is he? I know Jackie is supposed to be featured later at the college," Smith said.

Veeck shook his head.

"Last I read, he was considering pitching again for the Indianapolis Clowns," Veeck said. "But that was some time ago."

Veeck paused.

"I lost track of many people when I had my health issues," Veeck said.

In 1961, Veeck sold his Chicago White Sox when he had horrible recurring headaches. He was incorrectly diagnosed with a brain tumor.

Veeck noticed Smith was agitated by the reference to the Clowns.

"You never liked the Clowns," Veeck said.

"The last of the Negro teams," Smith said. "How they managed to stay alive this long is a stain on our race."

The Indianapolis Clowns, originally the Ethiopian Clowns, were owned by white owner Syd Pollock, who also ran a theater.

Wendell Smith found it particularly demeaning that until 1943, Clown players had to paint their faces with white "war paint" and wore wigs during games. In 1951, the Clowns dropped the Ethiopian name, and went with Indianapolis, and survived as the baseball counterpart to the Harlem Globetrotters. Goose Tatum of the Globetrotters even spent a year playing with the Clowns.

Smith found it insulting and demeaning.

"They are a fourth-rate Uncle Tom minstrel show," Smith said, shaking his head.

"You know, I never got the chance to give you my condolences on Abe," Smith told Veeck. "I know how close you guys were."

Globetrotters' owner Abe Saperstein had died two years earlier in 1966.

"We are at the age where life starts taking away from us," Veeck said.

Smith nodded.

"I feel bad. Our wives have kept in touch more than we have," Smith said. "Do you have anyone to walk with?"

Smith realized that Veeck was surrounded by a sea of grieving Black people.

Veeck brightened.

"Thank you, Wendell, for asking, but I'm meeting Sammy Davis Jr. and marching with him," Veeck said.

Veeck paused.

"Sammy promised me he wouldn't be wearing a tie, either," Veeck said. "We have a mutual acquaintance in Nate Dolin. Nate ran Sammy's investments for years, and after I found out my health issues weren't so bad, me and Nate tried to get back into baseball and buy the Senators five years ago."

Smith nodded.

"They still don't want you back," Smith said.

"Not a one," Veeck said, trying to hold back a smile he thought would be inappropriate.

"Are you staying here long?" Smith asked.

Veeck shook his head.

"I'm leaving right after this is done. I never liked the South,"

Veeck said. "I don't feel comfortable here. I don't even like driving through it."

Smith looked at Veeck and glanced at his leg.

"Are you going to be able to make the full four miles," Smith said. "I read in the newspapers you took quite a fall last year."

Veeck tapped his prosthetic leg.

"I'm going to do this," Veeck said. "I've got my prosthetic leg, and I'm going to make this without as much as a limp. I had surgery on my other knee after the fall. But I'll be OK."

Smith extended his hand. Veeck shook it.

Veeck started the four-mile walk. Grocery owners stood outside their businesses and handed out bread for free to the funeral procession.

The funeral procession route passed the Georgia state capitol building. Segregationist Georgia governor Lester Maddox refused to allow state workers off for the funeral. He had surrounded the state capitol with 160 helmeted armed guards. The soldiers had been ordered to shoot any protesters who came onto the state capitol grounds.

The spectacle made Bill Veeck ponder how his life had always been detached from the hardships Black people faced. He remembered something Abe Saperstein said when the two men sat in a New York Yankees Stadium box seat watching a Negro League game a quarter of a century earlier.

"You don't know a thing about what it means to have a Negro sports team or what the Negro players will go through for your latest stunt," Saperstein told Veeck in 1942.

Now, Veeck hoped he could say he understood. He witnessed so much since that 1942 game.

Bill Veeck had spent his career promoting a circus atmosphere. But he was unsettled walking with scores of Blacks crushed into silence. There would be no stunts or comic relief this day. Only this suffocating grief.

Veeck's thoughts flickered back to the past.

There was when Saperstein told him his Globetrotter players had to stay in a county jail in Nebraska after no hotel would take them in 1965.

Even Veeck's current home was not free from racism. His 20-acre home in Peach Blossom Creek in Maryland was three miles from the Wishing Well Club Motel that had a federal complaint filed against it for refusing to allow Blacks. Veeck would drive by it and see it advertising, "Restricted" – code for no Blacks allowed. Maryland had been a slave-owning state but didn't secede, although Veeck's home resided in an area that sympathized with the Confederacy. As he struggled to hide his limp, the Civil War didn't seem so long ago, but baseball seemed a million miles away.

CHAPTER 53

The Hall Of Fame Is Calling

April 30, 1998

Raheem Trotman landed his first journalism job at the local newspaper, The Montclair Times in New Jersey. During his one season on the Montclair State University football team, the 6-foot-2 Black player threw just one pass. He graduated with a minor in journalism and one of his first assignments with The Montclair Times was to interview Larry Doby.

Trotman grew up around sports but had never heard of Doby. The newspaper had the press release from the Baseball Hall of Fame in Cooperstown, N.Y. And Trotman got his hands on a baseball encyclopedia.

Doby currently lived in a modest home in Montclair Township, just nine miles from Paterson, N.J.

Trotman rang the doorbell and was greeted by Helyn Doby, Larry's wife. She led Trotman through the living room decorated with 15 years of baseball nostalgia. The walls were covered with photos of Doby with Jackie Robinson and Bill Veeck and numerous plaques Doby had received. And there was the 1948 photo of Gromek and Doby hugging and smiling.

Larry Doby was sitting in a lawn chair on the home's back patio.

Doby was now 74 years old. His hair was gone, and he was 30 pounds heavier than his playing days. Bill Veeck had been dead for 12 years. Jackie Robinson died 26 years earlier. The people who shaped his life and baseball career were gone.

Everything he had, Doby knew could be traced back to those two men and baseball.

The current interview request was triggered by the Baseball Hall of

Fame announcing its induction of Doby. He had done over a dozen interviews, responding graciously when the modern sportswriters confessed they knew almost nothing about his playing days.

But Trotman was the first Black sportswriter to interview him since the Hall of Fame announcement. That piqued Doby's interest. Looking at the young journalist, Doby's thoughts raced back 50 years to when another Black reporter convinced him to go public about the racism he faced trying to buy a house in his hometown.

Trotman took out his tape recorder and started the interview.

Trotman asked about a framed baseball card he saw in the den. It was a 1959 Topps baseball card of Doby, Minnie Minoso, and Rocky Colavito, all on the Cleveland Indians with the title "Destruction Crew."

Doby laughed.

"That was my last year on the Indians when that card came out," Doby said. "Then Bill Veeck bought my contract from the Tigers so I would finish my season with him."

"Bill Veeck?" Trotman asked. That was one person Trotman was unfamiliar with during his cramming for this interview.

Doby smiled.

"Bill Veeck was one of the most unique people I've ever met," Doby said. "He gave me a chance to play baseball in the major leagues, and baseball's establishment hated him for it."

Doby got up to retrieve the baseball card encased in hard plastic in the den. He walked back to his patio chair and identified the other players pictured in the card.

"This is Minnie Minoso," Doby said. "Let me tell you a story about my friends Minnie and Bill Veeck."

Doby paused and looked at the tape recorder to ensure it was still on.

"In 1976, Bill signed Minnie as a 50-year-old to pinch hit for the White Sox so Minnie could make baseball history by playing in four different decades," Doby said. "And he got a hit at age 50."

Trotman was shocked.

"Someone was still playing baseball at 50?" he asked.

Doby nodded.

"It gets better," Doby said with a laugh.

"Well, then some other player also played in four different decades. I can't remember his name. So, Bill signed Minnie to play at age 54 as a pinch hitter with the White Sox again in 1980. That way, Minnie would make history and claim to have played in five different decades," Doby said.

Doby paused.

"By the way, baseball banned Minnie from ever playing again. But he has his record thanks to Bill," Doby said.

Doby thought about it.

"Bill was always a step ahead of the baseball establishment," Doby said.

The tape recorder was clicked off. The interview was over.

Four days later, Doby walked into the Hall of Fame in Cooperstown. The Hall of Fame had assembled a large exhibit honoring him. Prominently displayed was the iconic photo of him and Gromek smiling together in 1948.

Doby froze, overwhelmed by the wave of 50-year-old memories and couldn't hold back the tears.

Helyn understood. She put her arm around her husband.

"That photo was a feeling from within, the human side of two people, one Black and one white," Larry told Helyn. "I would always relate back to that whenever I was insulted or rejected from hotels or other people and places. I'd always think about that picture. That's what America is all about, or what it's supposed to be all about. We could have rehearsed all day and never got that joy on our faces after hitting that home run for him."

Larry composed himself. He took a breath.

"Oh man," Larry told his wife in a what felt like a prayer. "I wish Bill could be here."

Helyn smiled.

"He is," she said, pointing to the Hall of Fame bust of Veeck in the same room. "And he'd probably have a midget pop out of a cake and hand you your Hall of Fame plaque."

Larry laughed.

"It's going to be tough for me to get through this," Larry said. "And I have to get through my speech."

Three hours later, at the outdoor venue of the Hall of Fame, Larry Doby sat in the front row as one of the people being honored for being inducted into the Hall of Fame. His family was seated in the crowd.

"Today, I am honored to introduce Larry Doby as a member of the Hall of Fame. Larry was a pioneer that broke the color barrier with a common, quiet dignity …."

Those last three words sat with Doby. Common. Quiet. Dignity.

His mind raced back to 1957 and a game between the visiting White Sox and the New York Yankees, who were managed by Casey Stengel.

Stengel had repeatedly called Doby a "jigaboo." When Doby told sportswriters about it years later, they were skeptical.

In 1957, Minnie Minoso was the only other Black starter on the White Sox. In a night game, he'd been knocked down by a pitch aimed at his head by Yankee pitcher Al Cicotte. Just two years earlier, a beanball left Minoso with a fractured skull.

Later in the game Minoso intercepted Cicotte on his way back to the dugout.

"You do that again, and I'll take care of you in my way!" he warned.

The two Black players on the White Sox worried the next day would be Larry Doby's turn.

Black players were frequent targets for beanball throwers. Al Smith, another Black who debuted in 1953, was hit by pitches 15 times in 1955. By comparison, white player Mickey Mantle was hit just 13 times over his 18-year career.

Behind the plate for the Yankees in that series was the New York team's first Black player, catcher Elston Howard. As Doby adjusted his stance for his first at-bat, Howard whispered, "Keep an eye out, Larry, Ditmar said he's going to hit you."

Larry had been a frequent target of bean ball throwers. In 1948 he was struck seven times, the most in the league. It would have been more if he hadn't learned to dodge the attacks.

Howard was right. Yankees' pitcher Art Ditmar threw a fastball aimed right at Doby's head. With the warning, Larry dropped to the ground, barely avoiding getting beaned. The wild pitch eluded the Yankee's catcher, allowing a runner on third to score.

While Howard chased down the ball, Ditmar rushed in from the mound to cover home plate. For a brief moment, he was standing shoulder-to-shoulder with Doby.

"Shoot, you were quicker than I thought. Next pitch I'll hit you!" he snarled.

Without a second thought Doby unleashed a left hook that hit Ditmar square on the jaw, dropping the opposing pitcher in a heap. Yankee second baseman Billy Martin ran in to tackle Doby, and within seconds both benches had cleared and an all-hands brawl began.

It lasted 30 minutes and was considered one of the worst in baseball's history.

The consequence-free assault-by-fastball of Black players by white pitchers had become an ongoing blemish on the leagues. For all but two of the 14 seasons from 1948 to 1961, a Black player led the American League in getting hit by pitches. It was open season on Major League Baseball's first Black hitters. In Jackie Robinson's second season in the National League in 1948, he was hit by a pitch a league-high seven times.

This was dangerous. Protective batting helmets mostly weren't available and wouldn't become mandatory until 1971. Players wore only their cloth caps while batting.

In 1920, Cleveland Indian Ray Chapman was killed at the age of 29 by a pitch thrown by Carl Mays. Chapman got up from the ground after being struck in the head, took a couple of steps, and then collapsed. His final words were, "...ring, Katie's ring." Left behind was Chapman's pregnant wife, Katie.

Larry Doby's response to the deliberate assault contradicted the sermons Black players had been hearing since their arrival in Major League Baseball.

"Don't do anything physical in retaliation - unless it involves hitting a baseball," Bill Veeck had told Doby in 1947. Brooklyn Dodgers' General Manager Branch Rickey gave similar marching orders to Jackie Robinson.

Doby slugging Ditmar signaled a change: Black players began fighting back.

An Ebony magazine article a few weeks after the event came to the same conclusion. While Doby's left hook didn't stop the epidemic, it did end the era of Black players "turning the other cheek."

Reality beckoned and tugged at Doby's sleeve. The memory was gone. The thundering applause snapped Doby out of his 40-plus-year-old daydream.

It was time for Doby to give his Hall of Fame speech.

Doby got up and walked to the microphone. He looked out over the crowd and was overwhelmed by the rush of memories.

Doby scanned the crowd, looking for his family.

He saw Helyn.

Doby recalled only two times in his life witnessing his wife cry. The first time was when her mother died. The only other time was when she answered the phone call that her husband was being inducted into the Baseball Hall of Fame.

Larry Doby smiled.

His Hall of Fame speech lasted about six minutes. Larry Doby was never a man of many words. As he walked off the stage to cheers, he was met by many baseball dignitaries. He shook the hand of fellow 1998 Hall of Fame inductee Don Sutton.

But then Doby recalled his old friend Ted Williams.

Williams was a Boston Red Sox star elected to the Hall of Fame 32 years earlier. That summer of 1966 featured race riots across the country. Just a week before Williams would be honored in Cooperstown, New York, the state witnessed its race riot in which 53 people were injured.

Minutes into his speech, Williams, a white man, looked into the crowd.

He made a plea to the white Lords of Baseball who ruled the sport and had not allowed any Blacks into the Hall of Fame, where he was now enshrined.

"I hope that Satchel Paige and Josh Gibson someday might be added to the Hall of Fame as a symbol of the great Negro players who are not here only because they were not given a chance," Williams said.

The message from Williams, revered as the game's greatest hitter, was greatly appreciated by the Black community.

And Williams' plea still echoed within Doby more than 30 years later at his Hall of Fame induction.

After Doby ended his speech and shook fellow 1998 Hall-of-Fame inductee Don Sutton's hand, he turned to see the empty podium. The next speaker had not arrived.

Doby hustled back to the podium. The murmuring crowd grew quiet with the sight of Doby returning to the microphone.

"I just got one thing I'd like to say," Doby told the crowd. "I got a telephone call from one of the greatest people I know and had the privilege of playing against – Ted Williams."

Doby struggled to eloquently remind people of the stance Williams had so boldly taken so long ago. Larry Doby, the last of the Negro League players, was finally honored with a Hall of Fame induction.

Doby looked one last time at the crowd.

"I thought I'd let you know that," he said.

CHAPTER 54

Epilogue

Pitcher Don Black eventually lost his battle with alcoholism. He couldn't recapture his pitching form and never played again in the majors after the aneurysm he suffered in 1948.

Without the support of Bill Veeck, Black let his membership with Alcoholics Anonymous lapse and returned to drinking. He spent all the money from Don Black Night and his World Series bonus, and his health issues escalated with bad headaches, fainting spells, loss of memory, and eventually lung cancer.

Black worked numerous jobs after baseball, including a sportscaster, a car salesman, an insurance salesman and a teacher.

Don Black died on April 21, 1959, at his home in Cuyahoga Falls, Ohio, while watching the Cleveland Indians play the Detroit Tigers on TV. He was penniless. The cause of death was lung cancer. He was 42 years old. He left behind his wife and two daughters, ages 17 and 15.

∞

Walter "Spike" Briggs Jr. lasted just nine months as the general manager with the new ownership of the Detroit Tigers. After he sold the team to them in 1956, Spike was forced to resign in April after the first nine games of the 1957 season. He complained to newspaper reporters the new owners only gave him the general manager position so he would sell them the team and, after the sale, fire him.

In 2017, Harvey Briggs, the great-grandson of Walter Briggs, Sr., wrote a column in the Detroit Free Press. Harvey Briggs wrote about his great-grandfather, "He was a racist. His factories employed thousands of African Americans, but based on news stories and other historical reports, conditions overall were less than ideal, and discrimination against Black workers was pervasive."

∞

Eddie Gaedel died in 1961. Bob Cain, the Detroit Tigers pitcher who faced Gaedel during that infamous plate appearance 10 years earlier, drove 300 miles to attend Gaedel's funeral.

Until he died in 1997, Cain honored Gaedel each year by sending out his personalized Christmas cards featuring a picture of Gaedel in his batting stance. The inside caption read, "Hope your target in the future is better than mine in 1951."

Once shunned by Major League Baseball, Gaedel is now embraced as a baseball icon. In the Baseball Hall of Fame, there is a life-sized cutout of the photo capturing Gaedel crouched in his batting stance. Alongside it is a 6-foot-11 mannequin of Jon Rauch, the tallest player ever to play in Major League Baseball.

Before he died, Gaedel was reinstated into the official record books. His perfect 1.000 on-base percentage is tied for the best ever.

∞

In 2020, the Baseball Writers' Association of America removed Kenesaw Mountain Landis' name from the plaques they awarded to the National League and American League Most Valuable Players. Some MVP winners didn't want the award to be named after the commissioner who permitted baseball to remain segregated during his 24-year reign.

∞

Satchel Paige didn't pitch in that 1952 all-star game. It was called due to rain after five innings. He did pitch in the 1953 all-star game. His dream was realized.

Abe Saperstein, who was working as Paige's agent, got Kansas City Athletics owner Charlie Finley to sign Paige as a promotion for one game in 1965. It was estimated Paige was 58 years old. Finley had the same spirit as Veeck. He proposed to the league owners in 1963 that they switch to green bats and orange baseballs.

The day before his game on "Satchel Paige Night" in his final 1965 appearance, Paige watched his new team sitting in a rocking chair with a nurse by his side in the bullpen, a jab at Paige's age. He started the next night's game and pitched three scoreless innings. The only person to get a hit off Paige was future Hall of Famer Carl Yastrzemski.

The Boston Red Sox won the game 5-2, scoring all their runs after Paige had left.

After Paige was taken out of the game in the fourth inning, he doffed his cap to the crowd and made his way into the dugout. However, he was summoned back to the field. The lights were turned off, the 9,300 fans lit a match, and the Public Address System serenaded Paige with the song "Darling, I Am Growing Old."

The crowd sang along with the song:

"LIFE IS FADING FAST AWAY

BUT, MY DARLING, YOU WILL BE, WILL BE,

ALWAYS YOUNG AND FAIR TO ME ..."

The Atlanta Braves signed Paige in 1968, 20 years after his major league debut. Paige, believed to be 62 years old, was put on the active roster. The Braves had no intention of using him. Instead, Paige remained on the roster to accrue 158 days to qualify for a $250-a-month pension.

At the press conference, reporters asked Paige his age.

"They've done a lot of research on that and asked me so much about it I've forgotten it myself," Paige told the reporters.

By the time his career was over, Paige estimated he had pitched for more than 250 teams. Who knows? There are few records left to document Paige's greatness.

In 1971, Paige became the first Negro League player elected to the Hall of Fame.

At first, the Hall of Fame wanted to put Paige in a separate part of the museum away from the players who made the Hall of Fame based on their Major League Baseball merits. But outraged sportswriters demanded the Negro League players be in the same area as the white players. Cooperstown relented.

∞

Abe Saperstein died from a heart attack in March 1966. His impact on the sport of basketball was enormous. In 1961, he founded the American Basketball League to compete against the NBA.

To make the games more exciting, Saperstein introduced a new rule: any basket made from 25 feet out or further would be worth three points. And with that, Saperstein invented the 3-point shot.

The news service United Press International wrote this about the first ABL game on Oct. 28, 1961.

In a story titled, "Baby Cage Loop Thrills Fans With 3-Point Shot" the article started with, "Basketball may never be the same since the American Basketball League has arrived on the scene."

∞

Tom Yawkey never realized his obsession with winning a World Series. In that pursuit, the game only delivered heartbreak in his 43 years as owner of the Boston Red Sox. His Red Sox teams did make it to three World Series and lost each time in the series-deciding seventh game.

The team owner's legacy of racism also dogged him to the end, and beyond. In 2018, the city of Boston stripped Yawkey's name from the street that had been named in his honor. Yawkey Way was once again Jersey Street.

The Yawkey Foundation protested the attacks: "As we have said throughout this process, the effort to expunge Tom Yawkey's name has been based on a false narrative about his life and his historic 43-year ownership of the Red Sox. The drastic step of renaming the street, now officially sanctioned by the City of Boston (and contradicting the honor the City bestowed upon Tom Yawkey over 40 years ago), will unfortunately give lasting credence to that narrative and unfairly tarnish his name, despite his unparalleled record of transforming the Red Sox and Fenway Park and supporting the city he loved through his philanthropy."

That same year, the team received a letter from Red Sox fan Joe Vignolo, who pointed out that the Red Sox players honored by a half dozen or so statues on Boston's Van Ness Street were all white. Vignolo suggested the team consider adding a Black player. He suggested Hall of Famers Pedro Martinez or Jim Rice. Another possibility could have been Pumpsie Green.

The Boston Red Sox replied to Vignolo. They told him that it was a good idea but getting permits to build the statues was difficult, and the statues were costly. The Boston Red Sox had total revenue of $516 million in 2018.

∞

Effa Manley became the first woman elected to the Hall of Fame in 2006, 25 years after she had passed away at the age of 81. Newspaper accounts at the time of her death described her as white and Black.

Manley depicted herself as Black in newspaper accounts. For

example, in 1942, she wrote a letter to Black sportswriter Buster Miller about the state of Negro League baseball and stated, "largely members of our race …"

However, Manley said in a 1977 interview that she was really a white woman. Manley said she was born out of wedlock, something the family hid. Her mother was white, and her father was white. Her mother later had a mixed marriage with a Black man, and it was assumed for years that Manley was a child of that mixed-race marriage.

∞

Bill Veeck was elected to the Baseball Hall of Fame in 1991, five years after his death.

At Bill Veeck's funeral in 1986, retired Black baseball player Minnie Minoso attended wearing the Chicago White Sox uniform he wore at age 54. Veeck had signed Minoso as a pinch-hitter so he could be the first player to appear in a Major League Baseball game in five decades.

Veeck was beloved by the common fan. Coming out of Chicago's Sears Tower in 1980 after signing the papers selling his White Sox team for the final time, he was greeted by a line of taxicab drivers all honking their horns in honor of the man known as Sports Shirt.

At the 1968 World Series, Bill Veeck asked recently-retired Black player Elston Howard to manage the Washington Senators if his 1969 bid for the team was accepted. This would have made Howard the first Black manager in Major League Baseball, but in the end Veeck was out-bid for the team.

And as of 2024, Cleveland has yet to win a World Series since the one Veeck brought them in 1948.

∞

In 1978, Bill Veeck hired Larry Doby to manage his Chicago

White Sox. Doby became the second Black manager in baseball history. Doby would later joke about being second-in-line when breaking baseball's color barriers.

Larry Doby was elected to the Hall of Fame in 1998. He died in 2003.

On July 25, 2015, with the Hall of Famer's son Larry Doby. Jr in attendance, the Cleveland Indians unveiled its statue of Larry Doby.

∞

ABOUT THE AUTHOR

Tom Gantert started in the newspaper business in 1983 when he was a senior in high school in Michigan. He began his career as a part-time sportswriter for the Jackson Citizen Patriot. Since then, he's worked at six daily newspapers, including USA Today. He is currently a managing editor of a non-profit national news site. Gantert covered baseball at every level during his career, from Little League to Major League Baseball. Gantert covered the Lansing Lugnuts, Chicago Cubs, Kansas City Royals, Detroit Tigers, Philadelphia Phillies and Pittsburgh Pirates during his career.

WHAT IS HISTORICAL FICTION?

This book is labeled as "historical fiction." The bibliography included at the end of this novel is in smaller type and takes up 22 pages. The dates, people and events in this book are real.

So, what is the "fiction" in Bad Penny?

Much of the dialogue in Bad Penny came from interviews in newspaper accounts of the day.

But there are other instances where dialogue is created for characters. In these instances, the words the characters speak are based on their documented views on the subject matter.

In the end, Bad Penny is historically and meticulously accurate. I included the bibliography as evidence of that for the reader. The bibliography cites just a fraction of the articles I read while writing Bad Penny.

ACKNOWLEDGMENTS

I want to thank the following people: Bob Poet, Laurel Lavery, Lisa Viger, Molly Wiltse, Jack McHugh, Nancy Maier, Jamie Hope, Gary Gantert, Steve Klein and Sandy Imanse. You know what you did.

BIBLIOGRAPHY

ONLINE

David Prince. The 'Ferocious Christian Gentleman' Behind Jackie Robinson's Famous Moment. Prince On Preaching. April 15, 2015. https://www.davidprince.com/2015/04/15/the-ferocious-christian-gentleman-behind-jackie-robinsons-famous-moment-2/

Marty Appel. National Pastime Museum: The Mexican League Raids And The Last Full-Season Suspensions. http://www.appelpr.com/?page_id=460

Mike Tighe. Minnesota Twins Cite Calvin Griffith's Racist Comments For Removing His Statue. WKBT. June 19, 2020. https://www.news8000.com/news/local-news/minnesota-twins-cite-calvin-griffith-s-racist-comments-for-removing-his-statue/article_fa96ea87-3eec-5ee0-96a8-d6073fba6cd2.html

Patrick Spranger. Sadness In Brooklyn: The American Housing Act Of 1949 And The Brooklyn Dodgers Move To Los Angeles. City University Of New York. May 30, 2019. https://academicworks.cuny.edu/cgi/viewcontent.cgi?article=1001&context=qc_etds

Andy McCue. Branch Rickey. Society For American Baseball Research. https://sabr.org/bioproj/person/branch-rickey/

Doug Pappas. Summer 1996: The MacPhail Report Of 1946. http://roadsidephotos.sabr.org/baseball/MACPHAILREPT.htm

Jackie Robinson. 1947. 75. 2022. Society For American Baseball Research. https://sabr.org/jackie75/signing/

Kevin Stiner. Veeck Launches Big League Career By Purchasing Indians. National Baseball Hall Of Fame. https://baseballhall.org/discover/inside-pitch/veeck-launches-big-league-career-in-1946

N/A. Chandler Repeals Sam Breadon Penalty. Daily Illini. July 27, 1946. https://idnc.library.illinois.edu/?a=d&d=DIL19460727.2.64&e=-------en-20--1--img-txIN----------

Peter Dreier. Mr. Rickey Calls A Meeting. Society For American Baseball Research. https://sabr.org/journal/article/mr-rickey-calls-a-meeting/

Baseball Vignettes – I. https://goldenrankings.com/baseballvignettes1.htm

Precious Sanders. Ken Burn's Baseball: The Sixth Inning. Archived Innings. Nov. 20, 2017. https://archivedinnings.com/2017/11/20/ken-burnss-baseball-the-sixth-inning/
Ralph Berger. Larry MacPhail. Society For American Baseball Research. https://sabr.org/bioproj/person/larry-macphail/

Andy McCue. Jackie Robinson And Baseball Owners. Society For American Baseball Research. https://sabr.org/journal/article/jackie-robinson-and-baseball-owners/

John Thorn. Jackie Robinson's Signing: The Real Story. April 15, 2012. https://ourgame.mlblogs.com/jackie-robinsons-signing-the-real-story-6e685f8e42de

A Negro Leagues Journal. Black Ball. Volume 1. Number 2. Fall 2008. https://www.larrylester42.com/uploads/1/9/5/4/19545937/can_u_read_printed_w_cover.pdf

Retro Simba. How Cardinals, Browns Discriminated Against Black Fans. May 1, 2019. https://retrosimba.com/2019/05/01/how-cardinals-browns-discriminated-against-black-fans/

David Stewart. BabeWatch: Barnstorming Against Negro League Teams. Aug. 8, 2016. https://davidostewart.com/2016/08/08/babewatch-barnstorming-negro-league-teams/

N/A. Feller All-Stars Vs. Paige's In "Racial Rivalry"; Sports Collectors Digest. Dec. 28, 2010. https://sportscollectorsdigest.com/news/fell-paige-all-stars

Michael Haupert. MLB's Annual Salary Leaders Since 1874. https://sabr.org/research/article/mlbs-annual-salary-leaders-since-1874/

N/A. 1948 Red Sox. The Diaries. FenwayParkDiaries.com. https://fenwayparkdiaries.com/1948%20red%20sox/1948%20red%20sox.htm

American Public Media. Whites Remember Jim Crow. AmericanRadioWorks. https://americanradioworks.publicradio.org/features/remembering/whitesremember.html

N/A. How Cardinals, Browns, Discriminated Against Black Fans. RetroSimba.com. May 1, 2019. https://retrosimba.com/2019/05/01/how-cardinals-browns-discriminated-against-black-fans/

Louis Moore. Doby Does It! Larry Doby, Race, And American Democracy in Post–World War II America. University Of Illinois Press. JSTOR. https://www.jstor.org/stable/10.5406/jsporthistory.42.3.0363

Ken Bresler. A Jew Challenged Boston's Racism 75 Years Ago. Racism Held On. JewishBoston.com. July 23, 2020. https://www.jewishboston.com/read/a-jew-challenged-bostons-racism-75-years-ago-racism-held-on/

Jeff Wallenfeldt. What Is The Origin Of The Term "Jim Crow"?; Brittanica. https://www.britannica.com/story/what-is-the-origin-of-the-term-jim-crow

Zoe Jackson. The Night Disco Died. BlkGirlCulture.com. https://www.blkgirlculture.com/blog-2/the-night-disco-died-the-racist-amp-homophobic-end-to-disco

Matt Cox. Keep Baseball Going. National Baseball Hall Of Fame. https://baseballhall.org/node/10106

Craig Muder. Ultimate Relief For Cardinals In 1926 World Series. National Baseball Hall Of Fame.https://baseballhall.org/discover/inside-pitch/alexander-1926-world-series

Iain Russell. Babe Ruth. ScotchWhisky.com. July 4, 2018. https://scotchwhisky.com/magazine/famous-whisky-drinkers/19736/babe-ruth/

David Zingler. Hack Wilson. Simply Baseball Notebook's Legend. October 2001. http://z.lee28.tripod.com/sbnslegends/hackwilson.html

Gary Livacari. The Sad Demise Of Hack Wilson. BaseballHistoryComesAlive. Nov. 27, 2016. https://www.baseballhistorycomesalive.com/the-sad-demise-of-hack-wilson/

Thomas E. Schott. Hack Wilson. Society For American Baseball Research. https://sabr.org/bioproj/person/hack-wilson/

1922 Babe Ruth Signed Contract Addendum Limiting His Drinking, Late Nights. Heritage Auctions. https://sports.ha.com/itm/baseball/1922-babe-ruth-signed-contract-addendum-limiting-his-drinking-late-nights-i-ll-promise-to-go-easier-on-drinking-an/a/707-19090.s?ic4=GalleryView-Thumbnail-071515

Chris Rainey. Nick Cullop (Henry). Society For American Baseball Research. https://sabr.org/bioproj/person/nick-cullop-henry/

L. Robert Davis. Nick Cullop, Minor League Great. Society For American Baseball Research. https://sabr.org/journal/article/nick-cullop-minor-league-great/

N/A. Veeck Begins Shopping, 1944. BorchertField.com. http://www.borchertfield.com/2015/12/veeck-begins-shopping-1944.html

N/A. The Sad Story Of Grover "Pete" Cleveland Alexander. DrunkPhilsFans.com. http://www.drunkphilsfans.com/2021/09/the-sad-story-of-grover-pete-cleveland.html

Kevin Birtha. The Story Of Rube Waddell And His Drinking. Bleacher Report. April 14, 2010. https://bleacherreport.com/articles/378614-the-story-of-rube-waddell-and-his-drinking

N/A. Radio. Encyclopedia Of Cleveland History. Case Western Reserve University. https://case.edu/ech/articles/r/radio#:~:text=Cleveland's%20first%20radio%20station%20was,clear%20channel%20at%20390%20meters.

Adrian Burgos. Remembering Mike Garcia, Cleveland's Original Latino All-Star Pitcher; LaVidaBaseball.com. July 6, 2019. https://www.lavidabaseball.com/cleveland-indians-mike-garcia-all-star/

N/A. The Demise Of Negro League Baseball. CNLBR.org. http://www.cnlbr.org/Portals/0/RL/Demise%20of%20the%20Negro%20Leagues.pdf

Gerald Holland. Feuds, Finale And A Fairy Tail. Sports Illustrated. Aug. 31, 1959. https://vault.si.com/vault/1959/08/31/feuds-finale-and-a-fairy-tale

Harold Uhlman. Two That Didn't Get Away. ThinkBlueLA.com. Feb. 23, 2013. https://thinkbluela.com/2013/02/two-that-didnt-get-away/

Ken Krause. Historian Recounts Medford African American Journalist's Role In Integration Of Baseball. WickedLocal.com. https://www.wickedlocal.com/story/medford-transcript/2013/02/15/historian-recounts-medford-african-american/39987579007/

Jim Pete. Celebrating Larry Doby On Martin Luther King Jr. Day: While We're Waiting. WaitingForNextYear.com. https://waitingfornextyear.com/2018/01/celebrating-larry-doby-on-martin-luther-king-jr-day-while-were-waiting/

N/A. Remembering Tom Yawkey. BaseballReflections.com. https://baseballreflections.com/2018/03/20/remembering-tom-yawkey/

N/A. Harlem Globetrotters International, Inc. ReferenceForBusiness.com. https://www.referenceforbusiness.com/history2/59/Harlem-Globetrotters-International-Inc.html

N/A. Sunset Lodge. South Carolina Encyclopedia. https://www.scencyclopedia.org/sce/entries/sunset-lodge/

N/A. Albert 'Runt' Pullins. HoopHall.com. https://www.hoophall.com/hall-of-famers/albert-pullins/

N/A. Albert 'Runt' Pullins. Black Fives Foundation. https://www.blackfives.org/albert-runt-pullins/

N/A. The People, The Place: Native Americans In Iowa. Iowa University Libraries. https://www.lib.uiowa.edu/exhibits/previous/native/

N/A. Early Basketball Season. RetroSeasons.com. https://www.retroseasons.com/leagues/early-basketball-leagues/

Number Of Inhabitants. Iowa. U.S. Census Bureau. https://www2.census.gov/prod2/decennial/documents/23761117v1ch06.pdf

History.com Editors. Native American History Timeline. History.com. https://www.history.com/topics/native-american-history/native-american-timeline

Larry Doby. Ohio Outdoor Sculpture. https://www.sculpturecenter.org/oosi/items/show/1275

Rebecca Alpert. Racial Attitudes Towards Jews In The 'Negro Leagues': The Case Of Effa Manley. Project Muse. Purdue University Press. https://muse.jhu.edu/pub/60/edited_volume/chapter/1662440/pdf

Luis Mayoral. The Odd Couple: Minnie Minoso And Bill Veeck. LaVidaBaseball.com. Feb. 5, 2019. https://www.lavidabaseball.com/bill-veeck-minnie-minoso-white-sox/

N/A. Revenue Of The Boston Red Sox (MLB) From 2001 To 2022.

Statista.com. https://www.statista.com/statistics/196639/revenue-of-the-boston-red-sox-since-2006/

Craig LeMoult. Yawkey Way Might Be No More But Fenway Statues Still Lack Racial Diversity. WGBH. Oct. 4, 2018. https://www.wgbh.org/news/local-news/2018/10/04/yawkey-way-might-be-no-more-but-fenway-statues-still-lack-racial-diversity

Tovia Smith. Boston Changes 'Yawkey Way' To 'Jersey Street' After Concerns Over Racist Legacy. NPR. April 26, 2018. https://www.npr.org/2018/04/26/605851052/boston-red-sox-want-to-strike-former-owners-name-off-street-sign

Bill Francis. Paige's Induction In 1971 Changed History. Baseball Hall Of Fame. https://baseballhall.org/discover/baseball-history/paiges-induction-changed-history

Ted Williams: Hall Of Fame Induction Speech – 1966. Speakola.com. https://speakola.com/sports/ted-williams-hall-of-fame-induction-speech-1966

Larry Doby 1998 Hall Of Fame Induction Speech. National Baseball Hall Of Fame. https://www.youtube.com/watch?v=SnictfRm-rl

Statistics Summary For 1993. Montclair State University Athletics. https://static.montclairathletics.com/custompages/football/1993.htm

N/A. John S. Hilson '47. Memorial. Princeton Alumni Weekly. https://paw.princeton.edu/memorial/john-s-hilson-%E2%80%9947

Angie Brown. The Harlem Globetrotters Were Often Victims Of Racism Off The Court And Behind The Scenes. AndScape.com. Feb. 13, 2017. https://andscape.com/features/the-harlem-globetrotters-behind-the-scenes/

N/A. Birmingham Sam – The Last Great Star Of The Indianapolis Clowns. BaseballHistoryDaily.com https://baseballhistorydaily.com/tag/dero-austin/

Wendell Smith. I Don't Know How Long I'm Gonna Last. BaseballHistoryDaily.com. Sept. 8, 2020. https://baseballhistorydaily.com/2020/09/08/i-dont-know-how-long-im-gonna-last/

Joseph Wancho. Don Black. Society For American Baseball Research. https://sabr.org/bioproj/person/don-black/

Brian Carroll. Black Baseball's 'Funmakers': Taking The Miami Ethiopian Clowns Seriously. Society For American Baseball Research. 2016. https://sabr.org/journal/article/black-baseballs-funmakers-taking-the-miami-ethiopian-clowns-seriously/

N/A. Remembering Thalia Beatrice Winfield. Milwaukee Times. Feb. 20, 2020. https://milwaukeetimesnews.com/christian-times-religion-ministry-counseling/remembering-thalia-beatrice-winfield

Gary Livacari. Al Smith. Society For American Baseball Research. https://sabr.org/bioproj/person/al-smith-4/

Cleveland Indians Vs Philadelphia Athletics Box Score: September 14, 1947. BaseballReference.com. https://www.baseball-reference.com/boxes/PHA/PHA194709142.shtml

N/A. Drum Major Instinct. The Marking Luther King, Jr. Research And Education Institute. Stanford University. https://kinginstitute.stanford.edu/encyclopedia/drum-major-instinct

Jimmy Swartz. The Life And Career Of Larry Doby (Complete Story). ProBaseballHistory.Com. https://www.probaseballhistory.com/larry-doby/

Tom Yawkey: Setting The Record Straight. Yawkey Foundation. https://yawkeyfoundation.org/tom-yawkey-setting-the-record-straight/

Dayn Perry. Photo: The Bill Veeck 'Bobble-Leg' Is Outstanding. CBS Sports. https://www.cbssports.com/mlb/news/photo-the-bill-veeck-bobble-leg-is-outstanding/

Margery Sly. Walt Whitman And Baseball. History News. Temple University. https://sites.temple.edu/historynews/2018/10/22/walt-whitman-and-baseball/

A.J. Desmond & Sons Funeral Directors. John Kelsey II. Obituary. https://www.desmondfuneralhome.com/obituaries/John-Kelsey-II?obId=12340320

Baseball Reference. Roy Campanella. https://www.baseball-reference.com/players/c/camparo01.shtml

Baseball Reference. Yogi Berra. https://www.baseball-reference.com/players/b/berrayo01.shtml

Baseball Reference. Al Kaline. https://www.baseball-reference.com/players/k/kalinal01.shtml

Baseball Reference. Mickey Mantle. https://www.baseball-reference.com/players/m/mantlmi01.shtml

Guide To U.S. Air Force Officer Ranks: Types And Definitions. Indeed.com. https://www.indeed.com/career-advice/finding-a-job/air-force-officer-ranks

Scottsdale, Arizona. History & Social Justice. Tougaloo College. https://justice.tougaloo.edu/sundowntown/scottsdale-az/

N/A. What Is A Flash Burn? Drugs.com. https://www.drugs.com/cg/flash-burn-of-skin.html#overview

Joyce Peterson. Black Automobile Workers In Detroit, 1910-1930. The Journal Of Negro History. Vol. 64. No. 3. Summer, 1979. https://www.jstor.org/stable/2717031

Thomas Sugrue. Driving While Black: The Car And Race Relations In Modern America. Automobile In American Life And Society. http://www.autolife.umd.umich.edu/Race/R_Casestudy/R_Casestudy5.htm#Briggs

N/A. Detroit Athletic Club. HistoricDetroit.org. https://historicdetroit.org/buildings/detroit-athletic-club

Jan Anschuetz. "Walter Owen Briggs." Ann Arbor District Library. Winter 2013. https://aadl.org/ypsigleanings/252683

Chris Lamb. "How Baseball's First Commissioner Led A Conspiracy Of Silence To Preserve Baseball' Color Line"; Oct. 16, 2020. The Conversation.com. https://theconversation.com/how-baseballs-first-commissioner-led-a-conspiracy-of-silence-to-preserve-baseballs-color-line-148076

N/A. The Ballparks. Comiskey Park. ThisGreatGame.Com. https://thisgreatgame.com/ballparks-comiskey-park/

Katelin Schroeder. Bards Room At Old Comiskey Park. Pinterest. https://www.pinterest.com/pin/312578030359956636/

N/A. Campbell-Ewald Advertising. Encyclopedia.com. https://www.encyclopedia.com/books/politics-and-business-magazines/campbell-ewald-advertising

Alan Cohen. Satchel Paige: Twilight With The Marlins. Society For American Baseball Research. https://sabr.org/journal/article/satchel-paige-twilight-with-the-marlins/

Branden Hunter. "Racism, Baseball, And The Detroit Stars Negro League Team"; Michigan Chronicle. March 30, 2018. https://michiganchronicle.com/2018/03/30/racism-baseball-and-the-detroit-stars-negro-league-team/

N/A. Odd Baseball Facts Archive – VI. GoldenRankings.com. https://goldenrankings.com/baseballoddfacts6.htm

John Robinson. The First Black Player To Play For The Detroit Tigers, 1958. WFMK. https://99wfmk.com/first-black-detroit-tiger/#google_vignette

N/A. Bill Veeck Quotes. Baseball Almanac. https://www.baseball-almanac.com/quotes/Bill_Veeck_Quotes.shtml

N/A. Satchel Paige Shakes Hands With Boxing Great Joe Louis In Chicago – 1948. ClevelandMemory.org. https://clevelandmemory.contentdm.oclc.org/digital/collection/press/id/2937/

N/A. Sport: Satchel The Great. Time. July 19, 1948. https://content.time.com/time/subscriber/article/0,33009,798876,00.html

Craig Calcaterra. You Need To Read About Del Webb, The Former Yankee Owner. NBC Sports. March 16, 2015. https://mlb.nbcsports.com/2015/03/16/you-need-to-read-about-del-webb-the-former-yankees-owner/

N/A. How To Catch Catfish: The Complete Catfishing Guide. FishingBooker.com. https://fishingbooker.com/blog/how-to-catch-catfish-complete-guide-to-catfishing/

Leslie Heaphy. Satchel Paige And Company. Essays On The Kansas City Monarchs, Their Greatest Star And The Negro Leagues. 2007. https://www.google.com/books/edition/Satchel_Paige_and_Company/GPmwCYht6lcC?hl=en&gbpv=1&dq=satchel+paige+%22stepin+hitit%22&pg=PA7&printsec=frontcover

George Castle. David Fletcher. Bill Veeck Sr. Society For American Baseball Research. https://sabr.org/bioproj/person/bill-veeck-sr/

Rory Costello. Clint Courtney. Society For American Baseball Research. https://sabr.org/bioproj/person/clint-courtney/

N/A. Traveling Through Jim Crow America. National Museum Of African American History & Culture. Smithsonian. https://nmaahc.si.edu/explore/stories/traveling-through-jim-crow-america

Charlie Bevis. Melville Webb. Society For American Baseball Research. https://sabr.org/bioproj/person/melville-webb/

N/A. Gunter Toody's Diner. The Lasting Effect Of 1950's Car Culture. https://gunthertoodys.com/es/1950s-car-culture/

N/A. 300 + Years Of Brewing Legacy. Our Story. Griesedieck Bros. http://www.gb-beer.com/our-story

Eric Robinson. The Peculiar Professional Baseball Career Of Eddie Gaedel. Society For American Baseball Research. 2015. https://sabr.org/journal/article/the-peculiar-professional-baseball-career-of-eddie-gaedel/

No. 1832. Treaty Of Peace With Japan. Signed At San Francisco, On 8 September 1951. https://treaties.un.org/doc/publication/unts/volume%20136/volume-136-i-1832-english.pdf

N/A. See Trains From The 1940s, When Passengers Could Ride The Railroad In Comfort And Class. ClickAmericana.com. https://clickamericana.com/topics/travel-tourism/trains-from-the-1940s-passenger-railroad-travel

N/A. Willard 'Home Run' Brown. Negro Leagues Baseball Museum. https://nlbemuseum.com/history/players/brownw.html

N/A. Walter Brown. Basketball Hall Of Fame. https://www.hoophall.com/hall-of-famers/walter-brown/

N/A. NBA. Career Opportunities. History. https://careers.nba.com/history/

Church Histories. First Baptist Church, Minot, North Dakota. North American Baptist Heritage Commission. https://www.nabarchives.org/wp-content/uploads/2011/10/First-Baptist-Minot.pdf

N/A. Minot International Airport. History. https://www.motairport.com/232/History

N/A. Memorable Manitobans: Gabriel Charles 'Barney' Mollot (1905-1987). Manitoba Historical Society. http://www.mhs.mb.ca/docs/people/mollot_gc.shtml

N/A. Minor League History: Mandak League. Dutch Baseball Hangout. https://dutchbaseballhangout.blog/2019/01/05/minor-league-history-mandak-league/

N/A. Minot Mallards Baseball. AtThePlate.com. https://attheplate.com/mallards/rosters.html

Curry Kirkpatrick. Watch Out. Tigers On The Loose. Sports Illustrated. Feb. 23, 1981. https://vault.si.com/vault/1981/02/23/watch-out-tigers-on-the-loose-after-devouring-22-straight-opponents-lsu-has-a-firm-grip-on-the-sec-lead

NA. Hello, Trouble, I'm Dale Brown. Sports Illustrated. Nov. 18, 1985. https://vault.si.com/vault/1985/11/18/hello-trouble-im-dale-brown

Nathalie Gomez. Little Chicago Pub District In Downtown Minot. KXMA. https://www.kxnet.com/news/little-chicago-pub-district-in-downtown-minot/

Steven Borjeson. Minot, North Dakota: Small City, Checkered Past, Bright Future. The Western Planner. https://www.westernplanner.org/arc/2016/1227/minot-north-dakota-small-city-checkered-past-bright-future

Bill Young. Charles Faber. J.L. Wilkinson. Society For American Baseball Research. https://sabr.org/bioproj/person/j-l-wilkinson/

N/A. Maurice Podoloff. Basketball Hall Of Fame. https://www.celticslife.com/2017/10/red-auerbach-walter-brown-and-gaming.html

N/A. Clifton, Nathaniel 'Sweetwater'. Encyclopedia.com. https://www.encyclopedia.com/education/news-wires-white-papers-and-books/clifton-nathaniel-sweetwater

N/A. Red Auerbach, Walter Brown And 'Gaming' The Draft. CelticsLife.com. https://www.celticslife.com/2017/10/red-auerbach-walter-brown-and-gaming.html

Alex Palmer. This Segregated Railway Car Offers A Visceral Reminder Of The Jim Crow Era. Smithsonian Magazine. June 13, 2016. https://www.smithsonianmag.com/smithsonian-institution/segregated-railway-car-offers-visceral-reminder-jim-crow-era-180959383/

1950 Census: Population Of North Dakota By Counties: April 1, 1950. https://www2.census.gov/library/publications/decennial/1950/pc-02/pc-2-17.pdf

N/A. Fire Commissioners And Chiefs Of Department. Boston Fire Historical Society. https://bostonfirehistory.org/personnel/fire-commissioners-and-chiefs-of-department/

Brad Ricca. The Secret History Of Chief Wahoo. Belt Magazine. June 19, 2014. https://beltmag.com/secret-history-chief-wahoo/

N/A. Sport: Life & Death; Time. Oct. 3, 1949. https://content.time.com/time/subscriber/article/0,33009,800840,00.html

Frank Drouzas. What's In A (Racist) Name?; TheWeeklyChallenger.com. July 24, 2020. https://theweeklychallenger.com/whats-in-a-racist-name/

The Kid From Cleveland. Internet Movie Database. https://www.imdb.com/title/tt0041545/?ref_=nm_flmg_t_6_dr

Andrew Meyer. Sean Fitzgerald. "'Our Team' Travels Back To Cleveland's Watershed Moment In Baseball History"; WKSU. April 5, 2021. https://www.ideastream.org/community/2021-04-05/our-team-travels-back-to-clevelands-watershed-moment-in-baseball-history

Dan Austin. Gotham Hotel. HistoricDetroit.org. https://historicdetroit.org/buildings/hotel-gotham

Chris Benedict. Sugar Ray Robinson, Jimmy Doyle, And A Dream Come Horribly True. RingSideReport.com. https://ringsidereport.com/?p=56377

1948 Boston Red Sox Roster. Baseball Almanac. https://www.baseball-almanac.com/teamstats/roster.php?y=1948&t=BOS

N/A. Detroit Wolves. Negro League Baseball Players Association. http://www.nlbpa.com/the-negro-league-teams/detroit-wolves

Emma Keith. Separate And Unequal. OUDaily. http://projects.oudaily.com/mclaurin/

Bruce Newman. The N.Y. Rens Traveled A Long Hard Road To Basketball's Hall Of Fame. Sports Illustrated. Oct. 22, 1979. https://vault.si.com/vault/1979/10/22/yesterday-the-ny-rens-traveled-a-long-hard-road-to-basketballs-hall-of-fame

N/A. "Branch Rickey Stole Negro League Stars, Author Finds"; Southern Bookman. April 16, 2021. https://louismayeux.typepad.com/southern_bookman/2021/04/branch-rickey-stole-negro-league-stars-author-finds.html

Ronald Auther. Abe Saperstein. 49 Days: The West Coast 'Baseball' Association. The Shadow Ball Express. https://shadowballexpress.wordpress.com/tag/abe-saperstein/

Warren Corbett. Steve Gromek. Society For American Baseball Research. https://sabr.org/bioproj/person/steve-gromek/

Dave Hoekstra. Mary Frances Veeck Turns 100. Aug. 26, 2020. https://www.davehoekstra.com/2020/08/26/mary-frances-veeck-turns-100/

Evin Demirel. "The Sweetest Thing"; Slam. Nov. 10, 2015. https://www.slamonline.com/news/nba/sweetwater-clifton-slam-feature/

Tom Kirvan. "Picture Perfect: Photo Links Two Baseball Families Forever"; Macomb County Legal News. July 22, 2022. https://www.legalnews.com/macomb/1513732/

Lisa Cooper. Larry Doby. Ebbets Field Flannels. July 1, 2022. https://www.ebbets.com/blogs/news-and-history/larry-doby

Dan Austin. Statler Hotel. HistoricDetroit.org. https://historicdetroit.org/buildings/statler-hotel

Larry Doby. Baseball Reference. https://www.baseball-reference.com/players/d/dobyla01.shtml

David Vergun. Sports Heroes Who Served: Baseball Legend Larry Doby Served In The Navy During WWII"; U.S. Department Of Defense. April 13, 2021. https://www.defense.gov/News/Feature-Stories/Story/Article/2562483/sports-heroes-who-served-baseball-legend-larry-doby-served-in-the-navy-during-w/

Matt Garcia. Alton Hornsby Jr. Steve Lawson. Susan Salvatore. Civil Rights In America: Racial Desegregation In Public

Accommodations. National Park Service. February 2004. https://archives.iupui.edu/bitstream/handle/2450/676/Racial%20Desegregation,%20Public%20Accomodations.pdf;jsessio nid=3C1BB85FE86BA843E904ECD760D86AC2?sequence=1

Mark Armour. Joe Cronin. Society For American Baseball Research. https://sabr.org/bioproj/person/joe-cronin/

C. Paul Rogers III. Rogers Hornsby. Society For American Baseball Research. https://sabr.org/bioproj/person/rogers-hornsby/

Francis Russell. The Last Of The Bosses; American Heritage. 1959. Volume 10, Issue 4. https://www.americanheritage.com/last-bosses

Bucky Fox. Baseball's Bill Veeck Changed The Pitch Of The National Pastime. Investor's Business Daily. June 11, 2016. https://www.investors.com/news/management/leaders-and-success/bill-veeck-brought-family-fun-out-to-the-ballgame/

Joseph Wancho. Sept. 28, 1948: Cleveland Celebrates Good Old Joe Earley Night. Society For American Baseball Research. https://sabr.org/gamesproj/game/september-28-1948-cleveland-celebrates-good-old-joe-earley-night/

Tim Wendel. "Bob Feller's Famous Motorcycle Test"; Huffington Post. Dec. 16, 2010. https://www.huffpost.com/entry/bob-fellers-famous-motorc_b_797564

N/A. Bill Veeck. Baseball Reference. https://www.baseball-reference.com/bullpen/Bill_Veeck

Cory Ross. James Blockett. The Cleveland Buckeyes. ClevelandHistorical.org. https://clevelandhistorical.org/items/show/867

Vince Guerrieri. Cleveland's Best Bars: Harbor Inn. Cleveland Magazine. Jan. 27, 2022. https://clevelandmagazine.com/things-to-do/articles/cleveland's-best-bars-harbor-inn

N/A. Friedman, Max R. Encyclopedia Of Cleveland History. Case Western Reserve University. https://case.edu/ech/articles/f/friedman-max-r

N/A. Owens, Jesse. Encyclopedia Of Cleveland History. Case Western Reserve University. https://case.edu/ech/articles/o/owens-jesse

William Rogers. Cool Papa Bell. Mississippi History Now. August 2008. https://mshistorynow.mdah.ms.gov/issue/cool-papa-bell

Danielle Rose. Millionaire's Row. ClevelandHistorical.org. https://clevelandhistorical.org/items/show/10

N/A. Chelmno. Holocaust Encyclopedia. United States Holocaust Memorial Museum. https://encyclopedia.ushmm.org/content/en/article/chelmno

Anthony Castrovince. The Crack-Of-Dawn Call To Larry Doby That Changed Baseball. MLB.com. Dec. 13, 2022. https://www.mlb.com/news/how-larry-doby-broke-al-color-barrier

Anthony Castrovince. Doby's Legacy, Too Often Forgotten, Lives On. MLB.Com. Dec. 13, 2021. https://www.mlb.com/news/larry-doby-legacy-as-first-black-player-in-american-league

N/A. The Second Coming. Larry Doby's Ignored Legacy. StudyLib.Net. https://studylib.net/doc/10250860/hist-498-senior-seminar-paper

Mia Bay. From Jim Crow To Now: On The Realities Of Traveling While Black. Lithub.com. March 25, 2021. https://lithub.com/from-jim-crow-to-now-on-the-realities-of-traveling-while-black/

Lit Century. How Baseball Legend Satchel Paige Sought To Pacify White Fans. LitHub.com. Nov. 30, 2021. https://lithub.com/how-baseball-legend-satchel-paige-sought-to-pacify-white-fans/

N/A. Satchel Paige Pitches For Chicago American Giants. Public Library. St. Joe County. Michiana Memory Digital Collection. https://michianamemory.sjcpl.org/digital/collection/p16827coll14/id/152/

N/A. Lot #151: 1940-50s. Spud Goldstein Traveling Secretary Cleveland Indians Team Trunk. MearsOnlineAuctions.Com. https://www.mearsonlineauctions.com/1940_50s_Spud_Goldstein_Traveling_Secretary_Clevel-LOT141509.aspx

Sarah Trembanis. They Opened The Door Too Late. William & Mary. 2006. https://scholarworks.wm.edu/cgi/viewcontent.cgi?article=3297&context=etd

Robert Creamer. The Comiskey Affair. Sports Illustrated. Feb. 24, 1958. https://vault.si.com/vault/1958/02/24/the-comiskey-affair

Jeff Miller. The 1950s Louisiana Law That Stalled Racial Progress In Texas Baseball. TexasMonthly.com. April 15, 2022. https://www.texasmonthly.com/arts-entertainment/texas-league-baseball-history-segregation/

George Bulanda. The Way It Was – Briggs Stadium, 1958. HourDetroit.com. https://www.hourdetroit.com/community/the-way-it-was-briggs-stadium-1958/

N/A. An Introduction To Larry Doby. MiscBaseballwordpress.com https://miscbaseball.wordpress.com/2013/08/20/an-introduction-to-larry-doby/

Joseph Wancho. Joe Gordon. Society For American Baseball Research. https://sabr.org/bioproj/person/joe-gordon/

N/A. Jackie Robinson 1947 2022. Society For American Baseball Research. https://sabr.org/jackie75/signing/

N/A. 1947 Texas League. BaseballReference.com https://www.baseball-reference.com/register/league.cgi?id=b5ef0fb7

David Rotenstein. A Big Numbers Hit In 1930 Created Pittsburgh Mob Legends. VeryLocal.com. Aug. 5, 2021. https://www.verylocal.com/pittsburgh-mob-woogie-harris-gus-greenlee/1271/

Brian McKenna. Gus Greenlee. Society For American Baseball Research. https://sabr.org/bioproj/person/gus-greenlee/

Luke Epplin. How Jackie Robinson Paved The Way For The Undersung Larry Doby. LitHub.com. April 1, 2021. https://lithub.com/how-jackie-robinson-paved-the-way-for-the-undersung-larry-doby/

Gary Waleik. "Forty Years Later, Disagreement About Disco Demolition Night"; WBUR. July 12, 2019. https://www.wbur.org/onlyagame/2019/07/12/disco-demolition-dahl-veeck-chicago-white-sox

Michael Rotman. Euclid Beach Park Riot. ClevelandHistorical.org. https://clevelandhistorical.org/items/show/562

Robert Creamer. The Good Days And The Bad Days Of Al Lopez. Sports Illustrated. July 1, 1957. https://vault.si.com/vault/1957/07/01/the-good-days-and-the-bad-days-of-al-lopez

Mickey Gallagher. Baseball's Larry Doby: #2 But First-Class All The Way Home. PeoplesWorld.org. April 17, 2018. https://www.peoplesworld.org/article/baseballs-larry-doby-2-but-first-class-all-the-way-home/

Tara Moriarty. More Than A Game: The Legacy Of Black Baseball. University Of Kentucky. https://uknowledge.uky.edu/cgi/viewcontent.cgi?article=1321&context=kaleidoscope

Thomas Brown Jr. Max Patkin. Society For American Baseball Research. https://sabr.org/bioproj/person/max-patkin/

Paul Dickson. Dickson: Larry Doby Integrates The Newly Formed Cactus League. Society For American Baseball Research. https://sabr.org/latest/dickson-larry-doby-integrates-the-newly-formed-cactus-league/

Reuters. South Africa: President Nelson Mandela Meets Basketball Legends Harlem Globetrotters. June 26, 1996. https://reuters.screenocean.com/record/170838

Terence Moore. Doby Was Second To None. BaseballHall.org. https://baseballhall.org/discover/doby-was-second-to-none

1947 Cleveland Indians Roster. Baseball Almanac. https://www.baseball-almanac.com/teamstats/roster.php?y=1947&t=CLE

1948 Cleveland Indians Roster. Baseball Almanac. https://www.baseball-almanac.com/teamstats/roster.php?y=1948&t=CLE

Vince Guerrieri. July 5, 1947: Larry Doby Integrates American League With Pinch-Hitting Appearance For Cleveland. https://sabr.org/gamesproj/game/july-5-1947-larry-doby-integrates-american-league-with-pinch-hitting-appearance-for-cleveland/

Don Jensen. Tris Speaker. Society For American Baseball Research. https://sabr.org/bioproj/person/tris-speaker/

N/A. 1947: The Arrival Of Jackie Robinson. ThisGreatGame.com. https://thisgreatgame.com/1947-baseball-history/

Kevin Czerwinski. Newcombe, Campanella Unsung Heroes. MILB.com. https://www.milb.com/news/don-newcombe-roy-campanella-bonded-as-nashua-dodgers-302553066

Japheth Knoop. Baseball's Integration Spells The End Of The Negro Leagues. Society For American Baseball Research. https://sabr.org/research/article/baseballs-integration-spells-the-end-of-the-negro-leagues/

Curt Smith. Ruppert Stadium (Newark, NJ). Society For American Baseball Research. https://sabr.org/bioproj/park/ruppert-stadium-newark-nj/

Frederick Bush. Mark Sternman. August 15, 1946: Newark Eagles Quartet Sparks East To Victory In Negro Leagues All-Star Game. Society For American Baseball Research. https://sabr.org/gamesproj/game/august-15-1946-newark-eagles-quartet-sparks-east-to-victory-in-negro-leagues-all-star-game/

Andrew Sharp. Jackie Price. Society For American Baseball Research. https://sabr.org/bioproj/person/jackie-price/

Warren Corbett. Buzzie Bavasi. Society For American Baseball Research. https://sabr.org/bioproj/person/buzzie-bavasi/

N/A. Hostetler, Joseph. Encyclopedia Of Cleveland History. Case Western Reserve University. https://case.edu/ech/articles/h/hostetler-joseph-c

N/A. Patkin, Max. Encyclopedia.com. https://www.encyclopedia.com/religion/encyclopedias-almanacs-transcripts-and-maps/patkin-max

Circus Clowns, OK. Rodeo Clowns, Sure. But Have You Ever Seen A Baseball Clown? CrazyAboutTV. https://www.youtube.com/watch?v=YaIHB65I6YI

Bing Crosby & Bob Hope – Baseball's Bustin' Out All Over – Feb. 1947. Bing Crosby. https://www.youtube.com/watch?v=PRGGWM0SeSY

N/A. Joe Bostic. Encyclopedia.com. https://www.encyclopedia.com/arts/educational-magazines/bostic-joe-1908-1988#:~:text=SIDELIGHTS%3A%20Joe%20Bostic%20was%20an,in%20baseball%20and%20as%20announcers.

N/A. The Private World Of The Negro Ballplayer. Sports Illustrated. March 21, 1960. https://vault.si.com/vault/1960/03/21/the-private-world-of-the-negro-ballplayer

N/A. Revised Book Reveals More About Life, Legacy Of Effa Manley. The Negro Leagues Up Close. https://homeplatedontmove.wordpress.com/2020/05/21/revised-book-reveals-more-about-life-legacy-of-effa-manley/

N/A. Is That All I Did. MLB.com. https://medium.com/joeblogs/is-that-all-i-did-4ecf70059113

N/A. Wilt, 1962. Hoopszone.com. https://www.hoopszone.net/Kansas/Kansas/Other/Articles/wilt%201962.htm

Doron Goldman. 1933-1962. The Business Meetings Of Negro League Baseball. Society For American Baseball Research. https://sabr.org/journal/article/1933-1962-the-business-meetings-of-negro-league-baseball/

N/A. McPhail Letter Shows Staunch Opposition To Integrate Baseball. MLB.com. Jan. 19, 2015. https://nlbm.mlblogs.com/mcphail-letter-shows-staunch-objection-to-integrate-baseball-c293bab9676

Thomas Whalen. John Henry Is Right. Yawkey Way Should Be Renamed; WBUR. Aug. 22, 2017. https://www.wbur.org/cognoscenti/2017/08/22/renaming-yawkey-way-thomas-j-whalen

Glenn Stout. Tryout And Fallout: Race, Jackie Robinson And The Boston Red Sox; GlennStout.com. https://glennstout.com/tryout-and-fallout-race-jackie-robinson-and-the-red-sox/

Glenn Stout. Denny Galehouse. Society For American Baseball Research. https://sabr.org/bioproj/person/denny-galehouse/

Gary Bedingfield. Al Schacht Entertains The Troops Overseas. BaseballInWartime.com. https://www.baseballinwartime.com/al_schacht.htm

Barney Frank. Jackie Robinson's Tryout With The Boston Red Sox, April 1945; Congressional Record. Volume 151, Part 3. March 2, 2005. https://www.govinfo.gov/content/pkg/CRECB-2005-pt3/html/CRECB-2005-pt3-Pg3327.htm

Bill Littlefield. The Biggest Trade That Never Was: Joe DiMaggio For Ted Williams; WBUR. July 7, 2017. https://www.wbur.org/onlyagame/2017/07/07/dimaggio-williams-trade-yankee-red-sox

N/A. Northern Cardinal. American Bird Conservancy. https://abcbirds.org/bird/northern-cardinal/

Walter Carrington. The Red Sox Were The Last Baseball Team To Integrate. This Is How It Happened. WBUR. July 17, 2019. https://www.wbur.org/cognoscenti/2019/07/17/red-sox-last-team-in-baseball-to-integrate-pumpsie-green-walter-c-carrington

N/A. Integration. Brittanica. https://www.britannica.com/sports/baseball/Integration

Chris Lamb. How Baseball's First Commissioner Led A Conspiracy Of Silence To Preserve Baseball's Color Line: The Conversation. Oct. 16, 2020.

https://theconversation.com/how-baseballs-first-commissioner-led-a-conspiracy-of-silence-to-preserve-baseballs-color-line-148076

Shayna Sigman. The Jurisprudence Of Judge Kenesaw Mountain Landis. Marquette Sports Law Review. Volume 15. Issue 2. Spring. https://scholarship.law.marquette.edu/cgi/viewcontent.cgi?article=1326&context=sportslaw

N/A. Gentleman's Agreement: A Brief History Of Negro League Baseball in America (From The Playbill). Marin Theatre Company.

https://www.marintheatre.org/productions/fences/fences-negro-leagues

1936 Baseball Judge Kenesaw Mountain Landis & Mrs. Tom Yawkey Vintage Photograph.

http://www.boxingtreasures.com/19bajukemola.html

N/A. Baseball And Opera.Sports Video.

https://www.sportsvideo.org/2014/05/05/baseball-and-opera/

N/A. Lincoln 'Stepin Fetchit' Perry. The Library of Congress.

https://memory.loc.gov/diglib/ihas/loc.music.tdabio.138/#:~:text=Lincoln%20Perry%2C%20the%20terrifically%20successful,Lincoln%20Theodore%20Monroe%20Andrew%20Perry.

Stephanie Roper. From Military Forts To 'Nigger Towns': African Americans In North Dakota, 1890-1940. Emporia State University. https://esirc.emporia.edu/bitstream/handle/123456789/633/Roper%20Vol%2027%20Num%201.pdf?sequence=1

1950 Minot Mallards Roster. StatsCrew.

https://www.statscrew.com/minorbaseball/roster/t-mm13037/y-1950

Gary Gillette. The True Greatness Of The Mandak League. Society For American Baseball Research. https://sabr.org/journal/article/the-true-greatness-of-the-mandak-league/

From The Buffalo Soldiers To Satchel: Early Black Baseball In North Dakota. NDBaseball. https://ndbaseball.weebly.com/uploads/2/1/1/9/21192418/black_baseball_in_nd.pdf

Justia US Law. Saul Henry Davis, Jr. Appellant, v. United States of America, Appellee, 229 F. 2d 181 (8th Cir. 1956).

https://law.justia.com/cases/federal/appellate-courts/F2/229/181/202246/

E.H. Allison. Bureau Of American Ethnology Catalogue Of Manuscripts No. 1755. Sioux. Surrender Of Sitting Bull. 1897. https://www.lib.montana.edu/digital/objects/coll2204/2204-B05-F34.pdf

Terry Bohn. Saul Davis. Society For American Baseball Research. https://sabr.org/bioproj/person/saul-davis/

Justia US Law. Shelley v. Kraemer, 334 U.S. 1 (1948). https://supreme.justia.com/cases/federal/us/334/1/

Interview With Larry Doby, November 15, 1979. Louie B. Nunn Center For Oral History. University Of Kentucky Libraries. https://kentuckyoralhistory.org/ark:/16417/xt7q5717nx51

Interview With Walter Wellesley "Red Smith", November 13, 1979. Louie B. Nunn Center For Oral History. University Of Kentucky Libraries. https://kentuckyoralhistory.org/ark:/16417/xt7fxp6v0282

Interview With Ned F. Garver, June 3, 1988. Louie. B. Nunn Center For Oral History. University Of Kentucky Libraries.https://kentuckyoralhistory.org/ark:/16417/xt7qv97znf64

Interview With Effa Manley, October 19, 1977. Louie. B. Nunn Center For Oral History. University of Kentucky Libraries.

https://kentuckyoralhistory.org/ark:/16417/xt798s4jnv7d

Super Disco Demolition: The 40th Anniversary Compilation. The Museum of Classic Chicago Television.

https://www.youtube.com/watch?v=kqDkBM9vxw8

Buck O'Neil Talks About Satchel Paige Facing Josh Gibson And Babe Ruth. Throwback Media. https://www.youtube.com/watch?v=lj7JPYOl3CY

Eleanor Cummins. No One Told Babe Ruth He Had Cancer, But His Death Changed The Way We Fight It; Popular Science. Feb. 6, 2018.

https://www.popsci.com/babe-ruth-cancer-treatment/#:~:text=While%20it%20cannot%20be%20confirmed,ethics%20of%20his%20doctor's%20decisions.

N/A. The Other Harry Webber. MadisonAveNew

https://madisonavenew.wordpress.com/?s=Harry+Webber

1922 University of Pittsburgh Yearbook. The Owl. https://digital.library.pitt.edu/islandora/object/pitt%3A1922e49702#page/1/mode/2up/search/1922+Owl+Yearbook

Billboard Hot 100. Billboard. https://www.billboard.com/charts/hot-100/1979-07-14/

Paul Tenpenny. Mr. Baseball & His 1943 Milwaukee Brewers. Borchertfield.com.

http://www.borchertfield.com/2009/10/mr-baseball-his-1943-milwaukee-brewers.html

Leroy 'Satchel' Paige In The New York State Library Collections. New York State Library. February 2021. https://www.nysl.nysed.gov/collections/satchelpaige/index.htm

Jules Tygiel. Revisiting Bill Veeck And The 1943 Phillies; Society For American Baseball Research. https://sabr.org/journal/article/revisiting-bill-veeck-and-the-1943-phillies/

T.S. Flynn. Showdown: Babe Ruth's Rebellious 1921 Barnstorming Tour. https://sabr.org/journal/article/showdown-babe-ruths-rebellious-1921-barnstorming-tour/

Warren Corbett. Bill Veeck; Society For American Baseball Research.

https://sabr.org/bioproj/person/bill-veeck/

N/A. Chicago's Harlem Globetrotters. WTTW. https://interactive.wttw.com/a/chicago-stories-harlem-globetrotters

Ron Fimrite. His Own Biggest Fan; Sports Illustrated. July 19, 1993. https://vault.si.com/vault/1993/07/19/his-own-biggest-fan-baseballs-first-commissioner-kenesaw-mountain-landis-was-part-hero-all-ego

George Castle. Bill Veeck: Remembering The Good, The Bad And The In-Between On His 100th Birthday. Chicago Baseball Museum. Feb. 7, 2014. https://chicagobaseballmuseum.org/wp-content/uploads/CBM-Bill-Veeck-20140207.pdf

Keri Pleasant. Honoring Black History World War II Service To The Nation. U.S. Army. Feb. 27, 2020. https://www.army.mil/article/233117/honoring_black_history_world_war_ii_service_to_the_nation#:~:text=During%20WWII%2C%20more%20than%202.5,the%20Army%20during%20the%20War.

NEWSPAPERS

Roy Grove. "Who Is The Bigger Man, Judge Landis Or Babe Ruth, The Baseball Swatter?"; Knoxville Sentinel. Oct. 20, 1921.

Associated Press. "Babe Ruth Caught In Toils Of Law"; Bristol Herald Courier. April 13, 1926.

N/A. "Miami To Run Eight Major Stake Races"; Times Union. Jan. 6, 1927.

Associated Press. "John Kelsey Dies"; Lubbock Avalanche-Journal. Jan. 23, 1927.

Philip O'Hara. "Briggs Plant In Flames After Blast In Detroit; Debris Traps Victims"; Windsor Star. April 23, 1927.

N/A. "Ty Cobb Will Sign With A's Comes Rumor"; Wilkes-Barre Times Leader, Evening News. Feb. 8, 1927.

N/A. "2 Are Dead; Blast Loss Is $3,000,000"; Detroit Free Press. April 24, 1927.

Associated Press. "Broken Light Caused Blast"; Lansing State Journal. April 25, 1927.

N/A. "Doniphan Wins In Two Events At Horseshow"; Detroit Free Press. July 2, 1927.

Frank Morris. "Briggs Blaze Brings Curb." Detroit Free Press. July 24, 1927.

N/A. "F.L. Moore Loses Suit For $36,000 Against Hornsby"; St. Louis Post-Dispatch. Dec. 22, 1927.

Associated Press. "Minor Draft War In Baseball Is Ended"; Jacksonville Daily Journal. Jan. 10, 1928.

N/A. "Briggs Gets Tigers' Stock"; Dec. 30, 1928.

N/A. "The Negro North And South"; Sioux City Journal. July 20, 1929.

N/A. "Negro Team Too Fast And Adroit For Seeger Men"; Globe-Gazette. March 13, 1930.

N/A. "Globe-Trotters Amuse On Court In 48-26 Battle"; Globe-Gazette. Dec. 29, 1930.

N/A. "Voyageurs Set For Invasion Of Globetrotters"; Winona Daily News. March 6, 1931.

N/A. "Oneida-Mohican Indians At Y.M." Globe-Gazette (Mason City). Dec. 2, 1931.

N/A. "Tent Men Upset Harlem Five By 19-6 In 'Prelim'"; Globe-Gazette. Dec. 7, 1931.

Associated Press. "Phils Again Crush Pirates; Hornsby Quits As Cubs' Manager"; Richmond Times-Dispatch. Aug. 3, 1932.

Dick Hackenberg. "Please Note"; Moorhead Daily News. Sept. 5, 1933.

Associated Press. "Yawkey Itches To Spend More"; Baltimore Sun. Oct. 27, 1934.

James Reston. "Pennants Are Won In December"; Lancaster New Era. Nov. 12, 1934.

N/A. "Semi-final Foes Both Confident"; Wichita Beacon. Aug. 26, 1935.

N/A. "Duncan Out For Revenge Tonight"; Wichita Beacon. Aug. 27, 1935.

N/A. "Great Negro Athlete Pitches Bismarck To Title"; Bismarck Tribune. Aug. 28, 1935.

N/A. "All Hail, Bismarck's First National Championship Team"; Bismarck Tribune. Aug. 28, 1935.

N/A. "Fist Fight Is Lost By MacPhail"; Cincinnati Enquirer. Sept. 26, 1935.

Associated Press. "Mickey Thinks His Tigers Can Repeat"; Palm Beach Post. Nov. 27, 1935.

Associated Press. "Tigers' New Boss Launched Cochrane Reign That Won Titles"; Fort Worth Star-Telegram. Dec. 27, 1935.

Daniel Daniel. "Yawkey Sees Game Through Rose Glasses"; Indianapolis Times. Dec. 28, 1935.

Associated Press. "Kraft Paper Mill At Georgetown"; The Item. Oct. 14, 1936.

Dale Stafford. "Detroit Park To Be Larger"; Escanaba Daily Press. Oct. 22, 1937.

Charles Ward. "Bengals' Park Will Be Rebuilt And Renamed"; Detroit Free Press. Oct. 22, 1937.

N/A. "Beaumont Club Office Is Given To Spike Briggs"; Detroit Free Press. Jan. 23, 1940.

Cumberland Posey. "Posey's Points"; Pittsburgh Courier. Feb. 17, 1940.

Harry Grayson. "Tom Yawkey Has Open Purse, Gets More Out Of Baseball Than Any Other Owner"; Guthrie Daily Leader. March 1, 1940.

N/A. "Hemsley On Waterwagon Is Improved"; Coshocton Tribune. April 18, 1940.

Eddie Brietz. "Sport Chatter"; Evening Review. Oct. 14, 1940.

N/A. "July 27 Set As Date Of East-West Game"; Pittsburgh Courier. June 28, 1941.

Associated Press. "Dykes Suspended By A.L. Prexy For Indefinite Period"; Baltimore Sun. July 7, 1941.

Grantland Rice. "Sportlight"; Southern Aegis (Ashville). July 10, 1941.

Jake Frong. "Press Box"; Journal Herald. Aug. 6, 1941.

Russ Cowans. "Through The Sports Mirror"; Detroit Tribune. Sept. 13, 1941.

Hardy Whritenour. "Kachadurian, Doby, Spark Great 'Undertakers' Offense For Grid Triumph By One-Sided Margin"; Paterson News. Nov. 21, 1941.

Jack Guenther. "MacPhail Tells Owners, Players Role Expected Of Them In War"; Ottawa Journal. Feb. 2, 1942.

Hardy Whritenour. "Doby, Eastside High Star, Honored at Testimonial"; The Paterson News. Feb. 20, 1942.

N/A. "There'll Be No More Games Staged At Briggs Stadium"; Michigan Chronicle. June 20, 1942.

Associated Press. "Negro Rapist Suspect Dies At Mob's Hands"; Cumberland Evening Times. July 13, 1942.

Alvin Moses. "Beating The Gun"; The Detroit Tribune. July 18, 1942.

N/A. "FBI To Probe Tex. Lynching Says Biddle"; Sunday Chicago Bee. Aug. 2, 1942.

Associated Press. "Negro Pitcher Scorns Majors"'; Spokesman-Review. Aug. 7, 1942.

N/A. "Satchel Paige Suggests An All-Negro Team For Majors"; The New York Age. Aug. 15, 1942.

Dan Parker. "Dan Parker Says"; The Camden Courier Post. Aug. 24, 1942.

Charles Neville. "Almost Unbelievable Comeback Of Rollicking Rollo"; News-Tribune (Tacoma). Sept. 13, 1942.

Jesse Haugabook. "Sports Fact"; Detroit Tribune. Sept. 26, 1942.

George Kelly. "War-Time Fighting Brings Change In Athletic Code"; Catholic Advance. Oct. 23, 1942.

N/A. "Branch Rickey Made Top Executive"; The Province. Dec. 30, 1942.

N/A. "Spike Briggs Air Force Captain"; Detroit Evening Times. Feb. 21, 1943.

Arthur Bystrom. "Swing Band And Vaudeville Draw Fans In Milwaukee"; Bennington Evening Banner. June 17, 1943.

N/A. "Acosta Is Birthday Present To Grimm, Milwaukee Pilot; Price Reported As $7,500"; Richmond Times-Dispatch. Aug. 29, 1943.

J. Roy Stockton. "1944 Baseball Season Set To Open April 18 And Close Oct. 1"; St. Louis Post Dispatch. Dec. 2, 1943.

Wendell Smith. "Frick Says Owners Were Impressed By Publishers"; Pittsburgh Courier. Dec. 11, 1943.

N/A. "Saul Davis Jailed On Wife's Complaint"; Minot Daily News. June 26, 1944.

N/A. "The Big Parade"; Detroit Free Press. Dec. 5, 1944.

N/A. "Governor Dewey Drives To Win"; Dayton Herald. March 2, 1945.

N/A. "Black Suspended; Broke Training"; Philadelphia Inquirer. June 7, 1945.

Roger Birtwell. "Fans In Danger When La Forest Bats"; Boston Globe. Aug. 13, 1945.

Associated Press. "Branch Rickey Gets Control Of Brooklyn Team." Tampa Tribune. Aug. 14, 1945.

N/A. "Baseball Jim Crow"; New York Age. Sept. 29, 1945.

Tommy Holmes. "Rickey Signs Negro Amid Complications"; Brooklyn Daily Eagle. Oct. 24, 1945.

N/A. "Boro Leader Support Rickey's Move"; Brooklyn Daily Eagle. Oct. 24, 1945.

Associated Press. "Wide Search Conducted By Dodger Head"; Hartford Courant. Oct. 24, 1945.

Joe Williams. "Frank Shaughnessy Has Sensible Approach To Baseball's Negro Problem; Right Type Welcomed"; Knoxville News-Sentinel. Oct. 25, 1945.

N/A. "Punted Paragraphs." Fort Worth Star-Telegram. Nov. 13, 1945.

Associated Negro Press. "Saperstein Heads West Coast Baseball Group"; Daily Bulletin (Dayton). Feb. 8, 1946.

N/A. "Not Expected To Heed Advice Of 'Hap' Chandler"; Pittsburgh Courier. Feb. 16, 1946.

Jimmy Powers. "The Powerhouse"; New York Daily News. March 6, 1946.

N/A. "Negro Major Loop Teams At Fireman's Park Today"; Corpus Christi Times. March 31, 1946.

Charles Einstein. "Veeck, Grabiner And Dykes In Deal – Cleveland Fans Approve Change"; Daily Dispatch (Moline). June 20, 1946.

Hugh Fullerton Jr. "Tribe Can't Be Hopeless With Bob In Control"; Rock Island Argus. June 22, 1946.

International News Serve. "Boudreau To Stay Says Tribe Prexy"; Tulsa World. June 24, 1946.

N/A. "Dykes Visits Cleveland; 'No Deal': Veeck"; Chicago Tribune. June 24, 1946.

Associated Press. "Bosox Trip Indians Twice, Rumor Has Dykes Taking Over"; Akron Beacon Journal. June 24, 1946.

Harry Grayson. "Grayson's Scoreboard"; Cushing Daily Citizen. July 2, 1946.

Dan Parker. "Rickey Visits Negro Contest With His Scout"; Camden Courier-Post. July 6, 1946.

Associated Press. "$300,000 Bid For Hurler Bob Feller"; Standard-Speaker. July 6, 1946.

United Press International. "Yanks Establish All-Time Attendance Mark"; St. Louis Star And Times. July 17, 1946.

Bo Whiting. "Time Out"; Morning Call. July 19, 1946.

Associated Press. "Tribe OKs Squatter's Rights"; Evening Star. July 30, 1946.

Associated Press. "Veeck Buys Shortstop For Entertaining Fans"; Cincinnati Enquirer. Aug. 3, 1946.

Joe Williams. "Cleveland's Newest Baseball Circus Veeck Is Master"; Memphis Press-Scimitar. Aug. 7, 1946.

Harry Grayson. "Lively Veeck Gives Indians Back To Fans; It Would Pay Other Owners To Do Likewise"; The News-Herald. Aug. 7, 1946.

Walter Parkes. "Fly Ball In The Tepee Rapidly Becoming Theme Song For The Cleveland Indians"; Mount Carmel Item. Aug. 9, 1946.

United Press International. "Pasquel Awaiting Spink Answer To Visit Mexico"; Rock Island Argus. Aug. 14, 1946.

Sid Keener. "Sid Keener"; St. Louis Star And Times. Aug. 21, 1946.

International News Service. "Major Leagues In Historical Joint Session"; Muncie Evening Press. Aug. 28, 1946.

Harry Grayson. "Long Time, But Red Sox Are Old Hands In Series"; Lancaster New Era. Sept. 13, 1946.

N/A. "Buster Miller's Time Out"; New York Age. Nov. 23, 1946.

N/A. "Larry Doby Accepts Montreal Offer"; Sunday News. Nov. 24, 1946.

Bill Lucas. "Press Box"; Tucson Daily Citizen. Feb. 20, 1947.

Sam Levitz. "Hall Of Fame Vets Get Together Here"; Arizona Daily Star. Feb. 21, 1947.

N/A. "$2,000 Raised At Wilberforce For Student Union Equipment"; Journal Herald. Feb. 26, 1947.

N/A. "Golf, Not Greenberg, Is The Topic"; Detroit Free Press. April 24, 1947.

Jackie Robinson. "Jackie Robinson Says:"; Pittsburgh Courier. May 17, 1947.

Jack Hand. "Rickey Explains Talk On Majors' Anti-Negro Action"; Charlotte Observer. Feb. 19, 1948.

UPI. "Text Of MacPhail's Reply To Branch Rickey's Charge"; Pittsburgh Press. Feb. 21, 1948.

Cleveland Jackson. "Veeck Impressed By Scout's Report On Negro Star"; Call And Post (Cleveland). June 28, 1947.

N/A. "Cleveland Announces Signing 22-Year-Old Paterson Negro For Reported $10,000 Price"; The News (Paterson). July 3, 1947.

Associated Press. "Indians Sign Larry Doby, Negro Player"; Alton Evening Telegraph. July 3, 1947.

Jim Schlemmer. "Cleveland Accepts Doby As Player Who May Give Them Added Strength" Akron Beacon Journal. July 6, 1947.

Associated Press. "Reformed Elbow Bending Pitcher Throws No-Hitter"; Reno Gazette-Journal. July 11, 1947.

Jim Schlemmer. "For The Records"; Akron Beacon Journal. July 11, 1947.

Bill Friel. "Baseball Has Hat Off To Its Former Bad Boy"; Reno Gazette-Journal. July 11, 1947.

International News Service. "Black Hurls No-Hitter Against A's!"; San Francisco Examiner. July 11, 1947.

Wendell Smith. "Cleveland Signed Doby In Nick Of Time"; Pittsburgh Courier. July 12, 1947.

N/A. "Mayor And McKee Agree To Go Along." Paterson News. July 14, 1947.

Associated Press. "Browns Sign Pair Of Negroes, Buy Option On Third"; Boston Globe. July 18, 1947.

Ken Gunderman. "The Sports Parade"; Escanaba Daily Press. July 24, 1947.

United Press International. "Bob Feller, Larry Doby Agree To Cuban Barnstorming Tour"; Scranton Tribune. Aug. 12, 1947.

Henry McCormick. "Playing The Game"; Wisconsin State Journal. Aug. 15, 1947.

George Lucas. "Pinch Hitting"; Morning Call (Paterson). Aug. 17, 1947.

C.M. Gibbs. "Refreshed By Layoff, Birds Open In Newark"; Baltimore Evening Sun. Aug. 21, 1947.

George Lucas. "Pinch Hitting"; Morning Call (Paterson). Aug. 27, 1947.

United Press International. "Bob Feller Gets Bonus Of $32,000"; Hartford Daily Courant. Sept. 4, 1947.

N/A. "Larry Doby Spends Day Off Watching Eastside Gridders"; Morning Call (Paterson). Sept. 10, 1947.

Joe Gootter. "Sport-O-Grams"; Paterson Evening News. Sept. 27, 1947.

Associated Press. "Boudreau 'Through' As Indians' Pilot"; Moberly Monitor-Index. Oct. 3, 1947.

United Press International. "Hint Al Lopez As New Mentor For Cleveland"; Nevada State Journal. Oct. 4, 1947.

Associated Press. "Browns Deal Still Red Hot, Veeck Signs In Cleveland"; St. Louis Globe-Democrat. Oct. 8, 1947.

International News Service. "Tribe Fans Sign Petitions To Retain Boudreau"; Daily Times (New Philadelphia). Oct. 8, 1947.

Wes Pedersen. "Salix Honors Hurler Don Black, Former High School Athlete: Pitches 5 Innings"; Sioux City Journal. Oct. 9, 1947.

Associated Press. "Rickey Will Appear In Jackie Robinson Movie"; Shreveport Times. Oct. 22, 1947.

Tommy Holmes. "Some Postseason Baseball Chatter"; Brooklyn Daily Eagle. Oct. 24, 1947.

United Press International. "Air Officials Eye DC-6 Deficiencies Listed By Engineer"; Spokane Chronicle. Oct. 25, 1947.

International News Service. "Select Boudreau Man Of The Year"; Camden Courier-Post. Nov. 6, 1947.

Ned Cronin. "Record Mat Purse"; Los Angeles Daily News. Nov. 7, 1947.

Frank Gibbons. "Boudreau Gets 2-Year Pact – Ruel Is Coach"; Dayton Herald. Nov. 25, 1947.

Grantland Rice. "Yawkey Shuns Spotlight But Likes Winning Team"; Tampa Times. Dec. 17, 1947.

N/A. "Paterson Team Sets Sights For Second Place In League Race, Doby In Debut With Local Club"; The News (Paterson). Jan. 5, 1948.

Jim Schlemmer. "Larry Doby, Tribe's Negro Outfield Candidate, Draws Rave Notices From Arizona"; Akron Beacon Journal. March 4, 1948.

Frank Gibbons. "Doby Poles Homer; A's Crash 10-1"; Akron Beacon Journal. March 4, 1948.

N/A. "Doby Expected To Stick If He Maintains Pace"; Paterson News. March 25, 1948.

Bill Lucas. "Doby, Seerey, Hit Homers In Intrasquad Game"; Tucson Citizen. March 4, 1948.

Associated Press. "Tribe To Scout Negro Players"; Spokesman-Review. May 5, 1948.

Burton Hawkins. "Doby's 450-Ft. Homer Helps Tribe Drub Nats, 6-1"; Evening Star (Washington). May 9, 1948.

C.E. McBride. "Sporting Comment" Kansas City Star, June 1, 1948.

Associated Press. "Indians Trade Seerey, Gettel For Bob Kennedy Of White Sox"; The New Journal. June 3, 1948.

Harold Burr "Kids Real Winners Of Flock-Indian Clash" Brooklyn Daily Eagle June 15, 1948

Roger Birtwell. "Red Sox Win, 8-6"; Boston Globe. June 17, 1948.

William Nunn Jr. "Jackie, Larry Having Their Ups And Downs," Pittsburgh Courier, June 19, 1948.

N/A. "Zulu Clowns To Play Nashville Cubs At Cardinal Park Friday"; Johnson City Press. Aug. 5, 1948.

N/A "'I'm Getting Into Shape' Says Satch"; Register-News (Mt. Vernon). Aug. 21, 1948.

A.S. Young. "Death Of Ruth Casts Pall Over World Of Sports"; Aug. 21, 1948.

Associated Press. "Satchel Paige Pays Reward"; Decatur Daily. Aug. 23, 1948.

Associated Press. "Paige Pays $500 Reward Offer For Proof Of His 1st Pro Job"; Winston-Salem Journal. Aug. 24, 1948.

Paul Menton. "Prospects For Boston Series Up To Red Sox"; Baltimore Evening Sun. Sept. 8, 1948.

Associated Negro Press. "Dodgers' Branch Rickey Flayed By Owner Of The Newark Eagles"; Alabama Tribune. Sept. 10, 1948.

Harry Grayson. "Satchel Amazed Boudreau, So Picked Up $55,000 Contract"; Okemah News Leader. Sept. 10, 1948.

United Press International. "Buc Home Attendance Sets Pace In National; Yankees Lead Majors"; Pittsburgh Press. Sept. 12, 1948.

Gordon Cobbledick. "Don Black's Greatest Victory"; Pittsburgh Sun-Telegraph. Sept. 12, 1948.

Associated Press. "Pitcher Don Black Given '50-50' Chance To Live"; Boston Globe. Sept. 14, 1948.

Frank Eck. "Beantown Series Would Mean Rubber Clash For Joe, Billy"; Sioux Falls Argus-Leader. Sept. 20, 1948.

Hy Hurwitz. "Johnson's Boner In Opening Game May Have Ruined Sox Flag Hopes"; Boston Globe. Sept. 20, 1948.

N/A. "Effa Blasts Fans, Press For NNL Flop; New York Age. Sept. 21, 1948.

Associated Press. "Everybody Else Had One, So Fan Gets His 'Night'"; Austin American-Statesman. Sept. 28, 1948.

Associated Press. "Jam For Series Tickets"; Kansas City Star. Sept. 28, 1948.

Al Wolf. "Sportraits"; Los Angeles Times. Oct. 4, 1948.

United Press International. "Fans Batter Gates For Sox Tribe Ducats"; Evening Express (Portland). Oct. 4, 1948.

N/A. "20 Of 22 Councilors At Sox Playoff Game; Meeting Called Off"; Oct. 4, 1948.

Robert Allen. "History Made At Fenway Park Ticket Battle"; Boston Globe. Oct. 4, 1948.

Gayle Talbot. "Indians Go On Warpath To Bury Boston Under Home-Run Barrage"; Billings Gazette. Oct. 5, 1948.

United Press International. "Cleveland Stages Big Celebration; Don Black Smiles"; Boston Globe. Oct. 5, 1948.

Grantland Rice. "Boudreau Performance In Tribe's Playoff Win Best Rice Ever Viewed"; Buffalo News. Oct. 5, 1948.

Associated Press. "False Alarm – For The Red Sox"; Pittsburgh Sun-Telegraph. Oct. 5, 1948.

Harold Kaese. "What WAS Matter With Our Red Sox?"; Boston Globe. Oct. 5, 1948.

N/A. "Name Fire Prevention Winners Here As Sirens Shriek And Chief Dashes"; Boston Globe. Oct. 5, 1948.

N/A "They're Really Our Indians"; Call And Post (Cleveland). Oct, 9, 1948.

Leo Petersen. "Indians Defeat Sain, 2-1, On 5 Hits"; Buffalo News. Oct. 9, 1948.

Associated Press. "Mom And Pop Come In For Presents When John Lynch Catches Doby Home Run Ball"; Sedalia Democrat. Oct. 10, 1948.

Carl Lundquist. "Boudreau Big Hero Of Series"; Akron Beacon Journal. Oct. 12, 1948.

Associated Press. "Only Four Boston Red Sox Sure Of Posts In 1949"; News-Journal (Mansfield). Oct. 14, 1948.

A.S. Young "Doby's Big Bat Tells The Baseball Story Of The Year" Call And Post, Oct. 16, 1948

A.S. Young. "Larry Doby Writes"; Call And Post (Cleveland). Oct. 16, 1948.

A.S. Young. "Gene Bearden Is Paige's Friend"; Call And Post (Cleveland). Oct. 16, 1948.

N/A. "Diamond Glovers Set For Doby Tribute; Fourth Armory Tourney Show Tomorrow"; Paterson News. Oct. 19, 1948.

N/A. "Picture Story Of City's Welcome Home Tribute To Larry Doby"; Morning Call (Paterson). Oct. 19, 1948.

N/A. "Our Hat Is Off To Larry Doby"; Morning Call (Paterson). Oct. 19, 1948.

N/A. "Larry Doby Makes A Hit At Gloves"; The News (Paterson). Oct. 21, 1948.

William Walker. "Down The Big Road"; Call And Post (Cleveland). Oct. 23, 1948

Marjorie McKenzie. "Pursuit Of Democracy"; Pittsburgh Courier. Oct. 23, 1948.

N/A. "Tom Yawkey"; Holdredge Daily Citizen. Nov. 6, 1948.

N/A. "Newark Eagles Nine Disband"; Brooklyn Daily Eagle. Nov. 10, 1948.

N/A. "New Officers Installed By YMHA Boosters At Annual Dinner"; The News (Paterson). Nov. 16, 1948.

Harry Webber. "Doby Can't Buy Decent N.J. Home"; New York Age. Dec. 18, 1948.

Associated Press. "Report Says Doby Can't Buy Home"; Des Moines Register. Dec. 25, 1948.

N/A. "Brooklyn Gives Up Monty Irvin"; Pittsburgh Courier. Jan. 22, 1949.

Associated Press. "'Healthy' Don Black Signs Cleveland Pact For '49"; Salt Lake Tribune. Jan. 30, 1949.

Dan Burley. "Now It's Campanella Vs. Mrs. Manley"; New York Age. Feb. 5, 1949.

Gordon Cobbledick. "Control? Old Satch Has That In Large Amounts"; News-Tribune (Tacoma). April 10, 1949.

Associated Press. "Tribe Rooter Ignores Police"; Winston-Salem Journal. June 8, 1949.

Associated Press. "Lawyers Say Lupica Can Stay On Perch"; Lexington Herald. June 9, 1949.

Ed McAuley. "Will He Become An All-Time Star?" St. Louis Post-Dispatch. July 7, 1949.

Frank Watson. "Despite Heat, Fatigue And An Expected Baby Lupica Remains Aloft"; Tampa Bay Times. July 16, 1949.

N/A. "Zulu Cannibal Giants Playing Nashville Cubs Here In Twin Bill Sunday, July 31st"; Macon Telegraph. July 30, 1949.

Red Smith. "Visiting Charley On The 'Flagpole'"; Miami News. Aug. 8, 1949.

N/A. "Pole Record Result Of Café Brag"; Circleville Herald. Aug. 11, 1949.

N/A. "Indian Sitter Establishes Unofficial Record; Anxious To See Newest Member Of Family"; Sidney Daily News. Aug. 11, 1949.

International News Service. "Owens, Paige To Receive Awards At Sox Game"; The Times (Hammond) Aug. 19, 1949.

Turner Dozier. "Reported Dead Year Ago, Indian Hurler Set To Resume Mound Career Next Year"; Ledger-Star. Aug. 20, 1949.

N/A. "Zulu Giants To Play Burlington"; Evening Times (Sayre). Aug. 31, 1949.

Joe Lovas. "The Sportsman Corner"; The Herald-News. Sept. 19, 1949.

United Press International. "Wobby Charley Off Perch, Kisses Family And Home Plate"; St. Louis Star And Times. Sept. 26, 1949.

Associated Press. "Pole Sitter 'Cured'"; York Dispatch. Sept. 26, 1949.

Bill Corum. "Veeck Champion Speech Maker"; Daily Sentinel-Tribune. Aug. 22, 1949.

Associated Press. "Wife Of Bill Veeck, Wins Divorce, Kids"; Springfield News-Leader. Oct. 30, 1949.

Dick Dugan. "Veeck Sells Tribe; Greenberg Signed As Executive"; Courier-Post. Nov. 21, 1949.

William Walker. "Down The Big Road"; Call And Post (Cleveland) Nov. 26, 1949.

Associated Press. "Gadsden's Ben Chapman Says He Plans To Sell Club At Season's End"; Montgomery Advertiser. Aug. 9, 1949.

Joe Gootter. "Sport-O-Grams"; Paterson Evening News. Oct. 17, 1949.

Jack Hand. "Bill Veeck Sells Cleveland Baseball Club For Reported $2,200,000"; Virginian-Pilot. Nov. 22, 1949.

N/A. "Globetrotters Slate 2 Cage Tilts For L.A."; Daily News (Los Angeles). Jan. 17, 1950.

N/A. "Veeck To Do Promotion For Harlem Globetrotters"; Tampa Bay Times. Jan. 25, 1950.

Kenny Brasel. "Veeck Assumes Responsibility For Cleveland's Poor Showing"; Springfield News-Leader. Feb. 1, 1950.

United Press International. "Indians Drop Satch Paige"; Republican And Herald. Feb. 11, 1950.

International News Service. "Mrs. Comiskey, Owner Of Chicago White Sox, Suffers Heart Attack"; St. Louis Star And Times. March 6, 1950.

New York News Service. "Pro Basketball Licking Lips Over Top Collegiate Talent"; Spokesman-Review. March 19, 1950.

United Press International. "Satchel Paige's Release Brings End To Legendary, Fiery Career"; Hopewell News. March 27, 1950.

Ernie Roberts. "Globetrotters Wallop All-Stars Here, 72-59"; Boston Globe. April 17, 1950.

International News Service. "Celtics Seeking Cooper Despite Trotters' Threat"; The Wilmington News Journal. April 28, 1950.

N/A. "Ice Capades Press Agent Weds Colorful Bill Veeck"; Pittsburgh Post-Gazette. May 1, 1950.

Jerry Nason. "Oddities Of The Derby; Trotters, Garden Agree; H.C. Coach Gets Break"; Boston Globe. May 6, 1950.

Associated Press. "Abe Saperstein's Father Succumbs"; Hamilton Daily News Journal. May 9, 1950.

Jack Case. "Crowds Largest Of Trip"; Bismarck Tribune. May 15, 1950.

Associated Press. "Mayor Pays Off On Census Wagers"; Evening World-Herald. May 18, 1950.

Satchel Paige. Earnest Mehl. "Scene Of Game In San Domingo"; Spokesman-Review. May 28, 1950.

N/A. "Wylie Stops Brandon As Teams Divide Pair"; Minot Daily News. May 31, 1950.

N/A. "Hands Brandon Initial Defeat"; Edmonton Journal. May 31, 1950.

N/A. "First Game Wed. Night"; Sheridan County Star. June 1, 1950.

Associated Press. "Chicago Withdraws From NBA, Circuit Fails To Keep Promises, Saperstein Says"; Democrat And Chronicle. Sept. 26, 1950.

Associated Press. "Simpson, Cleveland Rookie Negro Find, Rated Slugger"; Baltimore Sun. Jan. 16, 1951.

Associated Press. "Philadelphia A's Sign Johnson, Negro Scout"; Times Record (Troy). Jan. 25, 1951.

Dan Walton. "Sports-Log"; Tacoma News-Tribune. Feb. 2, 1951.

Jack Hand. "Walter Mulbry Will Take Over If Happy Chandler Resigns"; Elizabethton Star. March 16, 1951.

John Webster. "Sportscope"; Philadelphia Inquirer. April 3, 1951.

Tom Siler. "Will Harridge, AL Prexy, Is Little Known To Fans But He's Boss, Just The Same"; Knoxville News-Sentinel. March 28, 1951.

N/A. "Satchel Paige Helps Chicago Giants Win 2"; Chicago Tribune. May 21, 1951.

Wendell Smith. "Sports Beat"; Pittsburgh Courier. June 30, 1951.

Reno Hahn. "Veeck Has Inside Pitch Now"; St. Louis Globe-Democrat. July 4, 1951.

Associated Press. "Yes, Veeck Set To Give Browns Those Changes"' Dixon Evening Telegraph. July 6, 1951.

Associated Press. "Veeck Goes Into Action At Browns' Game With Music, Fireworks And Free Drinks"; Columbia Daily Tribune. July 7, 1951.

Associated Press. "Winnipeg Manager Admits Browns Contact 5 Negroes"; Chicago Tribune. July 11, 1951.

Arch Ward. "In The Wake Of The News"; Chicago Tribune. July 17, 1951.

Associated Press. "Sideshow Talent Putting Browns On Paying Basis." Nashville Banner. Aug. 20, 1951.

Harry Mitauer. "Win, 5-3, As Lollar, Wood Star"; St. Louis Globe-Democrat. Aug. 25, 1951.

Art Morrow. "1115 Managers Aid Browns, Garver Turn Back A's, 5-3"; Philadelphia Inquirer. Aug. 25, 1951.

Jack Rice. "Dykes Cries 'Wolf,' Veeck Flashes Book"; St. Louis Globe-Democrat. Aug. 25, 1951.

N/A. "Prize-Winning Coaches Banned By A.L. Office"; St. Louis Globe-Democrat. Aug. 25, 1951.

Bob Broeg. "Fun For Everyone, Except Indians, Whose Lose Lead; Lemon Vs. Sanford Tonight"; St. Louis Post-Dispatch. Sept. 8, 1951.

Wendell Smith. "A Gentleman From Texas Hedges"; Pittsburgh Courier. Oct, 13, 1951.

Red Smith. "Abe Saperstein Mulls Over Some Highlights In Harlem Globetrotters' First 25 Years"; Philadelphia Inquirer. Oct. 26, 1951.

N/A. "Falstaff Combines Two Departments"; St. Louis Globe-Democrat. Nov. 22, 1951.

Cy Kritzer. "New Bison General Manager Assured Under Tiger Regime"; Buffalo News. Nov. 28, 1951.

Associated Press. "Cleveland Indians Decide To Pay Don Black's Claim"; Dayton Daily News. Dec. 23, 1951.

Wendell Smith. "Mr. Veeck Defends His New Manager"; Pittsburgh Courier. Dec. 29, 1951.

Associated Press. "Spike Briggs Heads Tigers"; News And Observer. Jan. 27, 1952.

Lyall Smith. "Spike Briggs Is Named Tigers President"; Detroit Free Press. Jan. 27, 1952.

Bill Richardson. "Award, 1952 Contract Loom For Leavenworth's Murry Dickson"; Kansas City Times. Jan. 31, 1952.

N/A. "Rajah's 'Guy With Guts' On Deck For Bucs"; Valley Times (North Hollywood). March 8, 1952.

N/A. "Heinemann Says Golf Course Ban Temporary"; Corpus Christi Times. March 28, 1952.

United Press International. "Paige Fined $100 By Rogers Hornsby For Missing Game"; Muskogee Daily Phoenix and Times-Democrat. April 5, 1952.

N/A. "Negro Leader Praises Council, Gets 'Do What We Can' Pledge"; Corpus Christi Caller-Times. April 16, 1952.

Burt Newton. "Denver Inks Ed Steele"; Pittsburgh Courier. May 31, 1952.

Associated Press. "Hornsby Says He Won't Go For Any Of Veeck's 'Screwy Ideas'"; Knoxville News-Sentinel. June 11, 1952.

Jack Rice. "Veeck Says He 'Blew One' In Hiring Hornsby, Hopes Marion Can Patch Club"; St. Louis Globe-Democrat. June 11, 1952.

Milton Richman. "Players Hates Rogers Hornsby"; Columbus Ledger. June 11, 1952.

Associated Press. "Browns Present Veeck Trophy For 'Greatest Play'"; St. Louis Globe-Democrat. June 11, 1952.

Associated Press. "Roger Hornsby's Wife Is Seeking Divorce"; Lexington Herald. June 12, 1952.

John McCallum. "Max Patkin, Clown Of Diamond, Says He's Reformed Pitcher"; Evansville Press. June 19, 1952.

Carl Lundquist. Browns, Senators Fight 18 Innings; Game Is Called"; Sacramento Bee. June 21, 1952.

John Johnson. "Bill Veeck Loves Satch Paige"; The Call. June 27, 1952.

N/A. "Bill Veeck Asks Public To Urge Stengel To Use Satch In All-Star Game"; Alabama Citizen. June 28, 1952.

N/A. "Satch Is A Catcher, Too"; St. Louis Post Dispatch. June 29, 1952.

Milton Richman. "Satchel's Last Wish Granted"; Lubbock Evening Journal. July 1, 1952.

Wendell Smith. "Sports Beat"; Pittsburgh Courier. Aug. 23, 1952.

N/A. "City Mourns H.T. Ewald, Ad Executive"; Detroit Free Press. Jan. 10, 1953.

Prescott Sullivan. "Saperstein Is Top Promoter"; San Francisco Examiner. Jan. 15, 1953.

Associated Press. "Convicted Saigh May Possibly Dispose Of St. Louis Cards"; Daily Standard (Sikeston). Jan 29, 1953.

N/A. "Tribe, N.Y. Put Browns Off Radio"; St. Louis Globe-Democrat. Feb. 11, 1953.

Roy Stockton. "Claimed Loss Of $400,000 Included Price Paid For New Ball Players"; St. Louis Post-Dispatch. March 17, 1953.

Raymond Smith. "Veeck Offers To Sell Out For $2,400,000"; St. Louis Globe-Democrat"; March 17, 1953.

Associated Press. "Dispatch Says Ready To Sell Club, 'Lock, Stock And Barrell'"; Mexico Ledger. March 17, 1953.

N/A. "Veeck Ready To 'Face Music'"; St. Louis Globe-Democrat. March 18, 1953.

Associated Press. "Veeck Quoted As 'Victim Of Lying Owners'"; St. Louis Globe-Democrat. March 18, 1953.

Associated Press. "Detroit Tigers Sign Negro Outfielder"; Wilkes-Barre Times Leader The Evening News. Aug. 27, 1953.

International News Service. "Veeck Hanged In Effigy By Browns' Fans"; Columbia Daily Tribune. Sept. 26, 1953.

John Carmichael. "How Veeck Got In Bad"; St. Louis Post-Dispatch. Sept. 30, 1953.

Lyall Smith. "Approval Of Shift Is Unanimous"; Detroit Free Press. Sept. 30, 1953.

Associated Press. "Lane To Stay In Chicago"; Kansas City Star. Oct. 8, 1953.

United Press International. "Veeck Tells Woes To Circuit Judge"; The Tribune (Coshocton). Oct. 8, 1953.

Roy Stockton. "Players Need Actuary, Rather Than A Lawyer"; St. Louis Post-Dispatch. Dec. 6, 1953.

Associated Press. "Philadelphia A's Sign First Negro Baseball Coach"; Lancaster New Era. Feb. 4, 1954.

Dick Beddoes. "From Our Tower"; Vancouver Sun. Jan. 18, 1954.

Fred Pettijohn. "In The Press Box"; Fort Lauderdale News. Jan. 4, 1955.

Associated Press. "Detroit Tigers Sign Negro Catcher"; Corpus Christi Caller-Times. June 23, 1955.

Joe Doyle. "According To Doyle"; South Bend Tribune. South Bend Tribune. July 13, 1955.

Joe Gootter. "Sport-O-Grams." Paterson Evening News. July 16, 1955.

International News Service. "Briggs Family May Sell Tigers"; The Courier (Waterloo). Aug. 26, 1955.

Associated Press. "Briggs' Bid Turned Down"; Fort Worth Star-Telegram. Sept. 16, 1955.

Joe Falls. "Rebuffed By Sisters, Spike Briggs' Future In Baseball Is Uncertain"; Times Herald. Sept. 16, 1955.

Associated Press. "Detroit Tigers Sign Two Negro Pitchers"; Standard-Speaker. Oct. 13, 1955.

Associated Press. "Witnesses Say MacPhail Not Drunk At Race Track"; Cumberland Evening Times. Dec. 1, 1955.

Associated Press. "Bill Veeck Is Named To Lead New Miami Club In The IL"; Buffalo News. Dec. 20, 1955.

Associated Press. "Detroit Tigers Up For Sale But There's No Rush"; Gettysburg Times. Jan. 19, 1956.

Associated Negro Press. "Mississippi Team Withdraws From NAIA Tourney"; The Call (Kansas City). March 16, 1956.

Associated Press. "Gayle Talbot, 54, A Sports Writer; Columnist For A.P. Dies – Baseball Specialist Also Covered Two Olympics"; New York Times. March 30, 1956.

John Johnson. "A Salute To The Tan Players In Major Leagues"; The Call. April 20, 1956.

Charles Wartman. "Tiger Policy Has Definite Impact On Relations Here"; Detroit Tribune, June 23, 1956.

Ben Phlegar. "Bill Veeck Heads Syndicate After Detroit Tigers"; Corsicana Daily Sun. June 29, 1956.

Ben Phlegar. "Veeck Posts 'Good Faith' Money To See Tiger Books"; Times Herald. June 19, 1956.

John Cronley. "Once Over"; Daily Oklahoman. July 8, 1956.

Associated Press. "Four Groups Bid $5 Million For Detroit Tigers"; Tampa Tribune. July 11, 1956.

United Press International. "Detroit Group Backs Veeck In Reply To Sports Editor"; Boston Globe. July 12, 1956.

Dave Diles. "Veeck's Antics Dampen Chances"; Lansing State Journal. July 13, 1956.

Lyall Smith. "Tiger Unveiling Is Monday"; Detroit Free Press. July 13, 1956.

Tommy Devine. "Veeck Threatens Court Fight"; Detroit Free Press. July 17, 1956.

Associated Press. "Baseball Era Comes To An End"; The Record (Hackensack). July 17, 1956.

Lloyd Northard. "Spike Briggs Tiger Winner"; Baytown Sun. July 17, 1956.

Associated Press. "Only Money Considered"; Lansing State Journal. July 17, 1956.

Frank Corkin Jr. "Veeck Gets Knocked Down – Again"; The Journal (Meriden). July 17, 1956.

John Griffith. "Spike Jovial, Tense Revealing Tiger Sale"; Detroit Free Press. July 17, 1956.

United Press International. "Segregation Law May Doom Louisiana Sports"; Cincinnati Enquirer. July 18, 1956.

Wendy Foltz. "Sportalk"; Battle Creek Enquirer. July 19, 1956.

J.D. Kailer. "Observations, Reflections After Newsless Vacation"; Albuquerque Journal. Aug. 3, 1956.

N/A. "Detroit Fans Had Hoped Veeck Would Be Buyer Of Tigers"; Jackson Advocate. Aug. 4, 1956.

N/A. "Sixth Tan Player Enters Tigers Farm-Den"; The Detroit Tribune. Aug. 20, 1956.

N/A. "C.W. Schwefel, Hotel Man, Dies; Owner Of The Gramercy Park Was Active In Civic Groups And Trade Organizations." New York Times. Aug. 22, 1956.

Tommy Devine. "These Words Tell Why Briggs Hung Up Spikes: 'If I'm To Run Show, I Must Run It My Way'"; Detroit Free Press. April 27, 1957.

Associated Press. "Tigers Argue With Kaline Over Salary"; Miami News. Jan. 6, 1957.

Bob Glass. "Minoso Mad Over Bean-Ball Pitching"; Sidney Daily News. June 13, 1957.

United Press International. "Doby In Free-For-All As Yankees Nip White Sox, 4-3"; Morning Call. June 14, 1957.

N/A. "Ditmar Says He Wasn't Hit"; Berkshire Eagle. June 14, 1957.

Bill Beck. "Hutch Struggles To Stem Panic As Cards Wither"; Tampa Bay Times. Aug. 17, 1957.

Edward Prell. "Sox Trade Doby, Harshman To Orioles"; Chicago Tribune. Dec. 4, 1957.

Robert Burnes. "The Bench Warmer"; St. Louis Globe-Democrat. Jan. 16, 1959.

Jim Schlemmer. "What To Do For Don Black? It's A Many-Sided Puzzler"; Akron Beacon Journal. Jan. 17, 1959.

Robert Burnes. "The Bench Warmer"; St. Louis Globe-Democrat. Feb. 10, 1959.

Associated Press. "Francona Traded For Larry Doby"; Chattanooga Daily Times. March 22, 1959.

Milton Gross. "A Baseball First"; Kingston Whig-Standard; April 2, 1959.

David Condon. "In The Wake Of The News"; Chicago Tribune. April 15, 1959.

N/A. "Don Black Suffers Fatal Attack." Sioux City Journal. April 22, 1959.

Clif Keane. "Robinson's Day With Sox Told"; Boston Globe. April 29, 1959.

United Press International. "Detroit Tigers' Larry Doby Joins Chicago Outfield"; Simpson's Leader-Times. May 14, 1959.

N/A. "Cow Boots Sox Hopes In Milking Duel" Chicago Tribune. June 8, 1959.

Bob Holbrook. "Cows In Bullpen Latest By Veeck"; Boston Globe. June 8, 1959.

Associated Press. "Pulled Groin Muscle Idles Doby Few Days"; July 18, 1959.

Bob Murphy. "He Made A Million By Doing Nothing"; Minneapolis Star. July 20, 1959.

N/A. "Marie Green Planning To Join Husband Soon"; Boston Globe. July 24, 1959.

Associated Press. "Doby Sent To Minors"; Times Leader. Aug. 3, 1959.

United Press International. "Dodgers, Sox Divvy Biggest Series Take"; Bartlesville Examiner-Enterprise. Oct. 16, 1959.

N/A. "Manos Film Is Top Hit"; The Morning Herald. Dec. 10, 1959.

Joe Gootter. "Sports"; Paterson Evening News. Jan. 29, 1960.

Charles Chamberlain. "Veeck's New Toy Will Be Used Tonight"; Casper Star-Tribune. April 28, 1960.

United Press International. "American Loop Pennant To Get Axe At Chicago"; Salt Lake Tribune. May 1, 1960.

Doyle May. "Sports Beat"; Daily Ardmoreite. May 11, 1960.

Ken Ballstadt. "Ken's Korner"; Sault Star. May 16, 1960.

Gene Bludeauq. "Veeck Riles Over Piersall's Attack On Scoreboard"; Chicago Tribune. May 31, 1960.

Edward Prell. "Indians Beat Wynn, 4 To 1; Shaw, 9 To 4"; Chicago Tribune. May 31, 1960.

Associated Press. "Yankees Answer Sox Scoreboard With Sparklers"; Nashville Banner. June 18, 1960.

Associated Press. "'Dignified' Yankees Steal Veeck's Show"; Knoxville News-Sentinel. June 18, 1960.

Associated Press. "N.Y. Firemen Foil Sox' Mortar Blast"; Herald-Palladium. July 23, 1960.

Associated Press. "Yankees, Firemen Blasted"; Fort Worth-Star Telegram. July 24, 1960.

United Press International. "Baby Cage Loop Thrills Fans With 3-Point Shot"; Daily Republican-Register. Oct. 28, 1961.

Bill Veeck. "Why Veeck Couldn't Buy The Tigers"; Detroit Free Press. Aug. 12, 1962.

Wendell Smith. "Sports Beat"; Pittsburgh Courier. April 27, 1963.

United Press International. "Hotel Figurines Cause Furor At NAACP Meet"; Kingsport News. July 4, 1963.

Wendell Smith. "Sports Beat"; Pittsburgh Courier. Sept. 26, 1964.

Associated Press. "Rocking Chair Provided For Satchel Paige"; Springfield News-Sun. Sept. 16, 1965.

Richard Olive. "Satch Can Still Get 'Em Out"; Kansas City Star. Sept. 26, 1965.

Wendell Smith. "Sports Beat"; Pittsburgh Courier. April 2, 1966.

N/A. "Bill Veeck Has Operation"; The Sentinel (Winston-Salem). April 21, 1967.

Wendell Smith. "Sports Beat"; Pittsburgh Courier. Jan. 21, 1967.

Associated Press. "Civil Right Suit Filed In Easton"; Evening Sun (Hanover). Aug. 7, 1967.

Keeler McCartney. "False Alarms, Broken Glass But No Major Trouble Here"; Atlanta Constitution. April 10, 1968.

N/A. "Dr. King's Voice Rings Out Again"; Atlanta Constitution. April 10, 1968.

Ans Dilley. "Time In"; Verona-Cedar Groves Times. April 18, 1968.

Charlie Roberts. "Braves Pa(i)ge Ol' Satch"; Atlanta Constitution. Aug. 13, 1968.

Associated Press. "Jackie Robinson Calls Feller's Charges A Lie"; Ironwood Daily Globe. July 24, 1969.

N/A. "Spike Briggs Dies; Once Owned Tigers And Baseball Herd"; Buffalo News. July 3, 1970.

Phil Pepe. "The Satchel Paige Legend"; New York Daily News. Feb. 11, 1971.

Phil Pepe. "Everybody Talked Satch But Jackie Was 1st"; New York Daily News. Feb. 12, 1971.

Ron Coons. "Crafty Veeck's Intrigues, Arguments Save Gaedel His Place In Posterity"; Courier-Journal (Louisville). Aug. 20, 1971.

United Press International. "Veeck Sees Sports As Entertainment, 'Not Religion'"; Richmond Times-Dispatch. Dec. 17, 1972.

Jim Murray. "No Match For 'Old Pete'"; Tucson Citizen. April 27, 1974.

Red Smith. "Bill Veeck Ahead Of Time In Hiring Black Manager"; Spokesman-Review. Aug. 4, 1974.

Ed Sainsbury. "Armless Card Player Inspired Veeck"; Lebanon Daily News. May 20, 1976.

Edgar Driscoll. "Tom Yawkey, Red Sox Owner, Dies At 73"; Boston Globe. July 10, 1976.

David Condon. "Endurance Key To Doby Career"; Chicago Tribune. July 1, 1978.

Leslie Maitland. "Ernest Robert Beech, 81 Is Dead; Aviation And Automotive Official"; New York Times. July 5, 1978.

Bob Broeg. "Larry MacPhail Lit Up The Game"; St. Louis Post-Dispatch. Aug. 6, 1978.

Associated Press. "Disco Demolition Wrecks Game"; Abilene Reporter-News. July 13, 1979.

Bob Maisel. "Veeck's Anti-Disco Night Bombs"; Baltimore Sun. July 14, 1979.

Pat Truly. "Some Are Forfeited"; Fort Worth Star-Telegram. July 19, 1979.

John Schulian. "Bill Veeck Laughs At Baseball's Final, Bitter Twist"; Cincinnati Post. Feb. 6, 1981.

Thomas Boswell. "Satchel Paige: 'Best I Ever Saw' – Veeck"; Washington Post. June 9, 1982.

N/A. "Bill Veeck Was No Baseball Midget"; Los Angeles Times. Jan. 4, 1986.

Sam Smith. "For Doby, The Baseball Scars Are Deep"; Washington Post. July 7, 1987.

Steve Koehler. "'Mrs. Sherm' Headed For Comiskey"; Springfield News-Leader. Sept. 20, 1990.

N/A. "1948 Red Sox Had Booze To Blame, Not The Indians"; Standard-Times. Oct. 24, 1995.

Ira Berkow. "Larry Doby: He Crossed The Color Barrier, Only, He Was The Second"; New York Times. Feb. 23, 1997.

Terry Pluto. "Bill Veeck Had Some Good Intentions"; Daily Oklahoman. April 20, 1997.

Jack De Vries. "Eastside Product Remembers Historic Debut In Big Leagues"; Herald-News. July 5, 1997.

David Maraniss. "Neither A Myth Nor A Legend"; Washington Post. July 8, 1997.

N/A. "Lico, Trotman Join Times News Staff"; Montclair Times. Dec. 24, 1997.

Joseph Moore. "An Eagle Soars To The Pinnacle Of Baseball"; Herald-News. July 25, 1998.

Mike Neibart. "Fame Will No Longer Overlook Larry Doby"; Herald-News. July 26, 1998.

Raheem Trotman. "Hall Of Famer Stands Tall"; Montclair Times. July 30, 1998.

Elaine Woo. "Herbert Kline; Pioneering Documentary Filmmaker"; Los Angeles Times. Feb. 12, 1999.

Kid Sam. "The Straight Answer Ma'am." Winston-Salem Journal. Jan. 15, 2001.

N/A. "Sam Jethroe, 83; First Black Player For Boston Braves"; Boston Globe. June 18, 2001.

Associated Press. "Receptionist For Red Sox Past 60 Years Dies At 85"; Cap Cod Times. Oct. 14, 2001.

N/A. "Marjorie McKenzie Lawson"; Washington Post. Oct. 16, 2002.

N/A. "Indians Fan, 'Flagpole Sitter' Dies"; Tampa Bay Times. May 29, 2002.

Richard Goldstein. "Charley Lupica, 90, Dies; Fan Who Sat On Flagpole"; New York Times. Dec. 29, 2002.

Jim Litke. "Globetrotters Recall '48 Win Vs. Lakers"; Midland Daily News. Feb. 18, 2003.

Paul Sullivan. "A Memory That Will Never Be Demolished"; Chicago Tribune. July 9, 2004.

Joe Posnanski. "Lebovitz Was Always A Gentleman"; Kansas City Star. Oct. 20, 2005.

Marc Spears. "In Terms Of History, These Men Get Picture"; Boston Globe. Feb. 21, 2008.

Ed Koch. "'Bugsy' Siegel – The Mob's Man In Vegas"; Las Vegas Sun. May 15, 2008.

Grant Segall. "Nate Dolin, Indians Vice President, Ran Cleveland Arena And Front Row Theatre – Obituary"; Cleveland Plain Dealer. April 16, 2009.

Harvey Araton. "The Dixie Walker She Knew"; New York Times. April 11, 2010.

Bill Madden. "Yogi Remembers Happier Times With Doby"; New York Daily News. Dec. 16, 2010.

Charles Stanley. "The Commissioner's Wife"; The Times (Streator). July 17, 2011.

Jerry Izenberg. "Izenberg: Larry Doby Should Be Honored By Newark"; Newark Star-Ledger. July 7, 2012.

Michelle Jarboe. "Harbor Inn, A Legendary Cleveland Bar, Up For Sale; King Of The Flats Hopes To Retire (gallery)"; Cleveland Plain Dealer. May 2, 2014.

Tim Bannon. "Sports Flashback: The Story Behind Bill Veeck's Exploding Scoreboard"; Chicago Tribune. April 3, 2015.

Tony Lariccia. "Cleveland Indians Pitcher Don Black's No-Hitter 70 Years Ago Was A Triumph Over Alcoholism, But Tragedy Followed"; Cleveland Plain Dealer. July 9, 2017.

Nick Cafardo. "Book Could Dispel Yawkey's Racist Reputation"; Boston Globe. Aug. 20, 2017.

Harvey Briggs. "Great Grandson Of Former Tigers Owner: Turning A Racist Legacy Into One Of Hope"; Detroit Free Press. Aug. 22, 2017.

Rosalind Bentley. "Lester Maddox Turned The Capitol Into A Fortress During MLK's Funeral"; Atlanta Journal-Constitution. April 4, 2018.

N/A. "Walter O. Briggs, Captain Of Industry, Owner Of Tigers"; Detroit News. Sept. 1, 2018.

Richard Ruelas. "How The Cactus League Came To Be In Arizona: A Search For Racial Tolerance"; Arizona Republic. Jan. 18, 2019.

Gene Sapakoff. "Sapakoff: Tom Yawkey, Racism And A Better South Carolina Spin On Red Sox History"; Post And Courier. Sept. 14, 2020.

Rob Tannenbaum. "Commentary: Disco And The Bee Gees Are Beloved Today. But As Disco Demolition Night And A New HBO Documentary Demonstrate, That Wasn't True 40 Years Ago"; Los Angeles Times. Dec. 18, 2020.

Ken Dooley. "Opinion/Dooley: Abe Saperstein And The NBA Basketball Hall Of Fame"; Providence Journal. Feb. 11, 2021.

Chris Lamb. "J.G. Taylor Spink's Racist Baseball Legacy Lasted Decades, But In The End, Truth Won"; USA Today. March 13, 2021.

Pete Donovan. "Column: One Of Baseball's Oddities Is That Catcher Roy Campanella Took Pay Cut To Join Dodgers"; Desert Sun. June 1, 2021.

Bob Rose. "The Mysterious Case Of The Death Of Eddie Gaedel"; St. Louis Post-Dispatch. June 18, 2022.

Dave Perkins. "Minnie And Me: He Was This Typist's Favourite Player. Period"; Toronto Star. July 22, 2022.

Cesar Brioso. "How Integration Led To The Demise Of Negro League Baseball"; USA Today. Feb. 5, 2023.

WIKIPEDIA

American Baseball Guild. https://en.wikipedia.org/wiki/American_Baseball_Guild

Brother Can You Spare A Dime. https://en.wikipedia.org/wiki/Brother,_Can_You_Spare_a_Dime%3F

Walter O'Malley. https://en.wikipedia.org/wiki/Walter_O%27Malley

Jorge Pasquel. https://en.wikipedia.org/wiki/Jorge_Pasquel

J.G. Taylor Spink. https://en.wikipedia.org/wiki/J._G._Taylor_Spink

Amos 'n' Andy. https://en.wikipedia.org/wiki/Amos_%27n%27_Andy

Slaughter's Mad Dash. https://en.wikipedia.org/wiki/Slaughter%27s_Mad_Dash

Richard Muckerman. https://en.wikipedia.org/wiki/Richard_Muckerman

Johnson-Jeffries Riots. https://en.wikipedia.org/wiki/Johnson%E2%80%93Jeffries_riots

John R. Brinkley. https://en.wikipedia.org/wiki/John_R._Brinkley

Minnie Minoso. https://en.wikipedia.org/wiki/Minnie_Mi%C3%B1oso

The Pierre. https://en.wikipedia.org/wiki/The_Pierre

Happy Chandler. https://en.wikipedia.org/wiki/Happy_Chandler

Buck O'Neil. https://en.wikipedia.org/wiki/Buck_O%27Neil

Indian Citizenship Act. https://en.wikipedia.org/wiki/Indian_Citizenship_Act#Text

College Basketball. https://en.wikipedia.org/wiki/College_basketball

1948 American League Tie-Breaker Game. https://en.wikipedia.org/wiki/1948_American_League_tie-breaker_game

Ralph Houk. https://en.wikipedia.org/wiki/Ralph_Houk

Toni Stone. https://en.wikipedia.org/wiki/Toni_Stone

Syd Pollock. https://en.wikipedia.org/wiki/Syd_Pollock

Ryne Duren. https://en.wikipedia.org/wiki/Ryne_Duren

Hyatt Grand Central New York. https://en.wikipedia.org/wiki/Hyatt_Grand_Central_New_York

Eddie Gaedel. https://en.wikipedia.org/wiki/Eddie_Gaedel

H.G. Salsinger. https://en.wikipedia.org/wiki/H._G._Salsinger

Joe Falls. https://en.wikipedia.org/wiki/Joe_Falls

Canterbury School. https://en.wikipedia.org/wiki/Canterbury_School_(Connecticut)

Bougainville Campaign. https://en.wikipedia.org/wiki/Bougainville_campaign

Walter Briggs Jr. https://en.wikipedia.org/wiki/Walter_Briggs_Jr.

Briggs Manufacturing Company. https://en.wikipedia.org/wiki/Briggs_Manufacturing_Company

Grace Comiskey. https://en.wikipedia.org/wiki/Grace_Comiskey

Gramercy Park Hotel. https://en.wikipedia.org/wiki/Gramercy_Park_Hotel

Charles Erwin Wilson. https://en.wikipedia.org/wiki/Charles_Erwin_Wilson#

Ernest Breech. https://en.wikipedia.org/wiki/Ernest_R._Breech

Louisiana, Missouri. https://en.wikipedia.org/wiki/Louisiana,_Missouri

Clark Griffith. https://en.wikipedia.org/wiki/Clark_Griffith

Fred Lieb. https://en.wikipedia.org/wiki/Fred_Lieb#References

List Of First Black Major League Baseball Players. https://en.wikipedia.org/wiki/List_of_first_black_Major_League_Baseball_players

Basketball Association Of America. https://en.wikipedia.org/wiki/Basketball_Association_of_America

Chicago Stags. https://en.wikipedia.org/wiki/Chicago_Stags

Meadowlark Lemon. https://en.wikipedia.org/wiki/Meadowlark_Lemon

Goose Tatum. https://en.wikipedia.org/wiki/Goose_Tatum

Bob Douglas. https://en.wikipedia.org/wiki/Bob_Douglas

Red Klotz. https://en.wikipedia.org/wiki/Red_Klotz

National Basketball Association. https://en.wikipedia.org/wiki/National_Basketball_Association

Naval Base Ulithi. https://en.wikipedia.org/wiki/Naval_Base_Ulithi

Marjorie McKenzie Lawson. https://en.wikipedia.org/wiki/Marjorie_McKenzie_Lawson

Ebenezer Missionary Baptist Church (Chicago). https://en.wikipedia.org/wiki/Ebenezer_Missionary_Baptist_Church_(Chicago)

George Brent. https://en.wikipedia.org/wiki/George_Brent

1945 Boston Red Sox Season. https://en.wikipedia.org/wiki/1945_Boston_Red_Sox_season

Abe Saperstein. https://en.wikipedia.org/wiki/Abe_Saperstein

1944 Cleveland Indians Season. https://en.wikipedia.org/wiki/1944_Cleveland_Indians_season

James Michael Curley. https://en.wikipedia.org/wiki/James_Michael_Curley#

Kenesaw Mountain Landis. https://en.wikipedia.org/wiki/Kenesaw_Mountain_Landis

The Negro Motorist Green Book. https://en.wikipedia.org/wiki/The_Negro_Motorist_Green_Book

Chief Wahoo. https://en.wikipedia.org/wiki/Chief_Wahoo

The Catch. https://en.wikipedia.org/wiki/The_Catch_(baseball)

Alva Bradley. https://en.wikipedia.org/wiki/Alva_Bradley

Gerald Nugent. https://en.wikipedia.org/wiki/Gerald_Nugent

Tom Yawkey. https://en.wikipedia.org/wiki/Tom_Yawkey

Ford Frick. https://en.wikipedia.org/wiki/Ford_Frick#

Bill Veeck. https://en.wikipedia.org/wiki/Bill_Veeck

Paul Robeson. https://en.wikipedia.org/wiki/Paul_Robeson

Baseball Color Line. https://en.wikipedia.org/wiki/Baseball_color_line

Toots Shor. https://en.wikipedia.org/wiki/Toots_Shor

Hotel Theresa. https://en.wikipedia.org/wiki/Hotel_Theresa

Smoke! Smoke! Smoke! (That Cigarette). https://en.wikipedia.org/wiki/Smoke!_Smoke!_Smoke!_(That_Cigarette)

Ruppert Stadium (Newark). https://en.wikipedia.org/wiki/Ruppert_Stadium_(Newark)

Arthur Godfrey. https://en.wikipedia.org/wiki/Arthur_Godfrey

Lou Boudreau. https://en.wikipedia.org/wiki/Lou_Boudreau

Edna Mae Robinson. https://en.wikipedia.org/wiki/Edna_Mae_Robinson

Sugar Ray Robinson. https://en.wikipedia.org/wiki/Sugar_Ray_Robinson

Jesse Owens. https://en.wikipedia.org/wiki/Jesse_Owens
Los Alamos Ranch School. https://en.wikipedia.org/wiki/Los_Alamos_Ranch_School

BOOKS

Bill James. "The New Bill James Historical Baseball Abstract"; 2001.

Bruce Nash. Allan Zullo. "The Baseball Hall Of Shame"; March 2012.

Dave Halberstam. "Summer Of '49"; 1989.

Lou Boudreau. Russell Schneider, Jack Brickhouse. "Lou Boudreau: My Hall Of Fame Life On The Field And Behind The Mic"; 2017.

Paul Dickson. "Bill Veeck: Baseball's Greatest Maverick"; 2012.

Ron Thomas. "They Cleared The Lane"; 2004.

Bob Luke. "The Most Famous Woman In Baseball"; 2011.

Joseph Moore. "Larry Doby"; 2011

Lincoln Mitchell. "The Dodgers, The Giants, And Baseball Goes West The Shaping Of The Major Leagues"; 2018.

Ben Green. "Spinning The Globe. The Rise, Fall, And Return To Greatness Of The Harlem Globetrotters"; 2005.

Luke Epplin. "Our Team: The Epic Story of Four Men and the World Series That Changed Baseball"; 2021.

Bill Veeck. Ed Linn. "Veeck As In Wreck: The Autobiography Of Bill Veeck"; 2001.

Made in the USA
Monee, IL
10 April 2024

56767574R00246